Longman Co-ordinated
S-C-I-E-N-C-E

CHEMISTRY

Jean McLean

7 Day Loan

This book is due for return on or before the last date shown below.

Addison Wesley Longman Limited
Edinburgh Gate, Harlow, Essex CM20 2JE, England

First published 1996

© Addison Wesley Longman Limited 1996

Designed and produced by Gecko Limited, Bicester, Oxon

Printed in Great Britain by
Scotprint Limited, Musselburgh, Scotland

ISBN 0582 279852

The publisher's policy is to use paper manufactured from sustainable forests.

Acknowledgements

We are grateful to the following for permission to reproduce copyright material:

British Aerosol Manufacturers' Association for a graph and two data tables; Guardian Newspapers Ltd for extracts from articles from *The Guardian* 8.11.94 & *The Guardian* 20.9.94; IACR-Rothamsted for a data table; Thomas Nelson & Sons Ltd for an extract from *The Material World* by John Holman.

We are grateful to the following for permission to reproduce photographic material:

Front cover: David Parker/Science Photo Library
Polarised light micrograph of crystal line vitamin C
The photograph on page 78 bottom left is **"Crown copyright and is reproduced with permission of the Controller of HMSO"**
The photograph on page 120 is **Reproduced Courtesy of the Library and Information Centre, Royal Society of Chemistry**
AKG, London, Page 113
ARC Southern, page 233 top
Ace Photo Agency, page 26 top left (photo Jason Burns)
Allsport, pages 94 right (photo Tim Deerisco), 173 right (photo Stephen Munday), page 173 left (photo Vandystadt), 216 top right (photo Stephen Munday)
Audi, page 29 top right
Auto Alloys, pages 239 top left, 239 top right, 239 centre right
Bancroft Library, University of California, page 133
Bass Brewers, page 165
Beckett Newspapers, page 61 top
Becton Dickson, page 26 centre
Catherine Blackie, pages 2, 26 centre top, 115 bottom right, 173 centre, 174 right, 193 top left, 232 left
Anthony Blake Photo Library, pages 68 bottom right, 147 top right, 163 top, 164, 168
BP, pages 1 top right, 13 centre bottom,
BP Chemicals, page 23 bottom left
British Rail Civil Engineers, page 38 top
British Steel, Scunthorpe, page 52
Bubbles, pages 178, 189 top left (photo Loisjou Thurston)
Caradon Everest, pages 23 centre right, 193 top right,
Cern, page 1 bottom right
Chile Copper, pages 48-49, 49 top left, 49 top right, 49 bottom right, 181 right
Trevor Clifford, pages 22, 24, 62 bottom left, 62 centre bottom left, 62 centre bottom right, 67 bottom, 68 left, 70 centre bottom right, 73 bottom left, bottom centre and bottom right, 94 left, 141 right, 158 right, 162 bottom, 167, 173 centre top right, 226 centre, 232 right
Coca Cola, page 62 top centre left
Collections, pages 16 centre right (photo Brian Shuel), 23 centre bottom (photo Anthea Sievking), 77 (photo Alain Le Garsmeur), 117 left (photo Anthea Sicveking), 163 bottom (photo Brian Shuel), 193 centre bottom right, 193 bottom left, 193 bottom right, 205 top left (photo Brian Shuel), 207 top (photo McQuillan Brown)
Mary Evans Picture Library, pages 115 top, 127 top, 131 top
Finnigan Mat, page 130 centre left
Elizabeth Gage, page 29 top
Geoscience Features, pages 23 bottom right, 48 all pictures, 81 all pictures, 82 bottom left, 83 left, 88 centre, 88 bottom, 89, 105 centre, 105 bottom, 205 bottom left, 209 right, 217 top,
Griffin and George, page 32 top
Robert Harding Picture Library, pages 26 top right (photo Philippe Royer), 41 (photo Walter Rawling), 63 (photo Vulcan), 65 (photo E Simaner), 78 top right (photo David Hughes), 78 top left (photo Philip Craven), 84 top, 84 centre right, 120 (photo Ian Griffiths), 143 top, 189 top right (photo Ideal Home, IPC Magazines), 189 bottom (photo Asa Tallgard), 223 bottom (photo Robert Estell), 226 top (photo Duncan Maxwell)
HMSO page 78 bottom left
Holt Studios, pages 67 top (photo Primrose Peacock), 70 bottom left (photo Nigel Cattlin), 194 (all photos Nigel Cattlin)
Hydro Agri UK & Ireland, pages 70 top, 200 top, 200 centre, 200 bottom
Hydro Aluminium, pages 54 left, 54 right, 56

IACR – Rothamsted , page 195
Image Bank, pages 80 (photo Ken Huang), 96 (photo Antony Edwards), 103 (photo Wendy Chan), 117 centre right (photo Janeart)
ICI Chemicals and Polymers Ltd., page 73 top
ICI Fertilizers, page 197
ICI Paints, page 150
Johnson Matthey, page 141 left
LPU, page 162
Andrew Lambert, pages 8, 9, 11, 30, 31, 38 bottom, 39, 62 top right, 62 bottom right, 63 bottom, 71, 73 centre right, 118 left, 118 right, 121, 126 left, 126 centre, 126 right, 143 centre, 145 left, 145 right, 147 left, 147 centre right, 148, 149, 174 left, 179, 205 top right,
207 bottom, 208 left, 208 right, 209 left, 209 centre, 212 left, 212 right, 213 left, 213 centre, 213 right, 230 right, 237 top right, 237 centre left, 237 bottom, 241 left, 241 centre, 241 right, 246
Frank Lane Picture Agency, pages 1 left (photo Phil Ward) 13 bottom (photo H Hautala), 26 bottom (photo Peter Dean), 82 bottom right (photo S Jonasson)
Longman, page 62 top centre left
NASA, pages 79 top, 93, 142 centre
National Power, page 18
News Team, page 47
Nuffield Foundation, pages 136 (photo Derek Potter/Lynn Narvis), 228 top, 229, 230 left
Oxford Scientific Films, pages 45 top (photo Charlie Ott), 45 centre left (photo Doug Allan), 45 bottom (photo Daniel J Cox), 68 top (photo KG Vock), 82 top (photo CG Gardener), 83 top right (photo Breck P Kent), 84 bottom (photo TC Middleton), 85 top (photo Roger Jackman), 85 centre (photo Breck P Kent), 85 bottom (photo Breck P Kent), 181 left (photo Michael Fogden)
Popperfoto, page 127 bottom
RMH Foods, page 205 bottom right
Retrograph Archive, page 175 top
Rex Features, pages 13 top (photo Alexander Boulat, 13 centre top (photo Thierry Chesnot), 13 centre top, 40, 61 bottom left (photo Peter Brooker), 70 bottom right, 95 (photo Roy Garner), 98, 117 top right, 119 centre right, 119 left (photo Michael Friedel), 131 bottom, 142 left, 143 bottom (photo Sipa Press), 174 background, 175 bottom, 190 (photo DLR), 191 (photo Sipa), 193 centre left, 224 (photo David White)
Robinsons, page 148 left
Royal Society of Chemistry, page 112
RSPB, page 109 top (photo CH Gomersall)
Science Photo Library, pages 13 top right (photo SIU), 29 centre left, (photo Andrew Syred), 32 bottom (photo Amy Tristram Eve), 46 (photo Arnold Fisher), 62 centre top right (photo Jerry Mason), 83 bottom (photo Simon Fraser), 87 left, 87 right (photo George Whiteley), 88 top (photo Mike McNamee), 109 left (photo Scott Camazine), 109 bottom, 111, 115 bottom left 119 bottom right (photo Richard Megina/Fundamental Photos), 129 (photo US Naval Observatory), 130 bottom right (photo Simon Frascr), 157 top (photo David Scharf), 157 bottom left (photo Institut Pasteur), 157 bottom right (photo Dr Jeremy Burgess), 168 top left (photo Dr P Marazzi), 160 (LN Johnson, Oxford Molecular Biophysics Lab), 185 (photo European Space Agency), 217 bottom (photo Martin Land), 223 top, 228 bottom (photoJC Revy), 245 top left (photo Roberto De Gugliemo), 245 top right (photo Arnold Fisher), 245 bottom left (photo Martin Land), 245 bottom right (photo Roberto De Gugliemo)
Slazengers Ltd, page 216 left
Harry Smith Photo Library, pages 26 centre left, 61 centre right, 61 bottom right, 70 centre bottom left
Smithkline Beecham, page 159
Sothebys, page 214
Sumitomo Sitix Europe, page 233 bottom
Tarmac Quarry Products, page 16 top left
Thames Water, page 158 bottom left
Trek USA, page 216 bottom
University of Pennsylvania, page 114
John Walmsley, page 237 top left
Zefa Picture Library, page 105 top

Contents

How to use this book iv

1 Experiments and investigations 1

2 Oil 13

3 Metals 29

4 Ores 45

5 Acids and bases 61

6 Rocks and minerals 77

7 The Earth 93

8 The periodic table 109

9 Atoms 125

10 Rates of reaction 141

11 Enzymes 157

12 Energy in reactions 173

13 Using reactions 189

14 Structure and bonding 205

15 How much? 221

16 Chemistry help 237

Index 250

How to use this book

In Chapter One (Experiments and investigations) you will find out how to do experiments and what to think about when planning and carrying out investigations. Chapter Fifteen (How much?) is all about calculations and formulae. In Chapter Sixteen (Chemistry help) you will find general information and hints which you might need for your practical work.

All the other chapters are organised in the same way. The first page of each one is an introduction to the subject which you are going to cover. The second page is designed to remind you what you might have learned before. There are some questions to help test what you remember. The remaining pages cover what you need to know for your exam.

Experimental science

This book also contains introductions to the practical work which you might do. There are detailed worksheets to help you carry out your experiments. Use the practical summaries if you miss a lesson or need to revise.

The icons show you which skills you will be using;

planning   obtaining evidence

analysing   evaluating

▶ *There are questions marked with an arrow head like this. These are designed to help with your understanding of the text. For example, you might be asked a short question to check if you have understood the paragraph you have just read.*

Your teacher will tell you whether you need to cover material which is marked like this.

You will find a summary at the end of each chapter.

Finally, there is a selection of graded questions at the end of each chapter. These are similar to the questions that you might get in your exams. You may be asked to do the questions in class or as homework. Your teacher will tell you which questions to do.

We hope you enjoy using this book.

These boxes contain extra information

CHAPTER ONE

Experiments & investigations

■ How scientists work

Scientists collect and use information in many different ways. A biologist might observe the behaviour of an animal in its environment and then compare these observations with others of the same animal under different conditions. Statistics, a form of mathematics, can help to analyse the results and to discover if the differences observed mean anything.

Studying animal behaviour.

Investigating a group of newly discovered chemicals.

A chemist might try to solve a particular problem. For example, she might be trying to design a new type of antifreeze using a group of newly-discovered chemicals. She might have to analyse the chemical properties of all the members of this group before a suitable antifreeze can be produced. The scientist might have to run hundreds of separate tests, each involving the careful control of variables so that the results can be compared fairly. In this case, the scientist would have a good idea what to expect, but would not know exactly what the answers to the questions she was investigating were going to be.

A physicist might be trying to discover exactly what is in the centre of an atom. He might be part of a team of over a hundred scientists, working in different laboratories in different countries. Each of his experiments might cost millions of pounds and so his team cannot afford to do more than one a year.

An aerial view of the huge loop near Geneva where scientists study atomic structure.

The people on the previous page are all scientists but they all work in different ways. This book does not suggest that scientists work in the same way. Nor does it suggest that one method of working is better than any other. Instead, it suggests a range of methods that can be used in studying science. Some of these methods might be useful in other situations – at home or in a maths lesson, perhaps.

▶ *Make a list of some of the skills you think a scientist would need.*

Things to think about

Use practical work to help your learning. Try to explain the results you get from practical work in terms of **models**. Models are systems that can be used to help understand other problems and to predict what might happen in other situations. Using information from many different sources will help you understand your classwork better. Do not be afraid to ask for help, or to ask a friend to explain an idea to you. You may be given the chance to use computers to collect or to handle data, or to write up notes or experiments. Computers are very good at finding patterns in data.

▶ *Write down a list of all the possible sources of information you might use for a project in science.*

Try to apply what you learn to a real-life situation. Do not think of science as just something learned in a classroom. Look for it in your everyday life, but do not think that science can solve all the world's problems. Some problems seem just too difficult for even the greatest of scientists and others are just too expensive to solve.

▶ *Think of some problems that science has yet to solve. Can you think why we have failed to find a solution?*

Just as we study different types of scientific problems in different ways, you might like to write up your notes in different ways. Graphs, tables and diagrams help to explain complicated information. Presentations, models and posters can help to make the information more interesting.

▶ Write down all the ways you can think of for showing data from different experiments.

▶ Copy the list of words below and discover their meaning. You might need a dictionary. Two are done for you as examples.

- ■ *fair test*
- ■ *precise*
- ■ *accurate*
- ■ *hypothesis*
- ■ *reliable*
- ■ *variable*

Hypothesis *Based on earlier tests or some background research, this is an idea which can be tested by experiment. Usually, a hypothesis will involve predictions.*

Variable *This is a factor that can affect the outcome of an experiment.*

Experimental work

Scientists spend much of their time collecting and analysing data. To do this effectively they must have a clear idea of exactly what they are trying to discover or test. Following a series of steps is helpful for many people. You might like to use these general headings when planning your practical work.

Planning

- ■ Be clear about what you are trying to test or discover.
- ■ Can you write it out as a question?
- ■ Can you write it in a more general form as a **hypothesis**?
- ■ Can you support your hypothesis with knowledge that you already have?
- ■ Do you need to do any background research?
- ■ Are you sure that your method is safe?
- ■ Do you know what apparatus is available?
- ■ Which factors need to be controlled?
- ■ Which factors will you measure?
- ■ How will you measure these things?

Evaluating evidence

- ■ How could your experiment have been improved?
- ■ Are the results fair?
- ■ Can you explain any surprises in the results?
- ■ Would comparing your results with another group help?
- ■ What experiment needs doing next?

Obtaining evidence

- ■ Is it a **fair test**?
- ■ Will you collect enough data to form a **conclusion**?
- ■ Are you able to use all the apparatus correctly?
- ■ Can you make accurate measurements?
- ■ Do you need to repeat your experiment?

Analysing evidence

- ■ How are you going to record your raw data?
- ■ Can you show it as a table?
- ■ Can you convert it into bar charts or line graphs?
- ■ Are patterns or trends obvious?
- ■ Can you produce general statements from your data?
- ■ It it possible to produce a conclusion linking your **variables**?

🔺 Things to think about when planning and carrying out experimental work.

Safety

Remember, you will be doing a great deal of practical work. You, just as much as your teacher, will have to be responsible for your safety, so do not start any practical activity unless you are sure of what you are doing. You should carry out a **risk assessment** for each practical. One simple way of doing this is to write down each step of the practical, highlight any dangers and find a way of reducing your risk. Your teacher may give you a worksheet to help you each time you need to do a risk assessment.

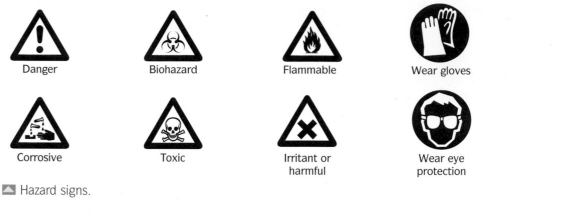

Danger	Biohazard	Flammable	Wear gloves
Corrosive	Toxic	Irritant or harmful	Wear eye protection

🔺 Hazard signs.

Apparatus

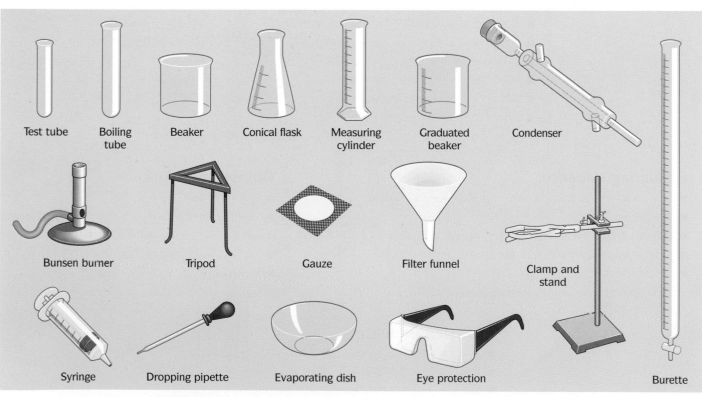

Test tube · Boiling tube · Beaker · Conical flask · Measuring cylinder · Graduated beaker · Condenser

Bunsen burner · Tripod · Gauze · Filter funnel · Clamp and stand

Syringe · Dropping pipette · Evaporating dish · Eye protection · Burette

🔺 Here are some examples of apparatus that you might use in your investigations.

Drawing apparatus

You may be given a worksheet so that you can practise drawing apparatus in two dimensions.

Measurements

This table shows you which pieces of apparatus you should use to make certain measurements.

Measurement	Units	Measuring device
Mass	grams (g) 1000 g = 1 kilogram (kg)	
Volume	centimetres cubed (cm^3) 1000 cm^3 = 1 litre (l)	
Time	seconds (s) 60 s = 1 minute (min) 60 min = 1 hour (hr)	
Length	centimetres (cm) 1000 cm = 1 metre (m) 1000 m = 1 kilometre (km)	
Temperature	degrees Celcius (°C)	
pH	pH number from 0 to 14	

Recording and presenting information

You should record information as you are going along. You should make sure it will be easy to process later. You might not do this on the same day or someone else might do it. Because of this, information should be recorded clearly showing exactly what was measured and the units used. Using a table can be a big help. It is a good idea to note down at the time whether you thought any of the readings might be wrong.

Time (minutes)	Temperature (°C)
0	23
1	35
2	45
3	59
4	77
5	80
6	92

▲ This table shows results for an experiment involving heating water. Notice the headings with the units in brackets.

Making the most of your results

Bar charts, pie charts and line graphs make results easier to understand and more interesting. You can either construct them by hand or use a word processing package and software.

Bar charts

Bar charts show how numbers compare in steps. Using graph paper is the best way to make a bar chart clear and accurate. Make sure the axes are properly labelled with what has been measured and the units used.

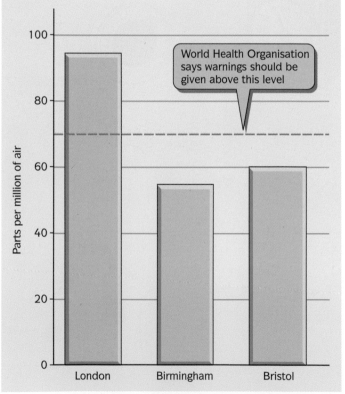

▲ Bar chart to show ground-level ozone levels in three cities in the UK, in July 1994. Notice how easy it is to compare the ozone level in each city and see if any of the values shown lie above or below a certain level.

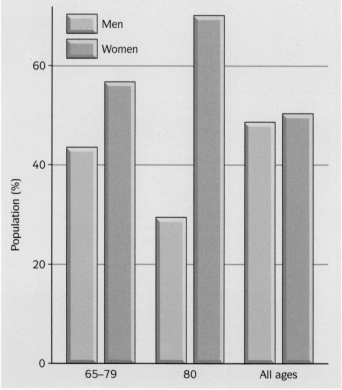

▲ This bar chart shows the distribution of the population by sex in different age groups. You can use bar charts to highlight comparisons among different groups.

Pie charts

You could use the information in the table on the right to draw a pie chart to describe the percentage composition by mass of stainless steel.

Element	Percentage %
Iron	73
Chromium	18
Nickel	8
Carbon	1

To draw the pie chart, you could use a computer spreadsheet if there is one available. Alternatively draw a circle with compasses. Divide it into 10 segments. Each segment is $\frac{1}{10}$ of the complete circle. If your results are expressed in percentages each segment is equal to 10 per cent. Work out how many segments or parts of segments are needed to represent each percentage. This is shown in the table below.

Elements	Percentage	Segments
Iron	73	$7\frac{1}{3}$ segments
Chromium	18	$1\frac{4}{5}$ segments
Nickel	8	$\frac{4}{5}$ segments
Carbon	1	A line to show small amount

If your results are not given as percentages you may find it easier to convert them to percentages of the whole before you work out what size segment should represent each one.

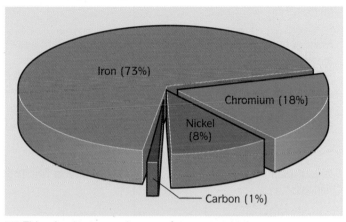

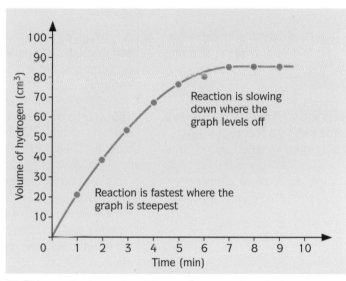

▲ This pie chart was drawn using a computer program.

Line graphs

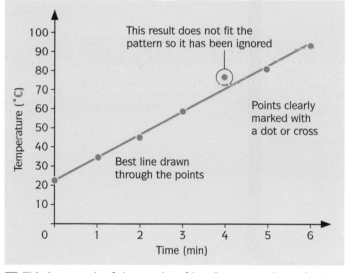

This result does not fit the pattern so it has been ignored

Points clearly marked with a dot or cross

Best line drawn through the points

▲ This is a graph of the results of heating water shown in the table on page 6.

Reaction is slowing down where the graph levels off

Reaction is fastest where the graph is steepest

▲ This graph shows the volume of gas produced when magnesium is added to dilute acid.

▶ *What can you tell from the graphs above?*

Notice that the points in the graphs above have been joined up into a smooth line. Any results not falling on the line have been ignored. You can tell a lot about the reaction of magnesium with dilute acid from the graph on the right. For example:

- the reaction is fastest where the graph is steepest
- the reaction slows down where the curve levels off
- the reaction has stopped when the curve becomes a straight horizontal line.

CHEMISTRY

Planning

To find out more about how to approach an investigation follow Natalie and Khalid as they investigate 'What makes packet jellies dissolve quickly in water'. Put yourself in their position …

What should you be thinking?	Action
You have to think of a problem worth investigating. It should be one you can tackle in your laboratory.	We are going to investigate the effect of heating the water on the time taken for the jelly to dissolve.
Make a prediction about what you expect to happen.	The hotter the water, the faster the jelly will dissolve.
Justify your prediction using scientific knowledge that you have already. It does not matter if you are not correct.	The hotter the water, the faster the particles will move and the more often they will hit the solid jelly making the jelly dissolve faster.
Is your planned experiment a fair test?	This will be a fair test.
The dependent variable is the one you are going to measure.	We are going to measure the time taken, so this is the dependent variable.
The independent variable is the one that you are going to change.	We are going to decide what the temperature of the water used will be, so temperature is the independent variable.
Factors that are going to be kept the same each time are called controlled variables or constants.	The volume of water used and the amount of jelly will be the same each time so these are controlled variables.
Carry out a risk assessment.	Jelly and water are not hazardous chemicals. We will wear eye protection when heating water. We will not eat the jelly (or anything else) in the lab.

▲ Natalie and Khalid are planning their investigation.

You may find it helpful to complete a table like the one below showing the variables. Circle or underline the dependent variable you intend to test.

Controlled variables (We will keep these the same)	Independent variables (We will alter one of these)	Dependent variable (We will measure this)
The volume of water The amount of jelly	The temperature of the water or the size of the bits of jelly	The time taken for the jelly to dissolve

Obtaining evidence

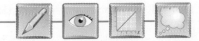

What should you be thinking?	Action
Make sure your plan is a fair test. If you decide to look at textbooks or other sources of information to help, you should mention this. Say or include a diagram showing what apparatus and what measuring instruments you are going to use.	Instructions on the packet say to dissolve the jelly in 500 cm³ of water. So each time, to keep the cost down we are going to dissolve 4 cubes (40 g) of jelly in 200 cm³ water (measured in a 250 cm³ measuring cylinder).
Mention how and how often you are going to make measurements giving reasons for your choice if you can. Remember, you must take at least five measurements to draw a valid graph from your results.	We are going to measure the time taken (using a stop watch) to dissolve the jelly at 50°C, 60°C, 70°C, 80°C and 90°C. We decided not to try temperatures below 50°C, because we thought the jelly might take too long to dissolve.
Have you made any changes to your plan as you have carried it out? If so, write them down and say why you made them.	The jelly was taking ages to dissolve, so we decided to stir the water and jelly. To keep the test fair, the rate of stirring was the same in each test.

▲ Natalie and Khalid are carrying out their plan.

Results and presenting them

What should you be thinking?	Action	
Before taking measurements design a table to write them in.	**Temperature (°C)**	**Time (minutes)**
Each column should have a heading and the units if appropriate.	90	3
	80	5
Do your results justice by choosing to present them in a bar chart, a pie chart or a line graph.	70	6
	60	10
	50	15
Bar charts are best for showing how things increase in steps.	We think a line graph is best here because looking at the table tells us that the time taken is slowly changing as the temperature of the water is increasing.	
Pie charts show how things are divided into sets.		
Line graphs are best when something is changing steadily.		

What should you be thinking?	Action
Construct your graph. Choose a sensible scale to make your results look good. Label both axes. (Don't forget the units.) Write a title beside the graph. Each point should be plotted with a cross. Join the points up smoothly ignoring any that do not quite fall on the line.	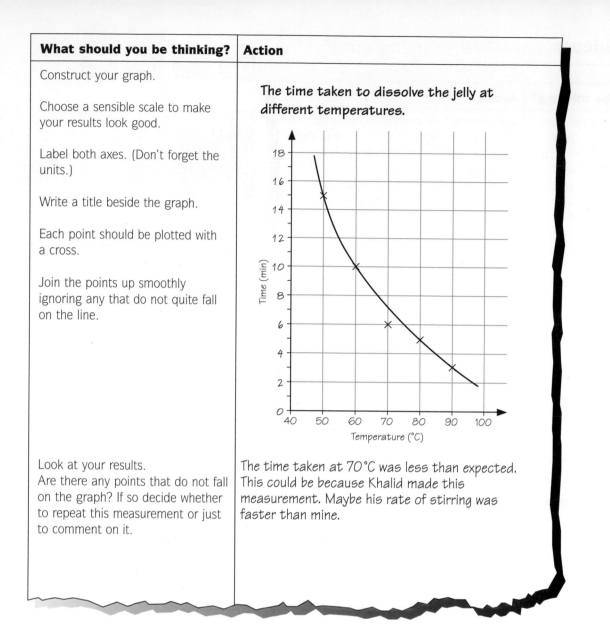 **The time taken to dissolve the jelly at different temperatures.**
Look at your results. Are there any points that do not fall on the graph? If so decide whether to repeat this measurement or just to comment on it.	The time taken at 70°C was less than expected. This could be because Khalid made this measurement. Maybe his rate of stirring was faster than mine.

Analysing your evidence and drawing conclusions

What should you be thinking?	Action
Look at your results and write down what you think they show. Do not worry if they do not agree with your original prediction, but do make sure you point out if they confirm or disprove your prediction.	Our results seem to show that the higher the temperature of the water, the faster the jelly dissolves.
If possible explain your results in a quantitative way. (This means using numbers and amounts.)	For every 10 °C rise in temperature the jelly dissolves about three minutes faster.
Do your results support your original ideas? Draw a diagram if this makes your theories clearer.	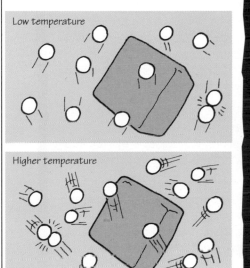

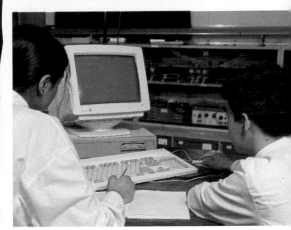

▲ Natalie and Khalid are using a computer to write up their investigation.

Heating water transfers energy to the water particles. This makes them move around faster and crash into (come into contact with) the solid jelly more often.

This makes the jelly dissolve faster.

Evaluating evidence

What should you be thinking?	Action
What problems did you have? How could you have improved this investigation?	We would have liked to repeat each measurement to improve the accuracy of this investigation but there was not enough time.
What was the main source of error or inaccuracy?	The main source of inaccuracy was the temperature of the water. It was difficult to be sure the temperature measurement was exact and the water was cooling all the time the jelly was dissolving. When the jelly took a long time to dissolve, the temperature of the water fell a lot from the start to the finish. It was also difficult to control the rate of stirring, making sure it was the same each time.
How could you improve this investigation?	We would like to use a water bath to keep the water at a constant temperature. A magnetic stirrer would give a constant rate of stirring.
Are your results enough to support your original prediction?	We feel confident that our results confirm our predictions, for the brand of strawberry jelly we used in this investigation. It would be interesting to compare different flavours and brands.
What further work could be done?	Other factors that might influence the rate at which jelly dissolves include the surface area of the jelly (which depends on the size of the pieces), the rate of stirring and the volume of water used.

Oil

■ Counting the cost

Supertankers carry oil across the oceans so that we can have all the fuel and plastic things we take for granted. Every so often though, oil gets into the sea by accident. In 1993 the tanker *Braer* crashed on the rocks of the Shetland Islands spilling most of its 85 thousand tonne cargo of oil into the sea.

Seven days after, most of the south-western tip of the main island was contaminated (polluted) threatening the lives of birds and animals, not to mention the cost and discomfort to the human population. It was only the ferocious storms and gale force winds at the time that that cleared the seas again.

For many people the mention of crude oil brings to mind pictures of birds and other wildlife covered in thick, black, evil-smelling liquid. Yet oil plays a central part in all our lives. A part that few of us are willing to give up.

The *Braer* breaking up in a storm.

Seabirds and seals were found dead or oiled.

NEW OIL RESERVES ARE PUT AT FOUR BILLION BARRELS

The go-ahead has been given to recover oil and gas from the Foinaven field, five hundred metres deep in the Atlantic, 190 kilometres west of the Shetlands. The field is expected to produce 85 thousand barrels a day and in the end produce as much as a third of the output of the North Sea.

A map of the Foinaven field.

■ Oil fields
30 miles

Foinaven

Sullom Voe

SHETLAND

Atlantic Ocean

ORKNEY

Flotta

Drilling for oil in the Foinaven field.

Disaster in Arctic

A map of the Komi region.

Barents Sea

Netetsky National Park

Area of detail

KOMI REGION

R. Kolva

Arctic Circle   Oil spillage here

R. Usa

Usinsk

R. Pechora

RUSSIA

Oil pipeline   60 miles

A massive Russian oil spill is threatening precious Arctic wildlife and tundra. Estimates of the size of the spill vary from 60 thousand to 270 thousand tonnes of oil. A pipeline burst spilling oil over a four mile stretch. The nearby Pechora river is flowing towards the Arctic taking the pollution with it.

The Komi region is home to about one hundred thousand reindeer.

Review

Before going any further, read this page and attempt the tasks. Write the answers in your notes.

An atom is the smallest part of an element. Atoms of any one element contain the same number of protons in the nucleus. Protons are tiny positively charged particles.

Each element can be represented by a symbol. For example, carbon is represented by C, bromine is represented by Br, hydrogen is represented by H.

Molecules are made when small groups of atoms join together. The atoms can be the same, for example oxygen, O_2, or different, for example carbon dioxide, CO_2.

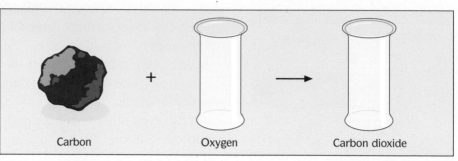

Carbon   Oxygen   Carbon dioxide

🔺 When two or more elements combine, a substance with completely different properties called a compound is formed. For instance, carbon and oxygen combine to make carbon dioxide. Carbon, oxygen and carbon dioxide all have different properties.

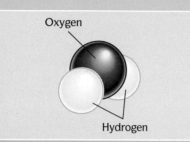

Oxygen

Hydrogen

🔺 The formula of water is H_2O. This means that the ratio of hydrogen atoms to oxygen atoms (H:O) is 2:1.

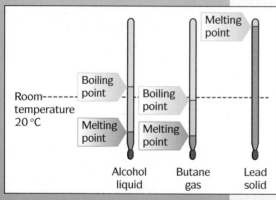

Melting point

Room temperature 20 °C

Boiling point

Boiling point

Melting point

Melting point

Alcohol liquid   Butane gas   Lead solid

🔺 All substances have an individual melting and boiling point.

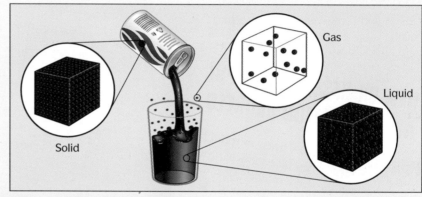

Solid   Gas   Liquid

🔺 Substances can exist as solids, liquids or gases. Heating a liquid makes the particles move faster and faster until they escape from each other, evaporating to form a gas. On cooling the particles in a gas slow down, move closer together and in the end condense to form a liquid.

CHECK TWO

1 What is the difference between:
a an element and a compound
b an atom and a molecule
c a mixture and a compound?

2 What are the three states of matter?

3 Explain in terms of particles the difference between a liquid and a gas.

4 Write down the name of the change when:
a liquid→gas
b gas→liquid.

5 a What technique could you use to separate a mixture of liquids?

b This method of separation depends on a property of these liquids. What is this property?

6 What symbol is used for:
a hydrogen
b carbon
c oxygen?

7 What are the elements combined and the ratio of the atoms in:
a sulphur dioxide, SO_2
b ammonia, NH_3?

8 What is the formula of a compound of carbon and hydrogen atoms in which the C:H ratio is 1:4?

Using Oil

Oil was formed millions of years ago. Dead plants and animals sank to the sea-bed and were covered in thicker and thicker layers of mud and sand. Over time, high temperature and pressure changed these remains into oil and natural gas.

Deep underground oil is stored in the **pores** (holes) in **permeable** sedimentary rock. The liquid tends to seep slowly upwards but is often trapped when it reaches layers of **impermeable** rock (rock which has no pores) where it collects.

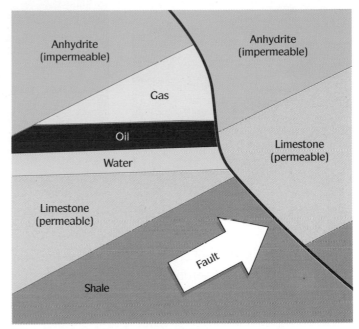

▲ A fault in the Earth can trap oil.

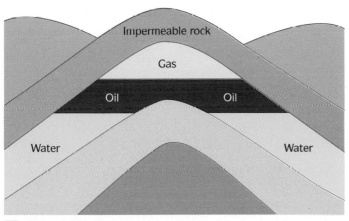

▲ Oil is often trapped under a dome of impermeable rock (an **anticline**).

Fractionation of oil

Crude oil pumped up from underground is a thick black mixture that you would not dream of using to oil a hinge or put in your car. It contains lots of different compounds, called **hydrocarbons** because they are made from the elements hydrogen and carbon. Oil is taken by sea tanker or in a pipeline to an oil **refinery** where it is purified.

The compounds in the oil mixture are separated from one another (or refined) using **fractional distillation**. Oil is heated to turn it into a gas and then the gas is passed upwards into a tower (**fractionating column**) where it is slowly cooled. As each of the compounds in the mixture cools to its boiling point, it turns back into a liquid. The liquids are removed from different levels in the column. In this way oil is separated into **fractions** (batches), each fraction containing compounds with similar boiling points.

▶ *Why is it possible to separate the fractions in crude oil using fractional distillation?*

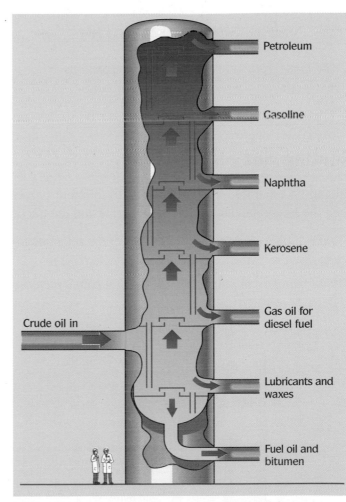

▲ The fractions removed from a fractionating column have different properties, which make them useful for different purposes.

CHEMISTRY

▲ Bitumen is mixed with aggregate and used in road surfaces.

▲ Diesel fuel is used by certain types of engine.

▲ Naphtha plays a part in manufacturing plastics, chemicals and drugs.

Most of the fractions from crude oil are used as fuels for lorries, cars, ships and aeroplanes or to heat our homes and workplaces.

▸ *Use the information given to make a simple poster to be used during a talk on the use of substances obtained from crude oil. Find out how much of each substance there is in crude oil, and display your findings as a pie chart or pictogram.*

▸ *Why must crude oil be separated into fractions before use?*

▲ Fuel oils are used in boilers to keep homes and schools warm, and to fuel factories and power stations.

Sorting out oil fractions

Oil can be separated into fractions with different properties. You may have seen the fractional distillation of oil and tested the fractions in class.

▸ *Make a table showing the properties of the fractions from crude oil. Use the results from the diagram below to fill it in.*

▸ *What pattern can you see as the boiling points increase?*

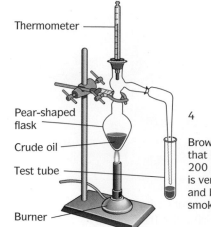

Thermometer

Pear-shaped flask

Crude oil

Test tube

Burner

4 Brown viscous liquid that boils between 200 and 250°C. It is very hard to light and burns with a smoky flame

3 Fairly viscous yellow/orange liquid that boils between 150 and 200°C. It is hard to light and burns with a smoky flame

2 Quite runny, yellow liquid that boils between 100 and 150°C. Lights fairly easily burning with a yellow flame and some smoke

1 Pale yellow, runny liquid that boils between room temperature and 100°C. Lights easily burning with a clear yellow flame

▲ Fractional distillation in the laboratory.

Investigating lubricants

Viscosity is the runniness of liquids. The viscosity of different fractions varies. Plan an investigation to find out what affects the viscosity of oils. Use Chapter One (Experiments and investigations) and Chapter Sixteen (Chemistry help) to help you. Check with your teacher before carrying out your plan.

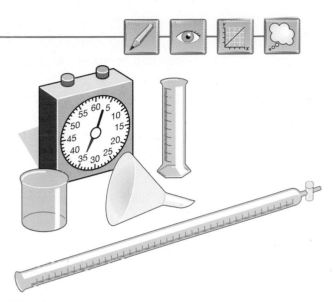

🔺 You could use some of these pieces of apparatus in your investigation.

Alkanes

Oil is a mixture of a very large number of compounds whose physical properties slowly change as their boiling points increase. Although the sizes of the molecules in these compounds are very different, they have a lot in common. They are all hydrocarbons and they all belong to a group or family called **alkanes**. Two of the simplest members of the group are methane and propane. Methane is North Sea gas. Propane is Calor gas.

Alkane	Formula	Melting point (°C)	Boiling point (°C)
Methane	CH_4	-182	-161
Ethane	C_2H_6	-183	-88
Propane	C_3H_8	-188	-42
Butane	C_4H_{10}	-138	-1

🔺 Melting and boiling points for the first four alkanes.

Formulae

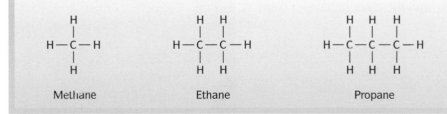

Methane   Ethane   Propane

🔺 The **structural formula** gives you an idea of how the atoms are joined together.

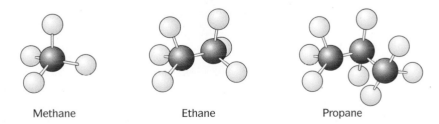

Methane   Ethane   Propane

🔺 This is how the atoms are arranged in space (**3D formula**) but it takes longer to draw.

Notice

- In the structural formula one line represents one single bond.
- Carbon can make four bonds and hydrogen can make only one bond.
- Names of alkanes end in -ane.
- The row of carbon atoms in the molecule is called a **carbon chain**, or sometimes the **spine** of the molecule.
- Alkane molecules get bigger as the carbon chain gets bigger but the general formula, $C_nH_{2n}+2$ (where n = the number of carbon atoms), is the same.

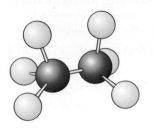

▶ *Butane has four carbon atoms. What is its formula?*

▶ *Use a modelling kit to make models of methane and propane.*

What's made when fuels are burned?

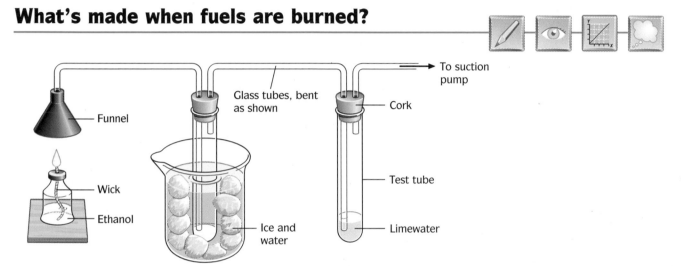

🔺 This apparatus was used to investigate what is given off when fuels burn.

Different fuels were burned as shown in the diagram. Any waste gases were drawn through the apparatus using a pump.

A clean liquid collected in the first test tube, and the clear limewater went cloudy. This happened for each fuel tested.

▶ *What can you learn from the investigation described above?*

Alkanes as fuels

Alkanes are good fuels. When burned in air, energy is transferred to heat things or move things around. The waste products are the same, carbon dioxide and water, whatever alkane is burned. For example:

methane + oxygen → carbon dioxide + water + energy

$$CH_4 + 2O_2 \rightarrow CO_2 + 2H_2O + energy$$

▶ *Give two reasons why alkanes are good fuels.*

🔺 Burning hydrocarbon fuels puts about five billion tonnes of carbon dioxide into the atmosphere every year.

Using models to help to write equations

Experiments can be used to discover that methane burns in air, combining with the oxygen to form carbon dioxide and water. Methane and oxygen are the reactants. Carbon dioxide and water are the products.

▶ *Write the word equation for burning methane in oxygen.*

▶ *Write the chemical symbols underneath the words.*

▶ *Using an atomic modelling kit, make models of the reactants (see page 17).*

▶ *Rearrange these atoms to make the products. Is this possible? What do you have to do?*

▶ *Count the number of atoms on both sides of the equation. It has to be balanced (i.e. have the same number of atoms on both sides).*

▶ *Write the balanced symbol equation for this reaction.*

Supply and demand

Hydrocarbons with larger molecules are very viscous and are difficult to ignite so they do not make very good fuels. Fractionally distilling crude oil gives more of these heavy, long-chain fractions than are needed, and less of the lighter fractions. We might get more fuel oil than we need and not enough petrol.

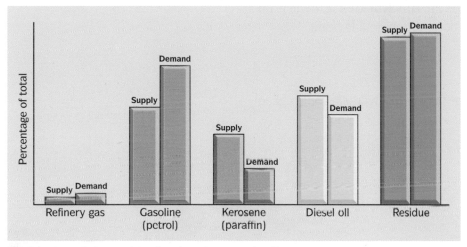

 Supply and demand for fractions from crude oil.

Cracking

To meet the demand for the short-chain alkanes, molecules with long chains of carbon atoms are broken up (**cracked**) to form more useful substances, with smaller molecules. When alkanes are heated strongly in the presence of a **catalyst** the molecules vibrate more and more until bonds are broken and new molecules with fewer carbon atoms are made.

A catalyst increases the rate of a reaction without itself being used up. Chemical catalysts are often metals like nickel and platinum.

▶ *Use the bar chart above to explain why it is necessary to crack fractions of crude oil.*

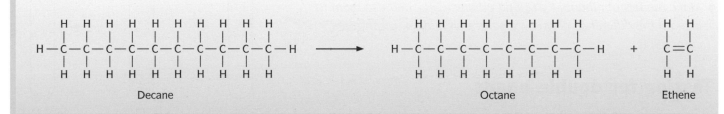

The equation shows what happens to decane (medicinal liquid paraffin) when its vapour is passed over a heated catalyst.

The octane formed in the reaction on the previous page can be blended with lighter fractions to make petrol. The other substance formed, ethene, is the reactive starting material used to make substances like polythene.

Ethene is not an alkane. Its general formula is different and the carbon atoms are joined differently.

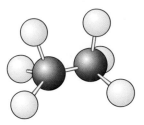

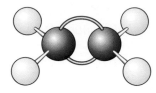

🔺 All the atoms in ethane are joined by single bonds.

🔺 Ethene has a **double bond** between the carbon atoms.

In alkanes the atoms are joined together with single bonds. Compounds like this are called **saturated** compounds. Alkanes are saturated hydrocarbons. Compounds with one or more double bonds are **unsaturated**. Ethene is an unsaturated hydrocarbon as it has one carbon-carbon double bond.

Alkenes

Ethene, C_2H_4, is the first member of a family of hydrocarbons called **alkenes**. All alkene molecules contain at least one double bond.

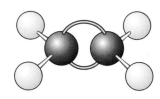

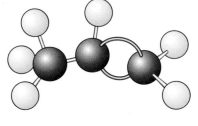

🔺 Ethene, C_2H_4. ($CH_2 = CH_2$)

🔺 Propene, C_3H_6. ($CH_3CH = CH_2$)

Notice

- Names of alkenes end in -ene
- The general formula for each alkene is the same, C_nH_{2n}.
- Alkenes contain one or more double bonds.

▶ *Make a model if you can and write the structural formula of butene, an alkene with four carbon atoms.*

▶ *Make models of ethane, C_2H_6, and ethene, C_2H_4, and use them to explain the difference between a saturated and an unsaturated compound.*

Testing for double bonds

You can test a compound to see if it is unsaturated (contains double bonds) by shaking it with bromine solution. If the compound contains double bonds, the reddish-brown colour of the bromine disappears.

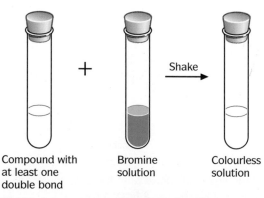

Compound with at least one double bond

Bromine solution

Colourless solution

🔺 This is how to test for double bonds.

Cracking decane

You may be given a worksheet to help you break up or crack an alkane in the lab.

Decane vapour is passed over a heated catalyst. The newly-formed gas is collected in test tubes.

The gas and samples of decane are tested as shown in the table below.

▶ *You know that some students are going to be cracking decane as shown in the diagram on the right. Carry out a risk assessment for safely collecting a gas over cold water from a heated test tube.*

▶ *Look at the table of results below. In what ways is decane different from the substance collected in test tubes in this reaction?*

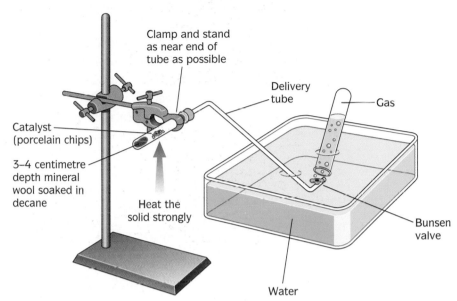

Clamp and stand as near end of tube as possible

Delivery tube

Gas

Catalyst (porcelain chips)

3–4 centimetre depth mineral wool soaked in decane

Heat the solid strongly

Bunsen valve

Water

▲ Apparatus used to crack decane in the lab.

Test	Results for decane	Results for gas
Appearance	Colourless liquid	Colourless gas
Does it burn?	Only burns with a wick	Readily ignites
Reaction with bromine solution	Reddish-brown colour remains	Solution becomes colourless

Reactive alkenes

Unlike alkanes, alkenes are very reactive compounds. The double bond readily opens up and joins on to other substances. Below you can see how it joins on to bromine. The two molecules add on to one another without giving any other products. So, this type of reaction is called an **addition reaction**.

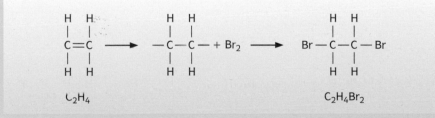

▲ An addition reaction.

▶ *In the presence of a nickel catalyst, ethene, C_2H_4, reacts with hydrogen, H_2, to form ethane, C_2H_6.*
   a *Write an equation for this reaction, using structural formulae.*
   b *Explain what an addition reaction is using the equation for this reaction to illustrate your answer.*

CHEMISTRY

Unsaturated and saturated fats

People's diets in the Western world contain about 40 per cent fats and oils. Oils and fats are mainly long hydrocarbon chains called **fatty acids**. In solid fats, like butter and lard, these molecules contain no double bonds. They are **saturated** fats. Liquid fats like sunflower oil and olive oil contain more than one double bond and so can be described as **unsaturated** fats.

Most people prefer a solid or semi-solid substance to spread on bread and crackers. To meet this demand food manufacturers convert liquid oils into solids like margarine. Unsaturated oils are reacted with hydrogen using a powdered nickel catalyst. You can read more about catalysts in Chapter Ten (Rates of reaction).

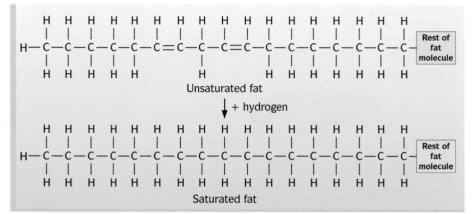

▲ Fats with many double bonds are described as **polyunsaturated** fats.

▲ Hydrogenation of liquid fats.

Hydrogen adds on to the double bonds in the fat molecule. This is called a **hydrogenation reaction**. This is another example of an addition reaction. Reaction conditions are chosen so that not all the double bonds are hydrogenated, just enough to 'harden' the oil.

Using alkenes

Cracking oil produces a valuable range of shorter chain hydrocarbons as well as producing alkenes. These reactive compounds readily add on to other molecules like bromine. They also, in conditions of raised temperature and pressure and with catalysts, join on to each other forming very long chains. This process is called **polymerisation**.

Polymerisation

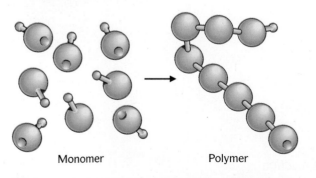

Monomer   Polymer

▲ A model of polymerisation is joining popper beads together.

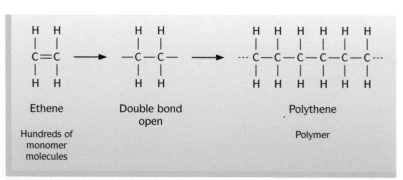

Ethene

Hundreds of monomer molecules

Double bond open

Polythene

Polymer

▲ An example of polymerisation.

The equation at the bottom of the previous page shows ethene molecules adding on to each other using the extra bonding from the double bond to form a new carbon–carbon single bond. The new substance, polythene, is a chain with hundreds of carbon atoms joined together. That is why the diagram above has dotted lines on either end to represent the rest of the carbon chain. If it was drawn out fully it would not fit on the page. In reactions like this, the small reacting molecule is called the **monomer** and the new, large molecule produced when the monomers join together is called a **polymer**.

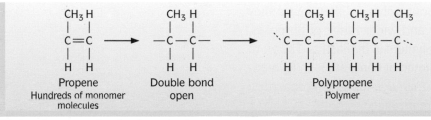

▲ Another example of polymerisation.

Notice that in both of these examples of polymerisation, the small alkene molecule adds on to itself. There are no other products so these are addition reactions, described as **addition polymerisation**.

Monomer	Polymer
Chloroethene (used to be called vinyl chloride)	PVC
Styrene	Polystyrene
TFE	PTFE (non-stick surface of pans)

▲ The monomers used to make some common addition polymers.

Making things from oil products

All these pictures show things that are made from oil.

▶ *Draw a section of the polymer made from each of the following monomers. Show about six carbon atoms.*

a
OH H
| |
C=C
| |
H   H

b
F   H
| |
C=C
| |
H   H

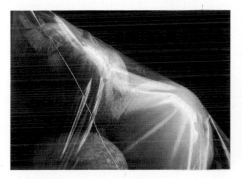

Synthetic and natural polymers

Synthetic (manufactured) polymers have been designed by chemists to fit a whole range of purposes, but the idea is not a new one. Living things have made natural polymers for millions of years. Starch and cellulose are polymers made from the monomer glucose joined together in different ways. Proteins are very complex polymers made from some 22 different small molecules called **amino acids** which are joined together into chains and rings. Silk is a protein.

As scientists came to understand more about polymers they found they could design and make polymers for a wider and wider range of purposes. One of the most common uses of synthetic polymers is in plastics. The word **plastic** just means that the substance was a liquid at some stage in its manufacture. There are two main types of plastics. To understand their properties, you have to look at how the polymer chains are arranged.

Thermosoftening plastics

To make products like washing-up bowls and atomic models, manufacturers buy in plastic granules, melt them and mould them into the desired shape. This type of plastic is like chocolate or jelly. Heating the substance softens it and allows it to be remoulded into a different shape. Polymers like this are known as **thermosoftening plastics** or **thermoplastic polymers**. Polythene and polypropene are examples.

Thermosoftening plastic

🔺 In a thermosoftening plastic the forces in the strands holding the atoms together are very strong but the forces between the strands are weak. On heating they can move past one another and the plastic softens.

🔺 You can feel the strands moving over one another in the plastic used to make these bags if you overload them.

Thermosetting plastics

Thermosetting plastics soften on heating but once cooled and hardened, they cannot be softened again. On cooling, new bonds form linking the polymer strands. These cross links do not break if the polymer is reheated, so instead of softening, the plastic chars and burns. Melamine, Bakelite and polyurethane are thermosetting plastics.

Thermosetting plastic
(showing cross-linking bonds)

🔺 On setting, strong cross links form between the polymer strands in a thermosetting plastic and so it cannot be resoftened.

Fibres

Some clothing is made from synthetic polymers like nylon and polyester.

The strands in a polymer are tangled up together. To make polymers into **fibres** the softened polymer is forced through small holes. This lines the strands up side by side to form a fibre.

▲ All of these clothes are made from oil.

Comparing synthetic and natural fibres

Jason was asked to investigate the properties of synthetic as compared to natural fibres. He decided to compare the strength of fibres made from wool and nylon. He fixed each thread in turn into a bung as shown in the diagram. The paper markers were stuck on to the thread ten centimetres apart.

He then added weights, 100 grams at a time, and remeasured the distance between the markers. He repeated this until the thread snapped.

Mass added to thread (g)	Distance between the markers (cm)	
	Wool	Nylon
0	0	0
100	20	20
200	24	26
300	28	31
400	31	36
500	36	39
600	37	44
700	39	46
800		49
900		52
1000		

▲ This table shows Jason's results.

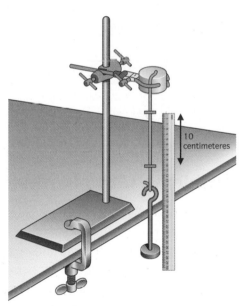

▲ This diagram shows the equipment that Jason used.

Help Jason by thinking about his results and writing up his investigation. You can read about writing up investigations in Chapter One (Experiments and investigations).

Making nylon in the laboratory

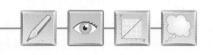

You may be given a worksheet to help you make some nylon. Nylon is a polymer made from two kinds of monomer molecules.

CHEMISTRY

Plastic performance

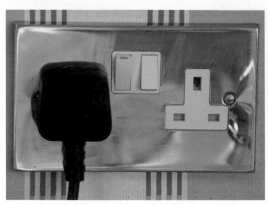

⬆ Plastics are good electrical insulators but they char and burn if heated.

⬆ Plastics can be easily coloured and moulded into shape.

⬆ Nylon ropes are strong, rot-resistant and not very elastic.

⬆ Plastics can be drawn out to give more strength along the length of the fibre. A strimmer head has a nylon line for trimming edges.

⬆ A disposable plastic, sterile syringe is used every time you have an injection.

Problems with plastics

Plastics are easily shaped, relatively cheap and can be easily coloured. They also do not rot. For nylon climbing ropes this is an advantage but for the tonnes of plastic waste that finds its way into refuse collection centres or that is discarded as litter this property is a disadvantage.

Discarded products made from natural materials are slowly broken down by microbes into harmless waste. They are **biodegradable**. So far plastics have proved resistant to microbes and so remain as unwanted rubbish for years on end. One solution would be to recycle them like, for example, paper. The trouble is that there are many different kinds of plastic and it is very expensive to sort them before recycling.

Another solution would be to develop biodegradable plastics, for example, Biopol made by fermentation. Some progress has been made in this direction although these polymers have not yet come into general use.

▶ *Make two lists, one showing the advantages and one showing the disadvantages of using plastics. Include as many points as you can.*

⬆ Plastics are usually strong in relation to their mass.

Summary

- Crude oil is a fossil fuel made from plants and animals that lived millions of years ago.
- Crude oil is a mixture of compounds made mainly from hydrogen and carbon.
- The compounds in oil have different boiling points and so they can be separated into more useful fractions by fractional distillation.
- The properties of hydrocarbons follow a trend as the molecules get bigger and bigger.
- Some fractions of crude oil are used as fuels.
- Compounds made from hydrogen and carbon are called hydrocarbons.
- Alkanes are hydrocarbons in which carbon atoms are joined in a chain by single bonds. Compounds like this with only single bonds are said to be saturated compounds.
- Alkenes are another group of hydrocarbons. They have one or more double bonds. Compounds containing one or more double bonds are said to be unsaturated compounds.
- Alkanes with long chains of carbon atoms can be cracked using strong heat and catalysts to form smaller alkanes and alkenes.
- Alkenes (for example, ethene) are very reactive and are used as starting materials to make many useful substances including polymers.
- Polymers (for example, polythene) are very large molecules formed when small molecules, like ethene, join together. The small molecule is called a monomer and the joining together process is called polymerisation.
- When monomers join together to produce a polymer and no other substance is made the reaction is called addition polymerisation.
- Plastics are compounds that were liquid at some stage in their manufacture. Plastics are polymers.
- You should know some examples of addition polymers (for example, polythene and PVC), their uses and some of the advantages and disadvantages of our widespread use of plastics.

Revision Questions

1 Draw a flowchart to show how oil and gas are formed from dead plants and animals.

2 List the properties of plastics that make them so useful. Give examples of plastics with different properties.

3 The uses of the fractions of crude oil and of the chemicals made from oil are outlined in this chapter. Cut out photographs from magazines, or make drawings to illustrate these uses. Make a chart called 'Crude oil and its uses' to use later for revision.

4 Early in 1993 the tanker *Braer* crashed on the rocks of the Shetland Islands spilling most of its 85 thousand tonne cargo of oil into the sea. After the accident the local people and the representatives from the oil company met to discuss the continued movement of oil using supertankers. List the occupations of some people who might contribute to the discussion. For each person, write down some of their interests and the main points they might want to make. If possible arrange a debate in which members of your group take the roles of people who would like to see the movement of oil limited in some way and of those who feel it is necessary.

5 Oil provides the starting chemicals used to make polymers, drugs, dyes and so on, but we burn most of the oil we pump up from underground. What could we do to cut down our use of oil fractions as fuels?

6 How are we affected now by the discovery of synthetic polymers? What would life be like without them?

7 Look back at the properties and formulae of the first four alkanes.
   a Write down the symbol and structural formula for:
      i pentane, the next member of the series
      ii decane, which has ten carbon atoms.
   b What is the general formula for alkanes?
   c What do you think the alkane with eight carbon atoms is called?

   d Draw a graph with the number of carbon atoms (allow up to ten) on the *x*-axis and melting point and boiling point (°C) on the *y*-axis.
   e Use your graph to predict the boiling point and melting point of decane. How accurate is your prediction likely to be?
   f What pattern can you see in the boiling and melting points of alkanes as the number of carbon atoms in the molecule increases?

8 The alkanes in the heavier fractions from crude oil are often cracked to give new products. What happens to alkanes if they are cracked? Give some similarities and differences between the starting compounds and the new products. Explain the meaning of:
   a monomer
   b polymer
   c n in $[-C_2H_4-]n$

9 Make a note to use for revision about the differences between thermosoftening and thermosetting plastics. It should include:
   a differences in their structure
   b differences in their properties
   c some examples of each type and their uses.

10
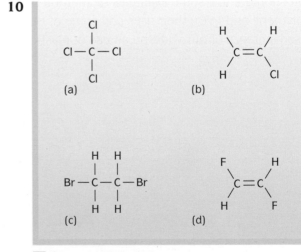
Structural formulae.

   a Which of these compounds is saturated and which is unsaturated?
   b Which of these compounds would decolour bromine solution?

Metals

The woman who received these gold earrings knew that the giver wanted to be more than just good friends.

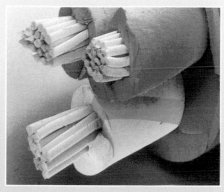

Metals like copper bring electricity to our homes and workplaces.

This car is made from aluminium. This element was not produced commercially until a little over a century ago although it's one of the most common metals in the Earth's crust.

It's hard to imagine life without metals. Metals are recovered from rocks and minerals taken from the Earth. At first people scraped and dug out minerals from the surface of the soil. Nowadays we mine deep into the Earth, and dynamite huge areas several kilometres across, to obtain metal-bearing rocks.

■ Metal reserves

Industry depends heavily on a whole variety of metals. At the moment we have a good supply of some metals, like iron and aluminium. Other metals that are critical to industry are in short supply. For example, chromium and manganese are needed to mix with other metals to produce stainless steel. Platinum is a valuable catalyst in many industrial processes, and cobalt is needed to make the heat-resistant, high-strength alloys used in the aerospace industry. (An alloy is a mixture of two or more metals.) All these metals are scarce. Shortages of zinc, tungsten and lead could also cause problems in the future.

The table on the right shows how many years of supply we have left for some important metals, if we keep using them at the current rate.

■ Conserving metals

Unless action is taken quickly, many important metals will simply run out within a century. There are several ways in which we can help to make metal reserves last longer.

Recycling not only saves metals but also conserves energy supplies. For example, getting usable aluminium from scrap uses only about five per cent of the energy needed to extract aluminium from rocks and ores. Scrap has now become a valuable resource.

Exploration might find new sources of metals, so they will be available for longer.

As the price of metals changes it might become become worthwhile to use poorer quality rocks and ores containing low quantities of metal. This would help maintain supplies for longer.

We could learn to use other materials instead of metals. In food packaging, tin has been replaced by glass and plastics. The vast majority of drinks cans are now made from aluminium instead of tin. Much copper piping has now been replaced by cheaper and lighter plastic piping.

Metal	Number of years of supply left, at our current rate of use
Copper	66
Lead	37
Platinum and other precious metals	176
Silver	24
Zinc	70
Cobalt	116
Gold	30
Manganese	186
Nickel	144
Tin	21
Chromium	374
Titanium	138

The Earth's reserves of some important metals.

Review

Metals and non-metals

Elements can be grouped in several ways, according to their properties. One way of grouping elements is as metals and non-metals.

This is what we learned last year about elements. We were asked to classify some elements according to their properties, by using tests and looking in the library. We found that the elements fell into two groups. One group contained metals, and the other group had completely different properties.

It wasn't difficult to pick out most metals because they were heavy, shiny solids. With some, we needed to scrape the surface layer to see the shiny surface underneath. Using a simple electrical circuit we found that all the metals were conductors of electricity. This made sense when we realised that insides of wires and cables are made from metal. This set us thinking about other uses of metals. Saucepans and baking tins are made from metal, so metals must be good conductors of heat. In the library we found information that said this was true. At the same time we discovered one metal that didn't quite fit into the group. Mercury is a liquid at room temperature, not a solid like other metals.

At first we couldn't see many similarities in the elements that were not metals. Most were gases like oxygen and chlorine. One was a liquid. That was bromine. Bromine is a reddish-brown liquid with red vapour above it. Sulphur, iodine and carbon (graphite) were solids. Their surfaces were dull, although iodine could be said to shine a bit. These elements weren't 'strong' like metals. They crumbled easily. Testing showed that although sulphur was a poor conductor of electricity, carbon was a good conductor which didn't quite fit into our scheme. In the library we found out that the elements we had left were classed as non-metals. They are almost all poor conductors of heat and electricity. Carbon, as we had suspected, is an exception to this rule.

CHECK THREE

1 Make a table comparing the properties of metals with non-metals.

2 Describe two elements that do not fit into the general patterns.

Marvellous metals

You can get an idea of how important and useful metals are just by looking around at home, or at school, or out in the street. Metals are used for hundreds of different jobs, because of their properties. To understand the properties of metals you have to know something about their structure. The structure of a substance is the way the atoms are arranged and joined together.

Metals are crystalline. The crystals are very small and so unless you have grown some metal crystals in the lab, or cleaned a metal surface with acid, you might not have noticed them. Millions of atoms are packed closely together in a regular pattern. The atoms make up a three-dimensional structure called a **giant metallic lattice**.

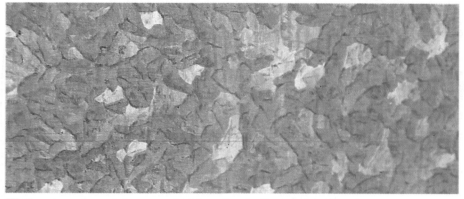

🔺 The atoms in metals are packed together in tiny crystals, like these.

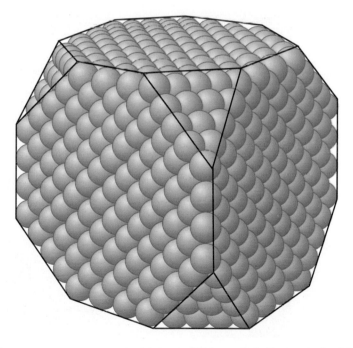

🔺 This shows copper atoms packed into a copper crystal. Copper is flexible, can be beaten into shape, has a high melting and boiling point, and is a good conductor of heat and electricity.

▶ *Try to stack some apples, oranges or polystyrene spheres into a structure like a metallic lattice.*

CHEMISTRY

Explaining metal properties

Strength

Almost all metals are strong and hard. They can support heavy loads which explains why they are used in building construction. This strength (called **tensile strength**) allows metals to support a big pull, which explains their use in cables for bridges and ski lifts. Metals are strong because the forces between the atoms (called **metallic bonds**) are very strong. These bonds are a bit like a flexible glue holding the whole structure together.

🔺 This machine slowly pulls samples of materials apart, to measure their tensile strength.

Heat-resistance

Most metals have high melting and boiling points, because of the strong forces between the atoms in a metal. They can be heated to high temperatures without becoming soft and changing shape, which explains their use in pans, casings for ovens and the elements in electric fires.

Density

Metals are generally heavy for their size. Some are very dense solids.

▶ *Try to explain why metals are dense solids, in terms of the arrangement of their atoms.*

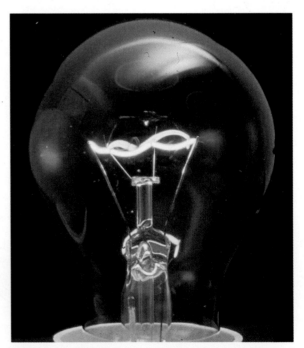

🔺 The coiled filament in a light bulb is made from the metal tungsten. As an electric current passes through the filament, it reaches extremely high temperatures, but it does not melt.

Flexibility

Metals are **malleable.** When you bend or hammer a metal, it does not break into pieces. Instead, the layers of metal atoms just move over one another and the overall shape changes. This explains why metals can be rolled out or squeezed into different shapes. In industry, metals are stretched into sheets to be later shaped into car doors or drinks cans, or squeezed into bars to be used for reinforcing concrete. Metals are also pulled out into wires to make ropes and cables.

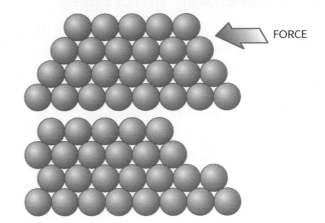
FORCE

◣ Metals can be hammered or bent into shape without breaking. This diagram shows how the layers of atoms in a metal can slip easily across one another when a force is applied.

Good conductors of electricity

Metals carry electricity into our homes. Metals do not change as they conduct electricity, so wires can be used for many years without being replaced. Metals are also good conductors of heat. The atomic model for metals shown earlier in this chapter cannot explain these properties as it is. To explain conduction, you need to look more closely at the structure of atoms. You may have read about atoms in Chapter Two (Oil). Atoms have a central nucleus containing positively charged particles called protons. Around the nucleus there is a kind of cloud of negative charge to balance the positively charged protons. When a metal is connected into an electrical circuit this cloud of negative charge flows from one atom to another. This flow of charge is an electric current. You will later learn that this mobile cloud is made from negatively charged particles called **electrons.** When heated, these charged particles move around more quickly, jostling their neighbours and transferring the heat energy throughout the metal.

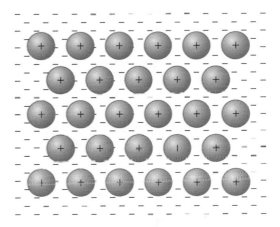

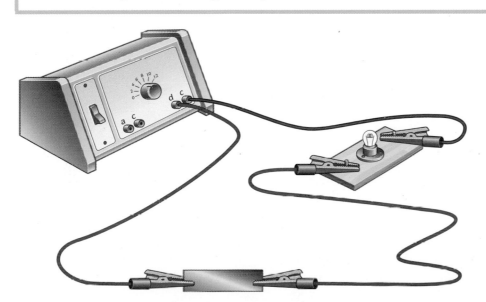

◣ This circuit can be used to test materials for electrical conductivity.

Metals have their differences

Different metals have some different properties. For example, a few metals are magnetic, like iron and nickel. Others are particularly dense, or soft, or resistant to corrosion. The metal you choose for any purpose depends on these differences.

Metal (symbol)	Density (g/cm^3)	Melting point (°C)	Tensile strength (MPa)	Electrical conductivity (Sm^{-1})	Properties
Aluminium (Al)	2.7	660	50–110	3.8×10^7	'Light', and resistant to corrosion
Copper (Cu)	8.9	1084	220–430	5.9×10^7	Excellent conductor of heat and electricity
Gold (Au)	19.3	1064	120–220	4.2×10^7	Expensive, but good conductor
Iron (Fe)	7.9	1540	210	1.0×10^7	Rusts in moist air
Lead (Pb)	11.3	327	15	4.8×10^6	Very 'heavy', and absorbs harmful radiation
Titanium (Ti)	4.5	1660	230	1.9×10^6	Expensive, but very resistant to corrosion
Zinc (Zn)	7.1	420	139	1.7×10^7	Resistant to corrosion

▲ Properties of some metals.

Comparing atoms

The following questions compare atoms of different elements. Use data tables to help you answer them. Use Chapters Fourteen (Structure and bonding) and Sixteen (Chemistry help) if you need to.

▶ Write down the relative atomic mass, A_r, for the following metals and non-metals.
a carbon, C
b magnesium, Mg
c sulphur, S
d sodium, Na
e hydrogen, H

▶ What type of atom is:
a 12 times as heavy as hydrogen
b twice as heavy as carbon
c twice as heavy as nitrogen?

▶ Write down the mass of 1 mol of atoms of:
a hydrogen
b sodium
c carbon.

▶ Work out the mass of:
a 2 mol of hydrogen atoms
b 0.1 mol of sodium atoms
c 10 mol of carbon atoms.

▶ How many mols of atoms are there in :
a 32 g of sulphur
b 10 g of hydrogen
c 4.6 g of sodium?

Reactions of metals

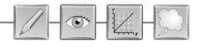

You may be asked to test and compare the reactions of different metals with water and acids and be given a worksheet to help you.

The problem with metals is that, although they have useful properties, they readily react with, or join on to, other elements. New compounds with totally different properties are formed and sometimes it's very difficult to get the metal back again. For example, you might have seen what happens when metal parts of cars and bikes react with oxygen in the air. But the reactions of metals can be useful, too. Knowing how metals react with other substances is the basis of the methods used to get metals from rocks and ores.

Metals and oxygen

Oxides of metals are often found in rocks because many metals join on to the oxygen in the air. Metals like potassium and sodium have to kept under oil because they are so **reactive** that they can catch fire spontaneously as they react with oxygen in air. Metals like iron and zinc react slowly with oxygen when heated. Calcium burns in oxygen forming calcium oxide.

metal + oxygen → metal oxide

calcium + oxygen → calcium oxide

$$2Ca(s) + O_2(g) \rightarrow 2CaO(s)$$

Metals like gold, silver and copper, that people have been using for hundreds of years, either don't react with oxygen at all or react very slowly. These metals are **unreactive**.

> Letters in brackets after a formula tell you more about the substance. For instance, Zn(s) means zinc which is a solid. You might also see (aq) which means **aqueous** or dissolved in water, (l) which means liquid and (g) which means gas.
>
> ▶ Put the correct letters in brackets after each the following formulae.
> **a** water, H_2O
> **b** iron, Fe
> **c** seawater, NaCl
> **d** mercury, Hg

Metals and water

If you have seen sodium and potassium reacting with water you will already know why there are no sodium or potassium mines in the world. These metals rush over the surface of the water, reacting with it very rapidly to produce hydrogen. Sometimes they catch fire. Other metals like aluminium, zinc and iron react with heated water (steam), while copper and gold do not react with water at all.

metal + water → metal hydroxide + hydrogen

magnesium + water → magnesium hydroxide + hydrogen

$$Mg(s) + 2H_2O(l) \rightarrow Mg(OH)_2(aq) + H_2(g)$$

▶ Why do we use copper for water pipes?

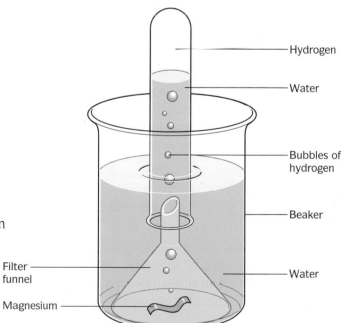

🔺 Magnesium reacts very slowly with water producing hydrogen. Collecting small amounts of hydrogen takes several days.

Metals and dilute acids

Some metals react with dilute acids, and give off hydrogen. This is one reason why acid rain can cause such damage to buildings. Like the reactions with water and air, there is a pattern in the way metals react with dilute acid. Gold and copper do not react at all. Sodium and calcium react violently, too violently to be tested in the lab. Magnesium, aluminium, zinc and iron all react with dilute acid, but each reacts less vigorously than the last.

$$\text{metal} + \text{dilute acid} \rightarrow \text{metal compound} + \text{hydrogen}$$

$$\text{magnesium} + \text{hydrochloric acid} \rightarrow \text{magnesium chloride} + \text{hydrogen}$$

$$Mg(s) + 2HCl(aq) \rightarrow MgCl_2(aq) + H_2(g)$$

The bubbles you can see when magnesium reacts with acid contain newly made hydrogen gas.

Metals and acid rain

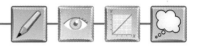

Plan

Ruth is planning an investigation into acid rain and its action on metals. (You may read about acid rain in Chapter Five (Acids and bases).)

'I know that one of the main causes of acid rain is sulphur dioxide. I wanted to investigate the effect of sulphur dioxide in the atmosphere on different metals so I asked our technician Margot how I could make an atmosphere that is acidic due to the presence of this gas. She said that I could use a solution of a compound called sodium sulphite that slowly releases sulphur dioxide into the air around it.

'I am going to stick strips of different metals of the same size into a piece of expanded polystyrene and put them into a transparent plastic box along with a beaker of sodium sulphite solution. I'm going to seal up the lid with sticky tape so that an acidic atmosphere develops inside the box, and look at it once a week over the next few weeks.

'The metals I am going to use are aluminium, copper, magnesium, nickel, tin, iron and zinc. I wanted at first to use calcium and sodium because they are very reactive metals. But I found out from a text book that these metals react quickly even with water so I thought it might be too dangerous.'

Risk assessment

'From a textbook I found that sulphur dioxide is a **toxic** (poisonous) gas. Breathing in small amounts causes breathlessness and coughing. The container of sodium sulphite solution must be kept covered until it's put into the plastic box. The lid of the box must fit and be sealed to prevent the gas escaping.'

▶ *Read Ruth's plan to investigate metals and acid rain.*

▶ *How do you think Ruth's investigation could be improved? (Look at Chapter One (Experiments and investigations) if you need help.) Include as many improvements as you can, explaining why they are necessary.*

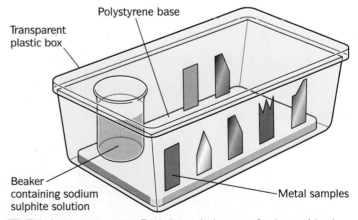

▲ This is the apparatus Ruth intended to use for her acid rain investigation.

CHEMISTRY

Patterns in reactivity

From their reactions with air, water and acids, metals can be arranged in a list with the most reactive metals at the top and the least reactive at the bottom.

▶ *Use the reactivity list on the right to explain why some metal objects have lasted in a better condition over the centuries than others.*

Using the reactivity list

The **reactivity** (or activity) **list** of metals allows us to make predictions about how metals and their compounds will react.

Metals at the top of the list readily react with other substances and the compounds they form do not easily **decompose** (or split up) again. For example, magnesium readily reacts with oxygen, forming white magnesium oxide. The forces (bonds) joining magnesium and oxygen together are very strong and so it takes lots of energy to separate magnesium from oxygen. Copper reacts slowly with oxygen on heating, forming black copper oxide. The forces holding copper and oxygen together are weak and so not much energy is needed to separate copper metal from oxygen.

▶ *From which of the following metal oxides would it be easiest to get the metal? Make a list putting the easiest at the top and the most difficult at the bottom.*
aluminium oxide, Al$_2$O$_3$
lead oxide, PbO
zinc oxide, ZnO

potassium	K	
sodium	Na	
calcium	Ca	
magnesium	Mg	
aluminium	Al	
(carbon	C)	
zinc	Zn	
iron	Fe	
tin	Sn	
lead	Pb	
(hydrogen	H)	
copper	Cu	
silver	Ag	
gold	Au	
platinum	Pt	

Increasing reactivity

◢ The reactivity list.

Competing for oxygen

Metals high in the reactivity list readily react with oxygen in the air. Metals will also take and combine with oxygen from another metal oxide, provided that the other metal is lower than itself in the reactivity list. For example, when aluminium and iron oxide are heated together, aluminium can grab oxygen from the iron oxide because aluminium is above iron in the reactivity list.

aluminium + iron oxide → iron + aluminium oxide

$$2Al(s) + Fe_2O_3(s) \rightarrow 2Fe(s) + Al_2O_3(s)$$

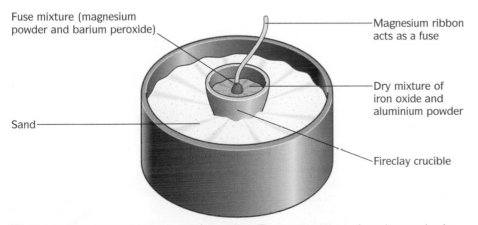

Fuse mixture (magnesium powder and barium peroxide)

Magnesium ribbon acts as a fuse

Dry mixture of iron oxide and aluminium powder

Sand

Fireclay crucible

◢ The lighted fuse starts this reaction going. Then you can see the mixture glowing and sparks being produced.

▶ *Can carbon be used to grab oxygen from iron oxide? Why?*

▶ *Your teacher may demonstrate the reaction shown in the drawing on the left.*

⬆ The reaction between aluminium oxide and iron (known as the thermit reaction) is used for on-the-spot welding. Here the heat produced by the reaction melts the metal railway tracks and welds them together.

▶ *What would you expect to happen if you heated:*
  a *iron with aluminium oxide*
  b *magnesium with copper oxide?*

Displacement reactions

If you dip a strip of zinc into a solution of blue copper sulphate, the surface of the zinc becomes coated with a layer of orange copper metal. The zinc has pushed out or **displaced** the copper from the compound. Zinc is above copper in the reactivity list. A metal will displace another metal lower than itself in the reactivity list from a solution of one of its compounds. These are called **displacement** reactions.

zinc + copper sulphate → copper + zinc sulphate

$$Zn(s) + Cu(SO_4)_2(aq) \rightarrow Cu(s) + Zn(SO_4)_2(aq)$$

⬆ A strip of one metal is dipped into a solution of a compound of another metal.

Displacement predictions

Copy and complete the table below. You are to predict whether or not the metal in the solution will be displaced from its compound in solution by another metal. Put 'yes' or 'no' in the appropriate boxes. One example has been done for you.

Metal	Solution				
	Zinc sulphate	Iron sulphate	Magnesium sulphate	Copper sulphate	Lead nitrate
Zinc				yes	
Iron					
Magnesium					
Copper					
Lead					

🔺 You can predict when a displacement reaction will happen using the reactivity list.

You may be given a worksheet to help you test these predictions about displacement reactions.

Investigating displacement reactions

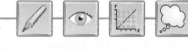

Plan an investigation to find answers to one or more of the following questions.

▶ *There is a temperature rise when iron displaces copper from copper sulphate solution. What affects this temperature rise?*

▶ *Do all metals produce a temperature rise when added to copper sulphate solution?*

▶ *What affects the amount of copper that is displaced from copper sulphate solution?*

🔺 You could use a temperature probe linked up to a computer to help you carry out your investigation.

Oxidation

When magnesium burns it joins on to oxygen in the air forming a white powder. The powder is a compound called an oxide. This is a simple example of an **oxidation** reaction. The magnesium is **oxidised** to magnesium oxide. The substance that does the oxidising is called an **oxidising agent**. In this reaction, the oxidising agent is oxygen.

magnesium + oxygen → magnesium oxide

$$2Mg(s) + O_2(g) \rightarrow 2MgO(s)$$

oxidised

It's not only metals that can be oxidised.

sulphur + oxygen → sulphur dioxide

$$S(s) + O_2(g) \rightarrow SO_2(g)$$

oxidised

▶ *In your notes write the equation for burning carbon in oxygen. Mark on the substance that has been oxidised, and the substance that is the oxidising agent.*

About 20 per cent of the air around us is oxygen. Without it we could not survive. Oxygen is a colourless gas with no smell or taste. We don't notice its presence but nearly all elements and compounds react with it.

If a glowing wooden splint is put into a test tube of oxygen, the splint will burst into flame. This test is used to identify oxygen gas.

Corrosion

🔺 The metal structure of the Eiffel Tower in Paris would not survive without a coat of paint every seven years. It has a surface area of about 50 acres, which takes 60 tonnes of paint to cover.

Corrosion is an example of an oxidation reaction. The surfaces of metal objects lose their shine because they get covered with a layer of oxide. Over time the whole object corrodes and has to be replaced. **Rusting** of iron is a special example of corrosion.

Rusting

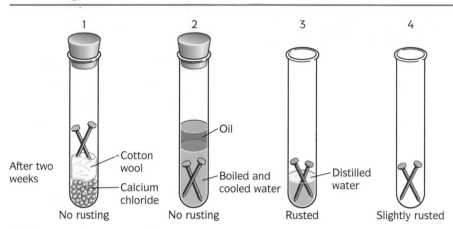

1   2   3   4

After two weeks

Cotton wool
Calcium chloride
No rusting

Oil
Boiled and cooled water
No rusting

Distilled water
Rusted

Slightly rusted

🔺 The experiment shown in the diagram above was set up to discover what makes iron rust. Iron nails were placed in four different sets of conditions, and left for two weeks.

▶ *What was the purpose of test tube 4?*

▶ *What makes iron rust?*

When iron rusts, it is oxidised by oxygen in the air. Iron oxide then joins on to water forming the crumbly orange solid we call rust. Rusting only takes place if both oxygen and water are present. This oxidation reaction causes lots of problems. Unless they are specially protected, objects such as car exhausts, that are made from iron or contain iron, slowly rust away and must be replaced.

iron + oxygen → iron oxide

$4Fe(s) + 3O_2(g) \rightarrow 2Fe_2O_3(s) \rightarrow$ joins with water and forms rust

Zinc corrodes very slowly. Every year two million tonnes of zinc are used to coat metals like iron and steel to stop them rusting. Metals coated in zinc are called galvanised metals.

🔺 Painted galvanised steel is used in London's Docklands Light Railway.

Burning

Burning is an oxidation reaction in which a lot of energy is transferred rapidly to the surroundings. When substances burn they react with oxygen from the air and form oxides.

methane (natural gas) + oxygen → carbon dioxide + water

$$CH_4(g) + 2O_2(g) \rightarrow CO_2(g) + 2H_2O(g)$$

oxidised

Compounds can be oxidised, as well as elements. The products of the reaction are the oxides of the elements in the compound. In the reaction shown above, methane is oxidised as it burns in air. The products are the oxides of carbon and hydrogen.

Food decay

You have probably noticed how foods taste quite different and unappetising if they are left open to the air for some time. Oxygen from the air attacks the food, oxidising it and producing acids that alter its taste. All sorts of different compounds are added to food to try to stop it 'going off' like this, including **antioxidants**. Antioxidants are substances that are more easily oxidised than the food itself and so the food stays fresh for a longer time.

▶ *Look at the ingredients lists on some food labels.*
What foods contain antioxidants?

Summary

- Most elements are metals, which have characteristic properties.
- The remaining elements, with different properties, are called non-metals, which have many different properties.
- Metals are shiny solids that melt at high temperatures. They are easily hammered or bent into shape. Metals are good conductors of heat and electricity.
- Non-metals are gases, liquids or solids. They have low melting and boiling points and are poor conductors of heat and electricity. Non-metal solids are brittle and crumbly with a dull appearance.
- Metals can be arranged into a list with the most reactive at the top and the least reactive at the bottom.
- You can find the position of any metal in the reactivity list by observing how easily it reacts with oxygen, water and dilute acid.
- A metal will take oxygen from the oxide of a metal that is lower than itself on the reactivity list.
- A metal will displace or push out a metal that is lower on the reactivity list from a solution of one of the lower metal's compounds.
- Burning is an example of an oxidation reaction.
- Fossil fuels, such as natural gas, burn in air producing carbon dioxide and water.
- Corrosion is another example of an oxidation reaction.
- Rusting is an oxidation reaction. Iron reacts with oxygen in the presence of water, producing rust. Only iron rusts.
- Antioxidants are added to foods to prevent them reacting with oxygen and 'going off'.

Revision Questions

1 Describe the tests you would carry out, and what you would expect to observe, if you were given a solid and asked to show it was a metal.

2 What tests would you do to find the place of an unknown metal in the reactivity list?

3 Look at the information about metals on page 34. Then copy the table below and complete it for six metals of your choice. One example has been done for you.

Metal	Use	Reason
Lead	Screens for X-ray departments in hospitals	Lead absorbs harmful radiation and so protects staff working in the area

4 What is an oxidation reaction? Use at least four examples to illustrate your answer.

5 Carry out some research into the dates when different metals were discovered. Make a time line describing your findings. Underneath, use the reactivity list to explain why you think they were discovered in this order.

6 Give two tests you could do to show that magnesium is a metal and sulphur is a non-metal.

Use the reactivity list on page 37 to help you complete the following questions.

7 Explain why some metals like gold are found as the pure metals while other metals like aluminium are always found in compounds, joined to other elements.

8

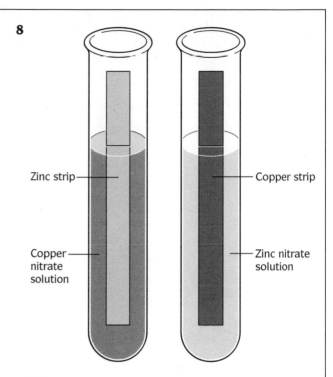

Zinc strip — Copper strip

Copper nitrate solution — Zinc nitrate solution

▲ Testing the reactivity of copper and zinc.

a What would you see happening in the test tubes drawn above?
b Write the word equation, and the symbol equation if you can, for any reactions taking place.
c Explain your answer to part a.

9 It's estimated that 80 per cent of all aluminium used could be recycled, and yet only 30 per cent of the world production of aluminium comes from scrap.
a Why has the recycling of metals become such an important issue in recent years?
b What could be done to make the recycling of used aluminium more efficient?

10 Use the diagram on page 33, showing how metal atoms are joined in giant metallic lattices, to help you explain why most metals:
a have a high density (are heavy for their size)
b have high melting and boiling points
c can be hammered into shape (they can change shape without breaking) and drawn into long wires
d are good conductors of electricity.

11

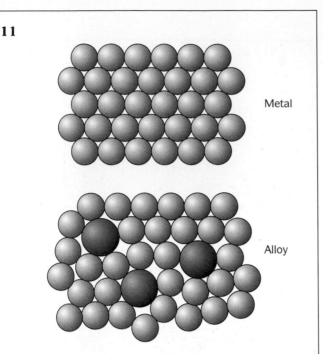

Metal

Alloy

🔺 The arrangement of particles in a pure metal and in an alloy.

When two or more metals are joined together they form an alloy. Use the diagrams above to help you explain why alloys are often tougher and stronger than the pure metals used to make them.

12

Compound	Result when compound is heated
sodium carbonate	Unchanged even after strong heating
calcium carbonate	Breaks down to calcium oxide and carbon dioxide when heated strongly for some time
copper carbonate	Breaks down to copper oxide and carbon dioxide immediately on gentle heating

The table shows the results of heating some metal compounds.

a Arrange the metals sodium, copper and calcium in the order of their reactivity.

b What pattern can you see in these results?

c What would you expect to observe on heating magnesium carbonate?

d Name a metal carbonate other than sodium carbonate that you would expect to be unchanged even after strong heating.

Ores

Without quarrying and mining, industry could not obtain the raw materials needed to manufacture all the products the developed world takes for granted. But as we dig into more and more of the Earth's crust, we scar the landscape forever, and disrupt or destroy natural habitats.

This used to be a mountain in Arizona, USA. Now it's a copper mine about two and a half miles wide and half a mile deep.

Madagascar is an island in the Indian Ocean, whose forests are home to endangered animals like the Sifaka in this photo. Plans are underway to mine for an ore called ilmenite $(FeTiO_3)$ on Madagascar. Ilmenite is processed to make a whitener used in paper and toothpaste. It's estimated that the planned mining would destroy 65 per cent of Madagascar's coastal forest.

In Antarctica the Sun can be seen for 24 hours a day in summer and the stars for 24 hours a day in winter.

As reserves of minerals and ores become depleted or used up people look around for new sources to develop for the future. Antarctica is one of the world's last wildernesses where humans have not yet interfered. But many countries are now interested in developing Antarctica's rich mineral deposits.

Antarctica's resources are protected for the next 50 years under the terms of an agreement drawn up in 1991, and it has been suggested that Antarctica should be kept forever as a World Park. But conservationists will have a very tough job persuading people to do without all their machines and materials in order to preserve Antarctica.

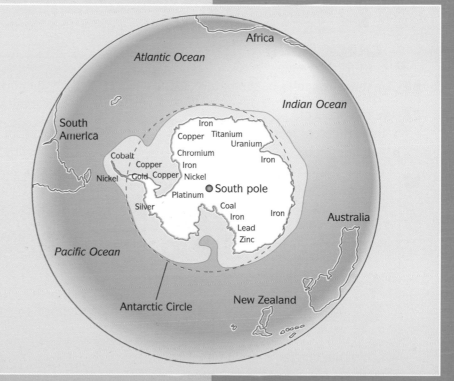

Scientists believe there may be over nine hundred major mineral deposits, the world's largest coalfield and extensive reserves of oil hidden away under the snow and ice of Antarctica.

Review

Before going any further, read this page and attempt the tasks. Write the answers in your notes.

Malachite is a mineral containing the compound copper carbonate.

Most elements join on to other elements forming new substances called compounds. Elements combine during chemical reactions. For example, zinc and oxygen react together to form zinc oxide. When oxygen joins on to another element, it is called oxidation.

zinc + oxygen → zinc oxide

$2 \text{ Zn(s)} + \text{O}_2\text{(g)} \rightarrow 2 \text{ ZnO(s)}$

Models and drawings are often used to describe elements and compounds.

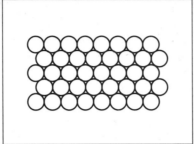

This represents the way a metal element is made up of atoms.

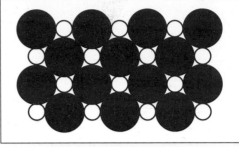

This represents the same metal element joined to oxygen, to form a metal oxide.

Name of compound	Elements joined	Explanation of the name
Magnesium oxide Sodium chloride Lead sulphide	Magnesium and oxygen Sodium and chlorine Lead and sulphur	-ide tells you only the two elements named are present
Copper sulphate Calcium carbonate	Copper, sulphur and oxygen Calcium, carbon and oxygen	-ate tell you the two elements named *and oxygen* are present

You can sometimes tell from the name of a compound what elements it contains.

CHECK FOUR

1 Give three examples of chemical reactions.

2 Give examples of:
  a three different metal oxides
  b two non-metal oxides.

3

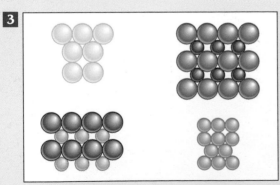

Which of the diagrams could represent
a metals
b metal oxides?

4 Write down the elements in each of the following compounds: potassium chloride, zinc iodide, copper carbonate, magnesium sulphate.

5 Write down the name of a compound made from:
  a zinc and sulphur
  b sodium and bromine
  c lead, carbon and oxygen.

6 Write a word equation for the oxidation of sodium.

Metals from rocks

Native gold

A prospector and a geologist are sure that they have found a vein of gold in Wales worth £2.5 million. All their observations have convinced them that they are in the right place. They have found small specks of gold spread throughout the rock. Gold is one of the only metals that can be found 'native'. That means it is not joined to other elements. When crushed rock is mixed with water, the gold sinks to the bottom, because it is more dense than the rock, and can be collected. This is called 'panning' for gold.

Panning for gold in the Welsh hills.

▶ *What effect do you think there will be on the local area if gold is found in the Welsh hills? Make two lists showing the good and bad points to help you decide whether finding gold in your area would be good or bad news.*

Metals have some very useful properties, that manufacturers put to good use in all kinds of products. The problem with most metals is that they readily react with other substances forming compounds with completely different properties. This means that only a few metals are found uncombined with other elements and can be dug out of the ground as pure metal, or **native**. Copper is sometimes found native, but only in tiny amounts, too small to be recovered. Most metals are found in rocks joined on to other elements, such as oxygen and sulphur.

Rocks, minerals and ores

Rocks can be any size from giant boulders to grains of sand. The compounds and elements that occur naturally in rocks are called **minerals**. Minerals are individual substances with names and formulae. Some minerals, like limestone, are found in rocks on their own. Most minerals are found in rocks mixed with other substances and often are not the main compounds in the rock. When these mixtures contain enough of the mineral for it to be profitably extracted, the mixture is called an **ore**.

Name of the ore	Name of the metal we extract or get from the ore	The chemical compound in the ore
 Chalcopyrite (copper pyrites)	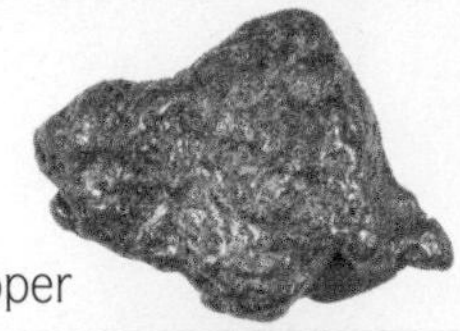 Copper	Copper and iron sulphides
 Galena	 Lead	Lead sulphide
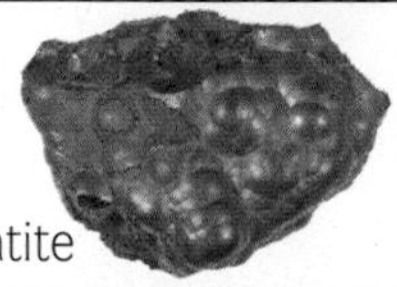 Haematite	 Iron	Iron oxide
 Halite	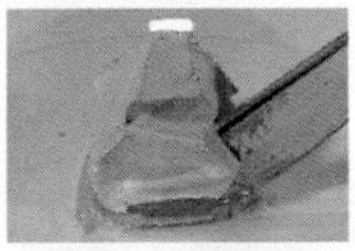 Sodium	Sodium chloride
 Malachite	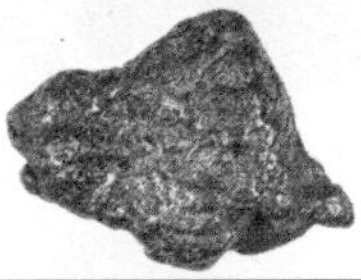 Copper	Copper carbonate
 Pyrites	 Iron	Iron sulphide
 Zinc blende	 Zinc	Zinc sulphide

The ores from which some important metals are extracted.

Comparing compounds

Use Chapter Sixteen (Chemistry help) if you need to.

▶ Write down the relative formula mass of:
  a magnesium oxide, MgO
  b sodium chloride, NaCl
  c calcium carbonate, $CaCO_3$
  d iron oxide, Fe_2O_3.

▶ Work out the mass of:
  a 1 mol sodium chloride
  b 0.1 mol calcium carbonate
  c 5 mol iron oxide.

▶ For magnesium oxide work out the mass of:
  a 1 mol
  b 0.5 mol
  c 2.5 mol.

▶ How many mols are in:
  a 80 g of magnesium oxide
  b 300 g calcium carbonate
  c 5.85 g sodium chloride.

▶ Copy and complete this table for three or more ores.

Name of the ore	What does it look like?	Names of elements in the ore

Mining and minerals

1 Rocks and ores can be obtained by underground mining or by mining from the surface of the soil. Some compounds, like salt, are dissolved in water and pumped up from underground.

2 The rocks and ores are crushed or ground into pieces of a suitable size for the next stage. Some ores, like iron ore, are ready for smelting with little further treatment.

3 Some ores are concentrated by **froth flotation**. The ore is mixed with water to form a **slurry** and then shaken with oil. Air is bubbled through the mixture producing a froth that moves to the surface taking the metal compounds with it. The froth is removed and the compounds separated from it.

4 Once the ore has been processed the next step is to separate the metal from the metal compound. This is called **extraction**. Most metals are found either as oxides or as compounds that are easily changed into oxides. Extraction removes oxygen from the oxide, leaving the metal. Some metals are extracted by **smelting** (heating) and some are treated with chemicals. For example, iron is recovered from haematite by smelting it with coke (carbon), and one stage in aluminium extraction involves treating the ore, bauxite, with sodium hydroxide. Aluminium hydroxide is produced which is then heated to form aluminium oxide or alumina.

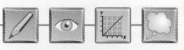

Grabbing oxygen from lead oxide

Your teacher may demonstrate this experiment.

Lead oxide and carbon (charcoal is a form of carbon) are heated strongly as shown in the diagram for about 20 minutes. On cooling, a silvery liquid is seen in the bottom of the crucible.

▶ *What is the silvery liquid?*

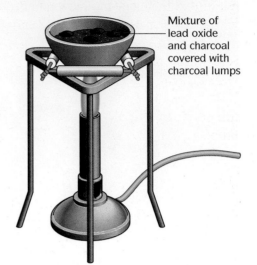

Mixture of lead oxide and charcoal covered with charcoal lumps

▲ Lead can be extracted from lead oxide by heating it strongly with carbon.

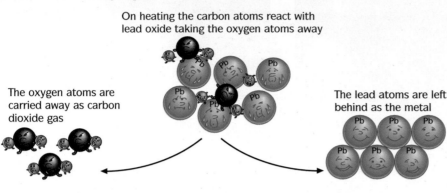

On heating the carbon atoms react with lead oxide taking the oxygen atoms away

The oxygen atoms are carried away as carbon dioxide gas

The lead atoms are left behind as the metal

▲ This cartoon illustrates what happens in this reaction.

▶ *Copy and complete the word and symbol equation for this reaction.*

lead oxide + carbon → _____ + _____

$2PbO(s) + C(s) →$ _____ + _____

▶ *What has been oxidised in this reaction?*

▶ *Could this method be used to get iron from iron oxide?*

Oxidation and reduction

Extracting metals from their compounds involves oxidation and another type of reaction called **reduction**. When lead oxide is heated with carbon, the carbon is oxidised to carbon dioxide. The oxidising agent is lead oxide.

$$2PbO(s) + C(s) → 2Pb(s) + CO_2(g)$$

oxidised

reduced

Notice carbon is more reactive than lead.

Oxygen is removed from the lead oxide. This is called reduction. The lead oxide is **reduced** to lead. Substances that grab oxygen from other compounds are called **reducing agents**. Here the reducing agent is carbon. Oxidation and reduction always take place together. Oxidation and reduction reactions are called **redox** reactions for short.

Here is another vigorous reaction you may have seen in the laboratory.

magnesium + copper oxide → magnesium oxide + copper

$$Mg(s) + CuO(s) → MgO(s) + Cu(s)$$

▶ *Copy the equation for this redox reaction. Show which substance has been oxidised and which has been reduced. Write down the names of the oxidising agent and the reducing agent.*

Getting iron from its ore

Iron and steel (a mixture of iron with other elements) account for about 95 per cent of the metal production in Britain. Iron is produced mainly from the two ores, haematite and magnetite. These both contain oxides of iron.

Blast furnaces can be anything up to thirty metres tall. The walls can be three metres thick. A blast furnace can run continuously for about twenty years, producing anything up to ten thousand tonnes of iron a day.

A charge of iron ore, coke and limestone is fed in at the top of the blast furnace. The coke burns in hot air blown in through pipes at the side. This produces carbon monoxide.

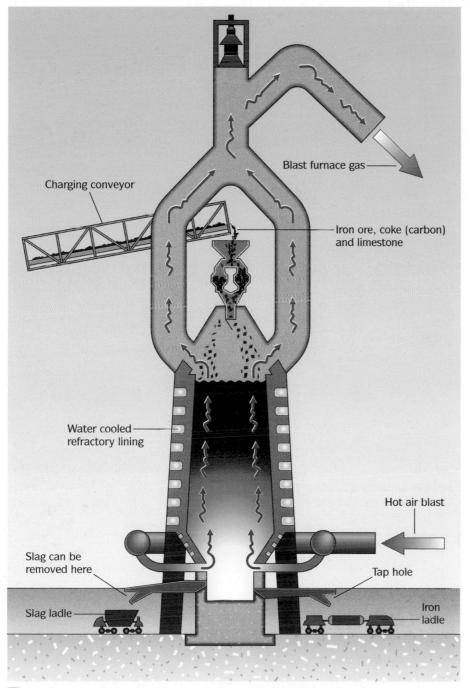

Charging conveyor

Blast furnace gas

Iron ore, coke (carbon) and limestone

Water cooled refractory lining

Hot air blast

Slag can be removed here

Tap hole

Slag ladle

Iron ladle

Iron is extracted from its ore in a furnace called a blast furnace.

At high temperatures carbon is more reactive than metals like iron and zinc, so carbon monoxide can be used as an oxygen grabber to reduce their ores to the metal.

Iron is produced in the two stages.

First stage

$$\text{carbon} + \text{oxygen} \rightarrow \text{carbon monoxide}$$

$$2C(s) + O_2(g) \rightarrow 2CO(g)$$

Second stage

$$\text{carbon monoxide} + \text{iron oxide} \rightarrow \text{iron} + \text{carbon dioxide}$$

$$3CO(g) + Fe_2O_3(s) \rightarrow 2Fe(s) + 3CO_2(g)$$

▶ *Copy the equation for the second stage of iron extraction. Show which substance is oxidised and which is reduced. Write the names of the reducing agent and the oxidising agent.*

Molten iron runs down inside the furnace and collects in the bottom where it can be run off through a tap. Impurities from the ore (such as sand and clay) would soon clog up the furnace if left inside. The limestone reacts with these unwanted substances to form a liquid called **slag**. Slag also runs to the bottom of the furnace and, because it is lighter than iron, floats on the surface. It is run out through another tap. Slag is used to make roads.

Molten iron is run into moulds to set. The iron produced is called **pig iron**. It still contains some impurities, mainly carbon, and is very brittle.

▲ The blast furnaces at Scunthorpe are named after four Queens: Bess, Victoria, Anne and Mary. Mary is shown here.

Reducing other metal ores using carbon

Where possible metals are extracted from their ores by heating with coke. This is a relatively cheap method but it only works with metals in the middle of the reactivity list like zinc, iron and lead. Carbon is less reactive than metals like aluminium and sodium, which are above zinc in the list, and so carbon monoxide cannot be used to grab oxygen from them.

Zinc sulphide and lead sulphide are the main ores of zinc and lead. First the ores are roasted in air to convert them to the oxide. Then the extraction process is similar to that for iron. The metal oxide is heated with coke. Carbon monoxide produced in the furnace reduces the ore to the metal.

▶ *Write the word and symbol equations for reducing zinc oxide, ZnO, to zinc with carbon monoxide gas, CO.*

▶ *Give two reasons why a coating of zinc will protect iron and steel from rusting.*

Getting reactive metals from their ores

Metals like sodium and aluminium were only discovered in the last century. They are very reactive metals and readily join on to other elements. They form bonds that are very strong. Heating sodium oxide or aluminium oxide on their own or with an oxygen grabber like carbon is not enough to separate the metal from the oxygen. Lots of energy is needed to prise the metal and the oxygen apart. This was not possible until the discovery of electricity.

Electrolysis

Your teacher may show you what happens when an electric current is passed through molten lead bromide, $PbBr_2$.

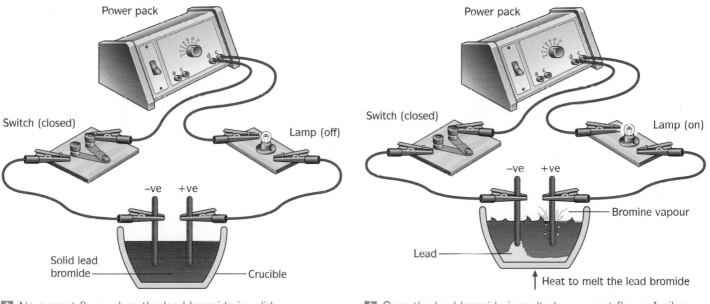

▲ No current flows when the lead bromide is solid.

▲ Once the lead bromide is melted, a current flows. A silver solid collects in the bottom of the crucible under the negative electrode and a red-brown gas collects around the positive electrode.

▶ *What has happened to the lead bromide in the second diagram?*

▶ *What forms:*
  a *at the negative electrode*
  b *at the positive electrode?*

When an electric current flows through molten lead bromide lead and bromine gas are formed. This is called **electrolysis**. Lead appears at the negative electrode and bromine collects at the positive electrode.

Molten compound	Element formed at the negative electrode	Element formed at the positive electrode
Sodium chloride	Sodium	Chlorine
Calcium iodide	Calcium	Iodine
Aluminium oxide	Aluminium	Oxygen

▲ This table shows what happens when an electric current is passed through some molten compounds.

▶ *Copy and complete this sentence: During electrolysis metals form at the _____ electrode and non-metals form at the _____ electrode.*

Explaining electrolysis

Lead bromide is a solid at room temperature. It is made from lead ions (Pb^{2+}) and bromide ions (Br^-) joined firmly into a giant lattice structure. **Ions** are like atoms with a positive or negative charge. You can read about ionic crystal structures in Chapter Nine (Atoms). Lead bromide crystals do not conduct electricity. However, melting the solid frees the ions allowing an electric current to pass through it. At the same time the current splits the compound up into lead metal and bromine gas.

Lead forms at the negative electrode.

$$Pb^{2+} + 2e^- \rightarrow Pb$$

lead ion + 2 electrons → lead atom

Bromine forms at the positive electrode.

$$2Br^- - 2e^- \rightarrow 2Br \rightarrow Br_2$$

2 bromine ions – 2 electrons → 2 bromine atoms → bromine molecule

▶ *Write the equations for the changes at the electrodes during the electrolysis of molten sodium chloride (NaCl). Sodium chloride contains sodium ions, Na^+ and chloride ions, Cl^-, joined together.*

Electrolysis of copper chloride

You may be given a worksheet to help you find out what happens when an electric current is passed through copper chloride solution.

Extracting aluminium from its ore

▲ 25 per cent of all aluminium produced is used in transport. Alloyed with other metals like copper it remains light but increases in strength.

▲ Aluminium is extracted from an ore called bauxite. This bauxite mine in Queensland, Australia, exports about 30 per cent of its production to Japan, Europe and Northern America.

Getting aluminium from its ore is an expensive and difficult process. Aluminium is found spread through the soil, but locked up in clay. In some climates the clay breaks down to form a fairly pure ore of aluminium called **bauxite**. In the first stage of extraction, bauxite is purified to produce aluminium oxide (alumina).

Vast amounts of energy would be needed to melt alumina (melting point 2045 °C). Instead, alumina is dissolved in molten **cryolite** (a compound containing fluorine) and other substances that conduct electricity. Electrolysis separates the pure metal from its oxide. The process still uses a great deal of electrical energy to melt the ore and to split it into its elements. Aluminium plants are often built near sources of relatively cheap electricity.

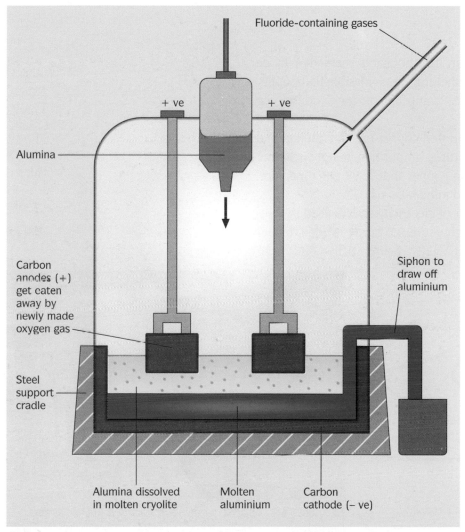

▲ Producing aluminium by electrolysis.

Aluminium forms at the negative electrode, called the **cathode**. Oxygen forms at the positive electrode, called the **anode**. The carbon anode has to be replaced every so often because the oxygen reacts with the carbon forming carbon dioxide gas.

At the negative electrode (cathode): $Al^{3+} + 3e^- \rightarrow Al$

At the positive electrode (anode): $O^{2-} - 2e^- \rightarrow O$

$$O + O \rightarrow O_2$$

CHEMISTRY

How much?

1 How much metal can you get from 100 g of:
   a iron oxide, Fe_2O_3
   b aluminium oxide, Al_2O_3?

2 How much carbon would you need to react with 446 tonnes of lead oxide? (A_r Pb=207, A_r O=16)

$$2PbO(s) + C(s) \rightarrow 2Pb(s) + CO_2(g)$$

Unreactive metals

Copper

The use of copper dates back more than 15 thousand years. It can be extracted from its ore using strong heat (smelting). It is possible that copper was first noticed by chance in an ordinary camp fire on rocks containing copper minerals.

To extract copper commercially, concentrated copper ores are melted and then blasted with hot air at high temperatures. Impurities, mainly iron and sulphur, are removed by oxidation leaving copper that is 98 per cent pure. This 'blister copper' is cast into bars called anodes.

After silver, copper is the best conductor of electricity so it is used in electrical wiring and cables. To ensure the high degree of purity needed, blister copper is further purified by electrolysis.

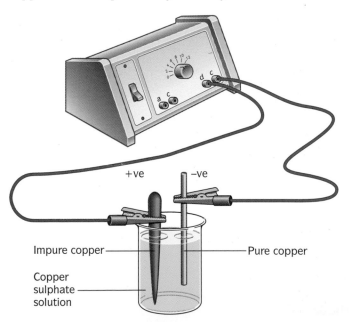

+ve   −ve

Impure copper ———— Pure copper

Copper sulphate solution

These cast copper anodes will be purified further using electrolysis.

This circuit can be used to purify copper. When the electricity is switched on, copper metal goes into solution at the anode and pure metal goes out of solution at the cathode.

▶ *Can you see why blister copper bars are called anodes?*

Purifying copper

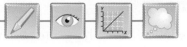

You may be given a worksheet to help you purify copper using electrolysis.

Carbon electrodes, which do not take part in the reaction, are often used for electrolysis. Here you will be using electrodes made from copper.

Understanding electrolysis

Electrodes used in school laboratories are mostly made from graphite which does not react. For industrial purification of copper the electrodes are made from copper and they are involved in the reaction. The anode is impure copper. The cathode is pure copper.

This is what happens at the anode or positive electrode:

$$Cu(s) \rightarrow Cu^{2+}(aq) + 2e$$

Copper from the electrode forms ions which dissolve in the solution.

This is what happens at the cathode or negative electrode:

$$Cu^{2+}(aq) + 2e^- \rightarrow Cu(s)$$

Copper ions from the solution move to the electrode and are deposited as copper on the electrode.

Copper from the impure anode forms positive ions. These are attracted to the negative electrode. Here they are discharged, reforming copper. The metal is deposited on the cathode as pure copper. In the end the positive electrode gets eaten away as the negative electrode increases in mass.

Investigating electrolysis

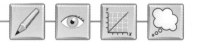

Copper can be purified using electrolysis as described above. Try to find out how you can influence the amount of copper that is deposited on the cathode. Use apparatus like that shown on page 56.

Extracting valuable metals

Metals can be extracted from their oxides by heating with a more reactive metal (one that is higher up the reactivity list). The process uses one reactive metal to produce another. It is an expensive option and is only used to produce exceptionally valuable metals.

Titanium metal has a high strength-to-weight ratio, and a high resistance to corrosion. These and other special properties mean that it is worthwhile to use another valuable metal, sodium, to displace it from a titanium compound. Sodium is above titanium in the reactivity list. In one process titanium is produced by reacting sodium with titanium chloride at high temperatures.

$$TiCl_4(g) + 4Na(l) \rightarrow Ti(s) + 4NaCl(l)$$

▶ *How much sodium would be needed to react with 100 tonnes of titanium chloride? (A_r Ti = 48, Na = 23, Cl = 35.5)*

Summary

- Ores contain naturally-occurring mineral compounds from which metals can be extracted.
- Ores often contain metal oxides or compounds that can easily be converted into metal oxides.
- To extract a metal from a metal oxide oxygen must be removed from the compound.
- When oxygen is removed from a compound reduction takes place.
- Sustances, like carbon, that remove oxygen from compounds are called reducing agents.
- Oxidation and reduction always occur together. These are called redox reactions.
- Ores can be reduced by heating with a reducing agent or with a metal higher up in the reactivity list.
- Metals above zinc in the reactivity list can be extracted from their ores using electrolysis.
- Some compounds are made from ions. They are called ionic compounds.
- When ionic compounds are melted, the ions are free to move. The molten substance conducts electricity.
- During electrolysis some molten compounds are decomposed into their elements.
- In electrolysis positive ions move to the negative electrode, the cathode, and negative ions move to the positive electrode, the anode.
- Some metals can be purified using electrolysis. The impure metal is used as the anode, and the pure metal collects at the cathode.

Revision Questions

1 Copy and complete this table.

Name of compound	Elements in the compound
Sodium sulphide	
Silver nitrate	
Zinc bromide	
Calcium carbonate	
Lead oxide	
Magnesium sulphate	

2 Copy and complete this table for at least six minerals.

Name of mineral	Compound in the mineral	Elements in the compound

3 A metal was heated above its melting point to 1500°C and allowed to cool. The temperature was taken at regular intervals and recorded in the table.

Time (minutes)	Temperature (°C)	Time (minutes)	Temperature (°C)
1	1500	8	1002
2	1340	9	1000
3	1210	10	1001
4	1150	11	985
5	1080	12	950
6	1020	13	830
7	1001	14	770

a Draw a graph showing the results in the table.
b What is the melting point of the metal?
c What metal is it likely to be?

4 Construct a flow chart showing the steps in the extraction of pig iron from a deposit of haematite ore.

5 A mineral resource has just been located near to your home. Use the library and any other resources to discover the factors involved in developing a mine. Consider what might be involved in extracting the metal.

6 You have been asked to give a presentation to another group at school about the extraction of aluminium. Write a plan for your talk. You may be able to watch a video of the process and could use this as part of your presentation. Try to include interesting facts and information about uses of aluminium. Remember to consider any adverse effects on the environment caused by the extraction process.

7

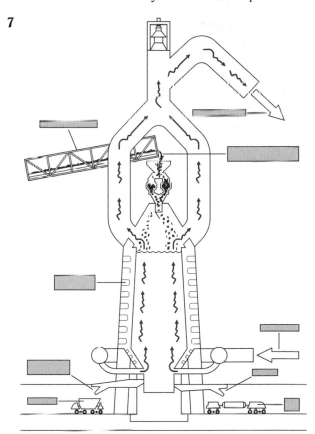

▲ A blast furnace.

a Trace or copy this drawing of a blast furnace.
b Complete the boxes to describe what is going on at each stage.

8

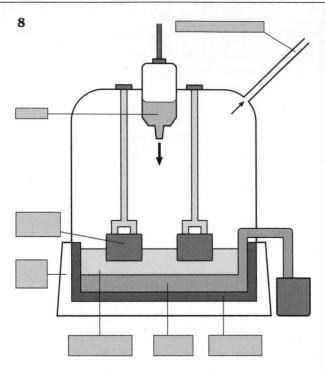

⏴ Extraction of aluminium by electrolysis.

a Copy or trace this drawing describing aluminium extraction.

b Use the snippets given below to label your drawing.

carbon cathode (negative)
carbon anodes (positive)
fluoride-containing waste gases
alumina
molten cryolite mixture
molten aluminium
steel support
$Al^{3+} + 3e^- \rightarrow Al$
$O^{2-} - 2e^- \rightarrow O$ $O + O \rightarrow O_2$

9 Using your knowledge of the reactivity list, put each of the following metals correctly into a copy of the table that follows.

aluminium	magnesium,
calcium	potassium
copper	silver
gold	sodium
iron	tin
lead	zinc

Metal or metals	Method of extraction from ore
	Electrolysis
	Reduction of the ore using carbon
	Heating strongly in air
	Found native

10 Silver can be purified in the same way as copper. Imagine you have been given a metal bar, some pure silver wire (Ag), a solution of silver nitrate ($AgNO_3$) and a low voltage power supply. Draw a labelled diagram showing how you would attempt to get pure silver from the metal bar. Include details of what would happen at each electrode.

11 Copy and complete these equations to show how during electrolysis:

   i metals are deposited (or discharged) at the negative electrode

   ii non-metals are deposited (or discharged) at the positive electrode.

   a $Na^+ + \underline{\quad} \rightarrow Na$

   b $\underline{\quad} + e^- \rightarrow K$

   c $Cu^{2+} + \underline{\quad} \rightarrow Cu$

   d $\underline{\quad} + 3e^- \rightarrow Al$

   e $Cl^- - e^- \rightarrow \underline{\quad}$ $Cl + Cl \rightarrow Cl_2$

   f $\underline{\quad} - e^- \rightarrow Br$ $\underline{\quad} + \underline{\quad} \rightarrow Br_2$

   g $O^{2-} - \underline{\quad} \rightarrow O$ $O + O \rightarrow \underline{\quad}$

12 The ore of a newly discovered metal (X) reacts with aluminium as shown:

   $$X_2O_3(s) + 2Al(s) \rightarrow Al_2O_3(s) + 2X$$

   a Copy the equation and draw arrows showing which substance has been oxidised and which has been reduced.

   b Does X come above or below aluminium in the reactivity list?

   c Aluminium is an expensive metal. Suggest how X could be extracted from its ore.

   d Write the formula for an ion of X showing its charge.

Acids & bases

Acids

Acids are important in all areas of our lives. The acidity of soil is important to gardeners and farmers, because the plants that grow on acidic soils are different to those that grow on alkaline soils. An alkali is chemically opposite to an acid.

Rain can become acidic as compounds in polluted air dissolve in it. Acid rain can cause serious damage both to the natural environment, and to stone and metal constructions in cities.

Many household cleaners contain acids and alkalis that react with dirt to remove it from objects. Sour-tasting foods and fizzy drinks contain acids, and some shampoos are made so that their pH matches that of your hair. pH is a measure of acidity or alkalinity.

These specially trained workers are cleaning up an accidental spillage of sulphuric acid on a road. Sulphuric acid is a strong acid, which is extremely corrosive and burns skin on contact.

The litmus test for gardeners. These flowers are blue in acid soils and pink in alkaline soils.

A couple wear masks against air pollution in London

The word 'acid' makes most people think of vinegar or lemon juice, or of dangerous chemicals used in smelly industrial processes. But acids do much more for us than taste sour and supply raw materials for industry.

Some shampoos and cleansers claim to do less damage to your hair or skin because their pH is similar to your own.

POLLUTION CAUSES ACID ATTACK

It is claimed that rain as acidic as lemon juice has fallen in Scotland. Acid rain has caused untold damage to wildlife, plants and trees in many countries around the world. Acid rain is a result of air pollution caused by burning fossil fuels containing sulphur and nitrogen compounds.

Review

Before going any further, read this page and attempt the tasks. Write the answers in your notes.

Indicators

Scientists use chemicals called indicators to find out about pH. Indicators are chemicals that change colour depending on whether they are in acidic or alkaline solutions. Alkalis are chemicals that behave in the opposite way to acids.

There are several different kinds of indicator, available as solutions or on paper strips. You have probably used litmus paper before to test pH.

Acidity	Acid	Neutral	Alkali
Colour of litmus paper			

▲ This table shows the colour of litmus paper in different conditions.

pH number

You can tell how acidic acid rain is by using universal indicator. Universal indicator is a mixture of indicators that change colour depending on the strength of an acid or an alkali. Each colour matches a number on the pH scale. The scale goes from 0–14. A neutral solution that is neither an acid nor an alkali has a pH of 7. The stronger the acid the lower is its pH number. Just as there are strong and weak acids there are strong and weak alkalis. The stronger the alkali, the higher is its pH.

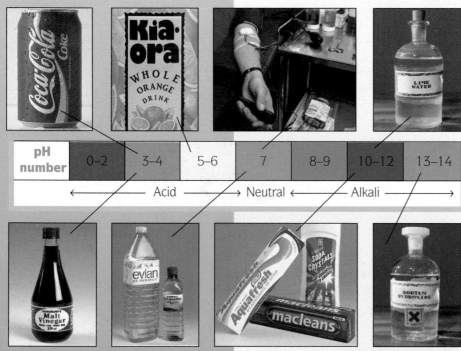

pH number	0–2	3–4	5–6	7	8–9	10–12	13–14

← Acid → Neutral ← Alkali →

▲ This shows the colours of universal indicator in solutions of different pH values.

CHECK FIVE

1 What numbers are on the pH scale?

2 What is the pH of a neutral solution?

3 Copy and complete these sentences:
   a The _____ the pH number the stronger the acid in solution is.
   b The _____ the pH number the stronger the alkali in solution is.

4 Explain how an indicator chemical works.

5 What colour would litmus paper turn in lemon juice?

6 Give an example of a substance that would turn litmus paper blue.

7 Why is universal indicator more useful than indicators like litmus?

8 Can you name any other indicators?

Forming acid rain

When volcanoes erupt they help to produce acid rain. You'll be able to see from the experiment and description below that we also have to take our share of the blame.

Sulphur dioxide and nitrogen oxides are the main causes of acid rain. Fossil fuels like coal and gas are made from the remains of animals and plants. They are mainly carbon and hydrogen but they also contain some sulphur, nitrogen and phosphorus. When fossil fuels are burned they produce, among other waste products, large amounts of sulphur dioxide and oxides of nitrogen.

Oxides of non-metals like sulphur and carbon dissolve in water, producing acidic solutions. Oxides of nitrogen also dissolve in water to produce acidic solutions.

Oxides of sulphur and nitrogen pour out of car and lorry exhausts and from factories every day of the year. These waste gases escape into the atmosphere and dissolve in water droplets in the clouds forming dilute solutions of sulphuric and nitric acids. When it rains these solutions fall back down to Earth.

▲ An active volcano in Iceland.

Burning some elements in oxygen

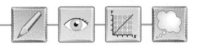

Your teacher may demonstrate this experiment.

Four elements were burned in oxygen, as shown in the diagram. After cooling, a small amount of water and a few drops of universal indicator were added. Elements burn in air forming oxides.

▶ Write word and symbol equations for burning the four elements in oxygen.

▶ What can you say about the oxides of:
  a calcium and sodium
  b sulphur and carbon?
    Can you see any pattern in these results?

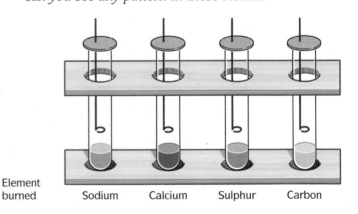

| Element burned | Sodium | Calcium | Sulphur | Carbon |

▲ This apparatus was used to investigate the oxides of some elements.

Acid strength

▲ The acids in our food are weak acids. The acid in descaling solution dissolves the unwanted scale but not the metal in the kettle. Safety rules have to be followed strictly when handling strong acids like sulphuric acid.

Comparing common fruits

Alex decided to compare the citric acid in some common fruits. Here are his results.

Per cent of citric acid: lemon 2.5, grapefruit 1.5, orange 1, strawberry 1, plum 0.2, banana 0.2.

Present these results in an interesting way. You may have read about ways of presenting results in Chapter One (Experiments and investigations).

Acids have different strengths but they all have a lot in common. The table shows the names and formulae of acids you are likely to come across at home and in science lessons. Some of the stronger acids are used in industrial processes. The weaker acids are often found in food and citric acid is a common flavouring in medicines.

Name	Formula	Strength
Hydrochloric acid	$HCl(aq)$	Strong
Sulphuric acid	$H_2SO_4(aq)$	Strong
Nitric acid	$HNO_3(aq)$	Strong
Ethanoic acid	$CH_3COOH(aq)$	Weak
Citric acid	$C_6H_8O_7(aq)$	Weak
Methanoic acid	$HCOOH(aq)$	Weak

🔺 Some common acids and their formulae.

▶ *Write down the names and formulae of two weak acids and two strong acids.*

Investigating the properties of acids

You may be given a worksheet to help you test the properties of acids.

Properties of acids

- Acids have a sour taste (though you should *never* taste a substance to see if it is an acid).
- The pH number of acids is below 7.
- Litmus turns red in acid solutions.
- Universal indicator turns from red through to yellow depending on the strength of the acid.
- Acids react with metals above copper in the reactivity list to produce hydrogen gas. Magnesium, zinc and iron react at a controllable rate. Metals near the top of the reactivity list, like sodium, react dangerously fast.

$$\text{magnesium} + \text{sulphuric acid} \rightarrow \text{magnesium sulphate} + \text{hydrogen}$$

$$Mg(s) + H_2SO_4(aq) \rightarrow MgSO_4(aq) + H_2(g)$$

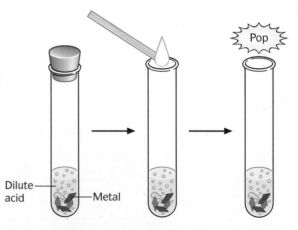

🔺 You can test to see if hydrogen is produced when metals react with acid, using a lighted splint.

ACID RAIN KILLS

Acid rain is thought to have caused the deaths of fish and trees all over Europe but scientists are not sure why. Aluminium is present in most soil minerals. Scientists think that acid rain dissolves aluminium and washes it into waterways. Aluminium is toxic to fish and other aquatic animals. It also affects the health of plants and animals including humans.

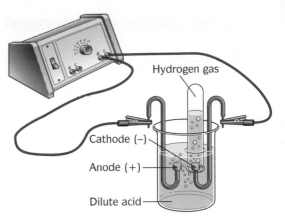

When a dilute acid is electrolysed, hydrogen gas collects at the cathode (negative electrode).

■ Acids conduct electricity. This shows that acid solutions contain charged particles called **ions**. Ions can be positively or negatively charged. You can read more about ions in Chapter Nine (Atoms). When a current is passed through an acid it is **electrolysed**. The acid decomposes and hydrogen gas is produced at the cathode.

Compounds of metals and the carbonate ion, CO_3^{2-}, are called carbonates. Compounds of metals and the hydrogencarbonate ion, HCO_3^-, are called hydrogencarbonates.

Name of compound	Formula	Where found
Sodium carbonate	Na_2CO_3	Washing soda
Calcium carbonate (marble, chalk or limestone)	$CaCO_3$	Used by farmers to treat acid soils
Copper carbonate	$CuCO_3$	In the ore malachite
Sodium hydrogencarbonate	$NaHCO_3$	Bicarbonate of soda
Calcium hydrogencarbonate	$Ca(HCO_3)_2$	Causes hardness in water

You can see how acid rain affects the weathering of limestone statues and buildings. Limestone, marble and chalk are all forms of calcium carbonate.

■ All carbonates give off carbon dioxide gas when they react with acids.

calcium carbonate + hydrochloric acid → calcium chloride + carbon dioxide + water

$$CaCO_3(s) + 2HCl(aq) \rightarrow CaCl_2(aq) + CO_2(g) + H_2O(l)$$

■ Acids react in a similar way with hydrogencarbonates.

sodium hydrogencarbonate + hydrochloric acid → sodium chloride + carbon dioxide + water

$$NaHCO_3(s) + HCl(aq) \rightarrow NaCl(aq) + CO_2(g) + H_2O(l)$$

▶ *Suggest why farmers add calcium carbonate to acid soils.*

▶ *Cakes made with bicarbonate of soda rise. What makes them rise?*

■ Acidity can be **neutralised** or cancelled out by other chemicals. Acids are neutralised by oxides and hydroxides of metals. These compounds are called **bases**. You will read more about bases in the next sections.

calcium hydroxide + hydrochloric acid → calcium chloride + water

$$Ca(OH)_2(aq) + 2HCl(aq) \rightarrow CaCl_2(aq) + 2H_2O(l)$$

zinc oxide + sulphuric acid → zinc sulphate + water

$$ZnO(s) + H_2SO_4(aq) \rightarrow ZnSO_4(aq) + H_2O(l)$$

▶ *Make a summary of the reactions of acids.*

SOME COMMON INDICATORS

Indicator	Acid	Alkali
Methyl orange	Red	Yellow
Phenolphthalein	Colourless	Red

CHEMISTRY

What makes a compound an acid?

If you look at the formulae for acids you will see that they all contain hydrogen. All acids produce hydrogen ions, $H^+(aq)$, when they dissolve in water. These are responsible for the characteristic properties of acids. Notice that not all compounds that contain hydrogen are acids. Ethanol, C_2H_5OH, and glucose, $C_6H_{12}O_6$, are not acids because they do not produce hydrogen ions in water.

Formula of acid	Ions formed in water
HCl(aq)	$H^+(aq) + Cl^-(aq)$
H_2SO_4(aq)	$2H^+(aq) + SO_4{}^{2-}(aq)$
CH_3COOH(aq)	$CH_3COO^-(aq) + H^+(aq)$

▲ All acids produce hydrogen ions when they dissolve in water.

▶ *Name the ion that is always produced when an acid dissolves in water.*

▶ *Copy and complete this equation for nitric acid, HNO_3, in water.*

$$HNO_3(aq) \rightarrow \underline{\hspace{2cm}} + NO_3{}^-(aq)$$

The production of sulphuric acid

Sulphuric acid is manufactured from sulphur, air and water. This acid is widely used to make fertilisers and detergents and it is used in batteries. The acid is made in three stages.

1) Sulphur is burned in oxygen.

   sulphur + oxygen → sulphur dioxide

   $$S(s) + O_2(g) \rightarrow SO_2(g)$$

2) Sulphur dioxide is reacted with oxygen forming sulphur trioxide. This is a **reversible reaction**. You can read about reversible reactions in Chapter Thirteen (Using reactions). The reaction conditions must be carefully chosen and a catalyst, vanadium oxide, is used to speed up the reaction.

   $$\text{sulphur dioxide} + \text{oxygen} \xrightarrow{\text{catalyst } (V_2O_5)} \text{sulphur trioxide}$$

   $$2SO_2(g) + O_2(g) \rightleftharpoons 2SO_3(g)$$

3) Sulphur trioxide is converted to sulphuric acid. Sulphur trioxide is not added directly to water as the reaction would be strongly exothermic. You can read more about exothermic reactions in Chapter Twelve (Energy in reactions). A dangerous mist of sulphuric acid would form. To avoid this problem sulphur trioxide is dissolved in extremely concentrated sulphuric acid. This is then diluted to give 98 per cent acid, or concentrated sulphuric acid as it is known.

   sulphur trioxide + water → sulphuric acid

   $$SO_3(g) + H_2O(l) \rightarrow H_2SO_4(l)$$

Bases

People with slightly acid soils have more choice about what they can grow. Most plants thrive on soils that are on the acidic side of neutral. If the soil is too acidic, the pII can be raised by treating it with substances like lime. Lime, or calcium oxide, is one of a group of compounds called **bases**. Bases react with acids neutralising them and raising the pH.

Metal oxides like zinc oxide and magnesium oxide are bases. Metal hydroxides like calcium hydroxide and copper hydroxide are bases too. Most metal oxides and hydroxides are insoluble in water. A few of them are soluble, like sodium hydroxide. Calcium hydroxide is sparingly soluble. These soluble hydroxides are called **alkalis**.

▲ Lime (calcium oxide), is used to neutralise soil acidity.

TESTING FOR CARBON DIOXIDE

Limewater is a dilute solution of calcium hydroxide in water. The clear solution goes milky when carbon dioxide gas is bubbled through it. You may have used this test to identify carbon dioxide. The clouding of the solution is caused by the formation of insoluble calcium carbonate or chalk.

calcium hydroxide + carbon dioxide → calcium carbonate + water

$$Ca(OH)_2(aq) + CO_2(g) \rightarrow CaCO_3(s) + H_2O(l)$$

Bases are oxides and hydroxides of metals.

Zinc hydroxide   Zinc oxide

Alkalis are soluble bases.

Sodium hydroxide

Potassium hydroxide

▲ Bases and alkalis.

Properties of bases

Like acids, bases also have properties in common.
- Soluble bases turn litmus blue.
- Strong bases are more dangerous than strong acids. They also burn skin on contact.
- Dilute solutions of bases feel 'greasy' because bases react with the oil in your skin making soap.
- Bases neutralise acids. If you add the correct amount of a base to an acid it 'cancels out' the acidity, giving a neutral solution.

base + acid → salt + water

sodium hydroxide + hydrochloric acid → sodium chloride + water

$$NaOH(aq) + HCl(aq) \rightarrow NaCl(aq) + H_2O(aq)$$

▶ *Carry out a risk assessment for someone using an oven cleaner containing sodium hydroxide.*

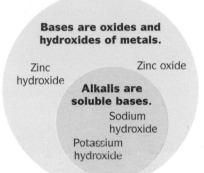
▲ Some oven cleaners contain sodium hydroxide.

- If you have ever looked at indigestion remedies you will be familiar with the term **'antacid'**. Bases and alkalis are antacids. They react with unwanted and painful acid in the stomach producing harmless, neutral substances called **salts**. This is an example of a neutralisation reaction.

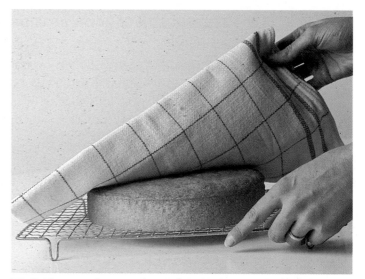

▲ A wasp sting contains a base and so it can be neutralised with a solution of a weak acid, like vinegar.

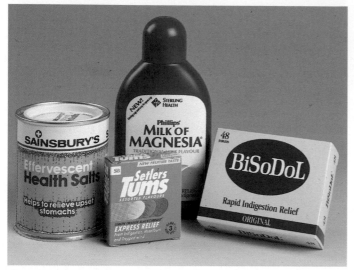

▲ Well over £1 million is spent on antacids every year in the UK. Milk of magnesia contains magnesium hydroxide. Some remedies contain aluminium hydroxide.

▶ *Write down some common uses of neutralisation reactions.*

- When an alkali dissolves in water, ions called hydroxide ions, $OH^-(aq)$, are produced. The pH of an alkaline solution is above 7 and the stronger the alkali, the higher the pH. Sodium hydroxide is a strong alkali.

$$NaOH(s) \rightarrow Na^+(aq) + OH^-(aq)$$

Calcium hydroxide is a weak alkali.

$$Ca(OH)_2(s) \rightarrow Ca^{2+}(aq) + 2OH^-(aq)$$

Carbonates (CO_3^{2-}) and hydrogencarbonates (HCO_3^-) are also bases.

- Ammonia, NH_3, is an unusual base because it does not contain a metal. Ammonia is a weak base. It is used to manufacture fertilisers and is often used in household cleaners. With water, ammonia produces hydroxide ions and so it turns litmus paper blue.

▶ *Write a summary of the properties of bases.*

▲ Baking powder contains sodium hydrogencarbonate and tartaric acid. When moist they react together producing carbon dioxide, the gas that makes the cake 'rise' in the oven.

What happens when an acid is neutralised by an alkali?

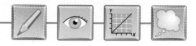

Adding an alkali changes the characteristic properties of an acid. You are going to find out what happens to the pH and temperature of an acid solution during neutralisation. You may be given a worksheet to help you with this experiment.

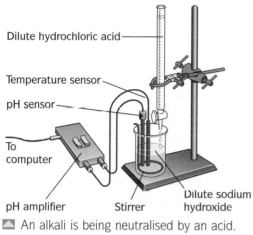

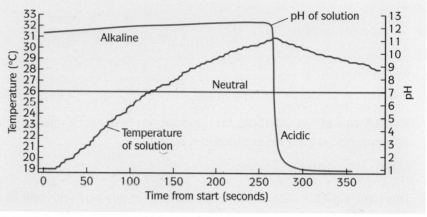

An alkali is being neutralised by an acid. A pH sensor is being used to monitor the pH.

A labelled trace showing pH against time for a neutralisation reaction using a pH sensor and a burette. Time is equivalent to the volume of acid added, if it is added at a constant rate.

When an acid is slowly added to an alkali, the pH suddenly drops to 7 when the alkali is neutralised. As more acid is added the pH drops even lower as an excess volume of acid is now present.

Understanding neutralisation

As you have already found out solutions of acids are conductors of electricity. Alkaline solutions also conduct. This tells us that they contain charged particles or ions. Look at the diagram below to find out what happens when acids and alkalis are added together.

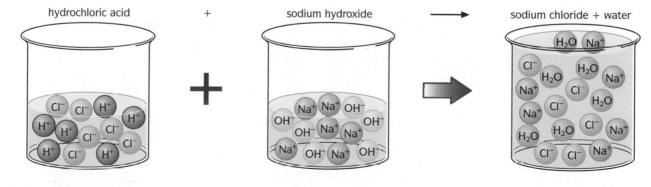

Adding acids and alkalis together.

When soluble substances made from ions are dissolved in water, the separate ions are free to move around. Notice that water is not an ionic substance, it is a molecule. You have already seen many word equations and many symbol equations. It is possible to show reactions as **ionic equations**.

word equation:

hydrochloric acid + sodium hydroxide → sodium chloride + water

symbol equation:

$$HCl(aq) + NaOH(aq) \rightarrow NaCl(aq) + H_2O(l)$$

ionic equation:

$$H^+(aq) + Cl^-(aq) + Na^+(aq) + OH^-(aq) \rightarrow Na^+(aq) + Cl^-(aq) + H_2O(l)$$

You can cancel out anything that appears on both sides, giving you the equation below for a neutralisation reaction.

$$H^+(aq) + OH^-(aq) \rightarrow H_2O(l)$$

This ionic equation describes neutralisation for any acid with any alkali.

▶ Write the word, symbol and ionic equations for the neutralisation of:
a potassium hydroxide, KOH(aq) with nitric acid, HNO_3(aq)
b sodium hydroxide, NaOH(aq) with sulphuric acid, H_2SO_4(aq).

Investigating neutralisation

▶ What affects the size of the rise in temperature when an acid is neutralised by an alkali?

Salts and their uses

For most people 'salt' means the substance that you put on fish and chips. This is sodium chloride, NaCl. However, if you think about it, you probably have heard of bath salts and the salts which are taken as a remedy for indigestion. **Salt** is the name given to a group of compounds that are made when an acid reacts with a base.

◢ Ammonium nitrate is used as fertiliser.

◢ Animals that graze don't get enough sodium chloride from plant foods. So, farmers provide blocks of salt called 'salt licks'.

◢ Iron sulphate is used in medicines, and as a moss killer on lawns.

◢ Epsom salts contain magnesium sulphate.

◢ Plaster of Paris contains calcium sulphate.

	Hydrochloric acid HCl(aq) forms chlorides	Sulphuric acid H_2SO_4(aq) forms sulphates	Nitric acid HNO_3(aq) forms nitrates	Ethanoic acid CH_3CO_2H(aq) forms ethanoates
Sodium hydroxide NaOH	Sodium chloride NaCl	Sodium sulphate Na_2SO_4	Sodium nitrate $NaNO_3$	Sodium ethanoate CH_3CO_2Na
Zinc hydroxide Zn(OH)₂	Zinc chloride $ZnCl_2$	Zinc sulphate $ZnSO_4$	Zinc nitrate $Zn(NO_3)_2$	Zinc ethanoate $(CH_3CO_2)_2Zn$
Calcium carbonate CaCO₃	Calcium chloride $CaCl_2$	Calcium sulphate $CaSO_4$	Calcium nitrate $Ca(NO_3)_2$	Calcium ethanoate $(CH_3CO_2)_2Ca$
Magnesium Mg	Magnesium chloride $MgCl_2$	Magnesium sulphate $MgSO_4$	Magnesium nitrate $Mg(NO_3)_2$	Magnesium ethanoate $(CH_3CO_2)_2Mg$

The left side labels: B A S E (Base) for Sodium hydroxide, Zinc hydroxide, Calcium carbonate; M E T A L (Metal) for Magnesium.

This table shows the salts that are made when different acids and bases are added together. You can see that the name of the salt depends on the metal and the acid from which it was made.

IONS IN SALTS

Compounds made from ions are neutral substances. Salts are made from two types of ions, a positively charged metal ion and a negatively charged ion. The negative ion is made from one or more non-metals. Once joined into a salt the charges on these ions cancel each other out. You can find out more about how to write the formula for a salt in Chapter Fourteen (Structure and bonding).

Purifying a salt

What is the best way to produce pure copper sulphate crystals from a mixture of copper sulphate and powdered copper metal? Use labelled diagrams to describe in detail what you would do. Use Chapter Sixteen (Chemistry help) if you need to. Check with your teacher before trying out your plan.

Insoluble salts

Some salts like lead iodide and silver chloride do not dissolve in water. You can make insoluble salts by adding together solutions of two soluble salts. For example if you add together solutions of lead nitrate and potassium iodide, bright yellow insoluble lead iodide appears in the solution. This is called a **precipitation reaction** and the newly formed solid is called a **precipitate**.

When you add together solutions of lead nitrate and potassium iodide, bright yellow insoluble lead iodide is formed.

Understanding precipitation

To understand precipitation you have to understand what happens to soluble salts when they dissolve into water. Salts are made from ions. On dissolving in water the ions in the solid are freed and able to move about in the solution.

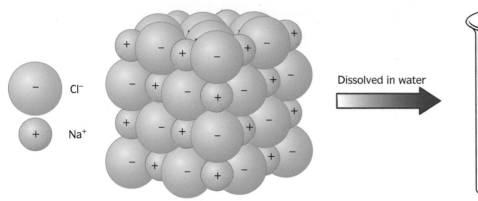

Cl⁻

Na⁺

Dissolved in water

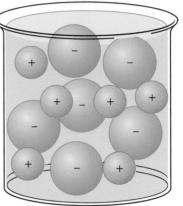

🔺 Solid sodium chloride does not conduct electricity because the sodium ions (Na^+) and the chloride ions (Cl^-) are held firmly together in a giant 3D lattice.

🔺 Sodium chloride solution conducts electricity. Once the solid is dissolved, ions are separated from the lattice and are free to move around.

The diagrams and equations below describe what happens when solutions of two different soluble salts are added together.

+

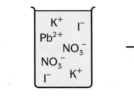

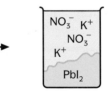

Lead nitrate solution contains a mixture of lead ions (Pb^{2+}) and nitrate ions (NO_3^-).

Potassium iodide solution contains a mixture of potassium ions (K^+) and iodide ions (I^-).

When the two solutions are added together, the ions are briefly mixed.

Lead ions and iodide ions form insoluble lead iodide and so appear as a solid. The potassium and the nitrate ions remain dissolved in the solution.

Symbol equation:

$$Pb(NO_3)_2(aq) + 2KI(aq) \rightarrow PbI_2(s) + 2KNO_3(aq)$$

Ionic equation:

$$Pb^{2+}(aq) + 2NO_3^-(aq) + 2K^+(aq) + 2I^-(aq) \rightarrow PbI_2(s) + 2K^+(aq) + 2NO_3^-(aq)$$
$$Pb^{2+}(aq) + 2I^-(aq) \rightarrow PbI_2(s)$$

▶ *Make drawings to describe these salts dissolving in water.*
  a *silver nitrate, $AgNO_3$*
  b *potassium chloride, KCl*

Precipitation reactions can be useful

■ **Purifying salt**. An impure solution of sodium chloride is pumped up from underground. The solution also contains salts of magnesium and calcium. These other metal ions are removed using precipitation reactions.

$$\text{calcium chloride} + \text{sodium carbonate} \rightarrow \text{calcium carbonate} + \text{sodium chloride}$$

$$CaCl_2(aq) + Na_2CO_3(aq) \rightarrow CaCO_3(s) + 2NaCl(aq)$$
$$\text{precipitate}$$

$$\text{magnesium chloride} + \text{sodium hydroxide} \rightarrow \text{magnesium hydroxide} + \text{sodium chloride}$$

$$MgCl_2(aq) + 2NaOH(aq) \rightarrow Mg(OH)_2(s) + 2NaCl(aq)$$
$$\text{precipitate}$$

⬆ Sodium chloride solution must be purified before it is used to make other chemicals. Precipitation is used in the purification process.

■ **Purifying citric acid**. Citric acid is made by **fermentation**. You can read more about fermentation in Chapter Eleven (Enzymes). After seven days of fermentation, calcium oxide is added to the broth (the liquid from the fermenter). Calcium citrate, an insoluble salt of citric acid, forms a precipitate and can be filtered off. It is then processed to produce pure citric acid.

■ **Identifying ions**. Precipitation reactions form the basis of many tests which are used to identify ions in solution.

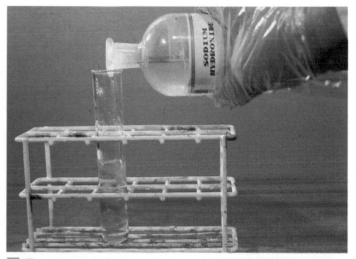

⬆ The presence of copper ions in a solution can be shown by the addition of sodium hydroxide solution. A blue precipitate forms.

Precipitation reactions can be a nuisance

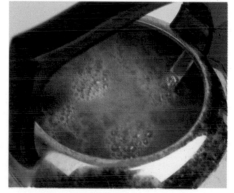

⬆ Insoluble calcium carbonate in hard water forms a precipitate called scale inside kettles and pipes. Kettles heat less efficiently if the element is covered in scale. These photos show how acid in a descaler dissolves the unwanted precipitate (the scale).

CHEMISTRY

Summary

- Oxides of non-metals dissolve in water forming acidic solutions.
- Oxides of metals that are soluble in water form alkaline solutions.
- Acids are corrosive substances with a pH less than 7.
- These equations summarise reactions of acids. Notice that in each reaction a salt is made.

    acid + metal → salt + hydrogen

    acid + base → salt + water

    acid + carbonate → salt + carbon dioxide + water

- Acids dissolve in water producing hydrogen ions, $H^+(aq)$.
- Bases are oxides of metals and hydroxides of metals.
- Alkalis are bases that are soluble in water.
- There are strong alkalis like sodium hydroxide and weak alkalis like calcium hydroxide (limewater).
- Bases neutralise acids forming a salt and water.
- The name of a salt depends on the metal and the acid used to make it.
- Uses of neutralisation reactions include treating indigestion with antacid preparations, treating acid soil with lime or powdered chalk, treating insect stings and making fertilisers.
- You can write the correct formula for a salt if you know the ions in it and their charges.
- Some salts are soluble in water. Others are insoluble.
- The method used to make a salt depends on its solubility in water.
- Sometimes, when two solutions are added together, an insoluble substance is formed and appears as a solid. This solid is called a precipitate and the reaction is called a precipitation reaction.
- Precipitation reactions can be represented by ionic equations.
- Precipitation reactions can be helpful in making new substances, in testing for the presence of metal ions and in removing unwanted ions from solution.
- Precipitation reactions can be a nuisance when unwanted solids form blocking up kettles, boilers and pipes.

Revision Questions

1 What colour would you expect these solutions to turn if a few drops of universal indicator were added?
   a lemon juice
   b hydrochloric acid
   c 'Bicarbonate of soda'
   d sodium hydroxide.

2 Strong alkalis can be bought as cleaners for use in the home. For example, many oven cleaners contain strong alkali. Design a label for an oven cleaner and say what the user should learn from it. Remember to include any relevent safety symbols.

3 Carry out a risk assessment for the safe use of bleach in disinfecting lavatories, sinks and drains.

4 a Copy and complete the following table.

Acid used in reaction	Name of salt
Hydrochloric acid Sulphuric acid Nitric acid Ethanoic acid	

   b Copy and complete the following word equations.

zinc + hydrochloric acid → _____ + _____

calcium hydroxide + _____ → calcium sulphate + _____

_____ + hydrochloric acid → magnesium chloride + _____ + _____

sodium hydroxide + _____ → sodium nitrate + _____

5 Make a poster for your classroom wall showing the formulae and the uses of as many salts as possible.

6
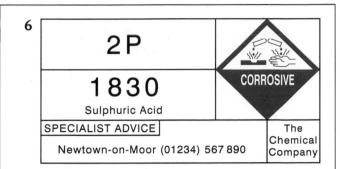

▲ Hazard warning panel for concentrated sulphuric acid.

Concentrated acids are transported around in tankers. The warning panel on the tanker advises the Police and the Fire Brigade what to do in case of accidents.
   a Find out the meanings of the symbols on the warning panel above.
   b Should tankers carrying dangerous chemicals be allowed to drive around busy cities and roads? Discuss this with your neighbour and make two lists of arguments for and against the idea. Decide which case you support and say why.

7
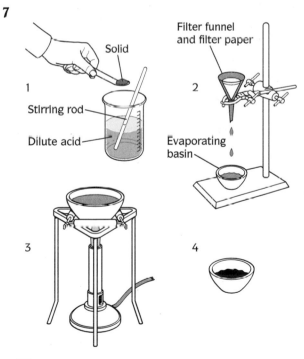

▲ Apparatus used to make a salt.

   a Give the name of a salt that could be made using the method above.

b Redraw the diagrams in 2D labelling each part and naming the metal and acid used.

c If you can, write the word and symbol equations for the reaction.

8 Use the snippets below and any other resources you can find to write an article about acid rain for a school magazine. Suggest any photographs and diagrams you would like to include.

- Acid rain is a result of air pollution.
- Acid rain affects the health of plants and animals.
- Acid rain speeds up the weathering of many of the world's historic buildings.
- About two thirds of the sulphur dioxide that we produce gets blown away by winds.
- Acid rain causes damage miles away from the source of the air pollution.
- Hundreds of Scandinavian lakes no longer contain fish.
- Many forests in Europe are dying or are affected by acid rain.
- Acid rain can dissolve aluminium in the soil and wash it into waterways.
- People with some forms of senility have high aluminium levels in their brains.
- Aluminium sulphate is used in drinking water treatment.
- Many vehicles have catalytic converters to reduce the production of oxides of nitrogen. But much more carbon dioxide is released from exhausts as a result.
- Most of the sulphur dioxide produced in Britain comes from power stations.
- Gases from power stations can be 'scrubbed', or cleaned, before being released into the atmosphere.
- 'Scrubbing' sulphur dioxide from gases in power stations takes up a finite amount of their output. This means more carbon dioxide is produced for the same amount of fuel burned.
- Sulphur can be removed from fuels used in power stations before they are burned.
- Other sources of energy could be used to generate electricity.
- Other sources of power (e.g. nuclear) can be expensive and carry their own hazards.

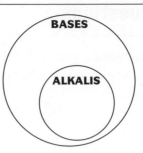

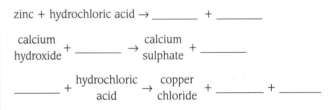

▲ All alkalis are bases, but not all bases are alkalis.

9 Copy and complete the diagram above. Put these compounds in the correct category: sodium hydroxide, zinc oxide, magnesium oxide, zinc hydroxide, calcium oxide and calcium hydroxide.

10 Use the table on page 223 to help you write the correct symbol formulae for the following: potassium chloride, magnesium bromide, potassium sulphate, copper sulphate, potassium nitrate, calcium hydroxide, ammonium bromide and ammonium sulphate.

11 Copy and complete the following word equations. Write the balanced symbol equation underneath each one.

zinc + hydrochloric acid → _____ + _____

calcium hydroxide + _____ → calcium sulphate + _____

_____ + hydrochloric acid → copper chloride + _____ + _____

sodium hydroxide + _____ → sodium nitrate + _____

12 Give the word equation, and if you can, the symbol equation for the reaction of hydrochloric acid with:

a magnesium

b magnesium oxide

c magnesium carbonate.

13 Silver chloride (AgCl) is insoluble in water. It can be made from solutions of sodium chloride (NaCl) and silver nitrate ($AgNO_3$).

a Explain how you could make a solid sample of silver chloride.

b Write the word and the symbol equation for the reaction.

c Explain in terms of ions how solid silver nitrate is formed.

Rocks & minerals

Consider where sand comes from. Every sand grain has its origin somewhere. Perhaps you have wondered why some rocks form scars and ridges extending out to sea and others form tors on high mountains, while elsewhere the land is low and flat with no rock features at all. The shape of the Earth's surface is the result of processes that have been going on since the planet first formed.

Review

Before going any further, read this page and attempt the tasks. Write the answers in your notes.

▲ Houses are made from rocks. Originally solid lumps of rock were used. Now rocks are used to make bricks and concrete to construct all kinds of buildings.

▲ People pay lots of money for minerals that sparkle.

▲ Clay is the rock used to make china. It is also used in paper making. Tiles, baths, sinks, cups, plates and building bricks are also made from clay. Gypsum is used in plaster and plasterboard.

CHECK SIX

1 Make a list of the rocks that were used to make your home. Include rocks that are used as they are and rocks that are used to manufacture other construction materials.

2 Give the names of some minerals that are used to make jewellery.

3 How is clay used? What property of clay makes it so useful?

4 Give the names of some of the Earth's mineral resources and examples of their uses. Here are some examples to start you off: metal ores, salts, clay, coal, oil, calcium carbonate.

5 What rocks are made from the remains of plants and animals? How are they used?

The Earth

The rocky ball you know as the Earth came into being about 4600 million years ago. It had a large atmosphere probably consisting of hydrogen and helium, and a rocky core which was probably molten. It is likely that it also had a molten surface. As the Earth cooled down, the surface solidified and steam changed into water which became the sea. The early atmosphere was stripped away and was replaced gradually by gases from the cooling Earth. These gases were carbon dioxide, steam and nitrogen. But there was no oxygen. The oxygen in the air comes from plants which make oxygen during photosynthesis. The first oxygen-producing plants were algae. These appeared about 2000 million years ago. Humans appeared just 2 million years ago.

Inside the Earth

Finding out what goes on inside the Earth is difficult because it's 13 thousand kilometres in diameter. One of the world's deepest mines is in South Africa. It is 3.5 km deep and the temperature inside it is 50 °C. This provides evidence that the Earth's temperature increases closer to the centre. The deepest hole that has been drilled is in the Comecon States (formerly the USSR), north of Finland. It is 11 km deep. Even this only scratches the surface of the Earth. Most of what we know about the deep interior of the Earth comes from evidence of natural movements in the Earth's surface. Earthquakes and volcanoes tell a story. You can read more about earthquakes and volcanos in Chapter Seven (The Earth). Scientists also send shock waves through the Earth and can find out, by analysing the resulting signals, about the structure and likely composition of the interior of our planet.

The **crust** is the thin outer layer. It can be compared to the cracked outer shell of a soft-boiled egg. The crust is broken in places, but it still stays together. At the bottom of the crust the temperature is 1050 °C

The **mantle** is a dark coloured, sometimes semi-solid, rock layer which is rich in magnesium and silicon. The temperature of the mantle can be as high as 3700 °C. Very slow movements take place in the upper mantle due to convection currents. Rock rises in the mantle and then slowly sinks again as it cools.

The **Moho** (short for **Mohorovičić discontinuity**) is the boundary between the crust and the mantle.

The core is probably made of nickel and iron. The **outer core** is molten because of high temperatures. Heat from radioactive decay in the core produces convection currents. This keeps the core mixed by strong swirling movements. High temperatures combined with extremely high pressure keep the **inner core** in a solid state. The temperature ranges from 2200 °C at the edge of the core to 4500 °C deep inside the centre.

▲ This is what the Earth looks like from space.

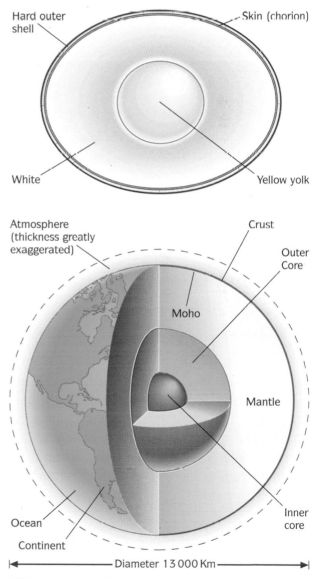

Hard outer shell

Skin (chorion)

White

Yellow yolk

Atmosphere (thickness greatly exaggerated)

Crust

Outer Core

Moho

Mantle

Ocean

Continent

Inner core

|◄——————— Diameter 13 000 Km ———————►|

▲ Nowadays the Earth is thought to be made from a series of layers, a bit like a spherical soft-boiled egg. Compare the diagram of the Earth with the diagram of the egg above.

CHEMISTRY

Part of the Earth	Crust	Mantle	Outer core (liquid)	Inner core (solid)
Depth (km)	200	2700	2300	1200
Density (g cm⁻³)	2.6–3.0	3.3–9.0	12.3–13.3	13.6

$$\text{density} = \text{mass (g)/volume } (cm^3) = g/cm^3 = gcm^{-3}$$

Dense objects, like lead weights, are heavy for their size. Substances like expanded polystyrene have a low density. They are light for their size.

▸ *Draw a cross section through the Earth naming each area and showing its depth and density.*

▸ *The overall density of the Earth is much higher than the density of the crust. What does this tell you about the material deep down in the Earth?*

The crust

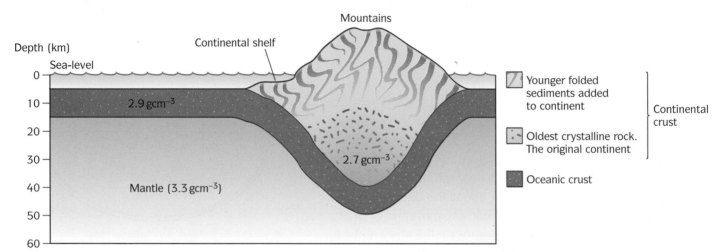

The structure of the Earth's crust.

Continental crust and **oceanic crust** 'float' on the mantle layer. Remember that the mantle is semi-solid and that currents flow within it.

▸ *Where on Earth is the crust thinnest?*

▸ *Why does the crust float on the semi-solid rocks in the upper part of the mantle?*

More is known about the crust than about other layers of the Earth because scientists can collect rock samples from it. The crust is comparatively thin, like a postage stamp stuck onto a football, and can be divided into two types. Continental crust forms the Earth's continents and reaches some distance into the sea. It can be 70 km thick under high mountain ranges. Oceanic crust is found under the deep sea and is, on average, 6 km thick.

Minerals

The Earth's crust provides the natural materials for most of our needs. Minerals are solid chemicals that are formed naturally in the Earth. You may have read about minerals in Chapter Four (Ores). They can be elements like diamond (carbon) or compounds like haematite. They all have a formula. Galena is a mineral – it is a compound of lead and sulphur.

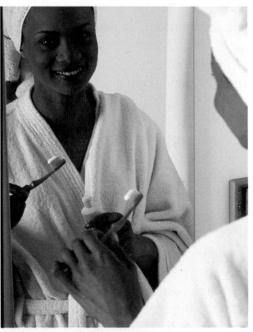

Powdered limestone is found in toothpaste. Soapstone contains the mineral talc. Ground up it provides soft, absorbent talcum powder. Some talc is also made from china clay.

Its formula is PbS. Rocks are made from minerals. Some contain only one mineral. Limestone contains only calcium carbonate. Some rocks contain several minerals. Granite contains quartz, feldspar and mica. Some minerals are used as they are, for example marble and rock salt. Others are used as a source of other substances, often metals. Iron is extracted from haematite and aluminium from bauxite.

Identifying minerals

Minerals have properties just like any other substance. It is possible to use standard tests to identify them.

Observation

The colour of the mineral can provide a clue to its identity but is not always reliable. Minerals sometimes show a range of colours.

Ask yourself these questions:

- What is its colour and crystal shape?
- How is light reflected by the mineral?
- Is it dull, does it shine like a metal, or does it have a 'glassy' look like broken glass?
- Does the mineral break or 'cleave' easily along certain lines? These faint parallel lines are often visible on the surface of the mineral.

Hardness

The scale of hardness goes from 1 (for example, talc which is the softest mineral known) to 10 (for example, diamond). A soft mineral can be scratched by a harder one and that in turn by an even harder one. For convenience, seeing how easily the mineral is scratched by your fingernail, a copper coin or a knife blade gives a rough guide to hardness.

Mohs' scale of hardness			
10	diamond	**4**	fluorite ← copper
9	corundum		← 10p coin
8	topaz	**3**	calcite
7	quartz		← fingernail
6	feldspar ← steel nail	**2**	gypsum
5	apatite ← glass	**1**	talc

🔺 A scale of hardness used to help identify minerals.

Density

Most minerals have a density of 2–3 gcm^{-3}. Some are denser and feel 'heavy' for their size.

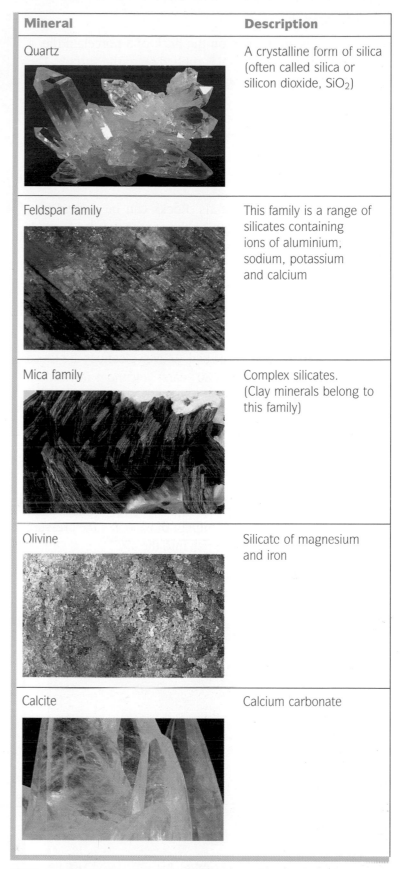

Mineral	Description
Quartz	A crystalline form of silica (often called silica or silicon dioxide, SiO_2)
Feldspar family	This family is a range of silicates containing ions of aluminium, sodium, potassium and calcium
Mica family	Complex silicates. (Clay minerals belong to this family)
Olivine	Silicate of magnesium and iron
Calcite	Calcium carbonate

🔺 The most common types of rock-forming minerals.
Notice: a carbonate contains carbon and oxygen, and a silicate contains silicon and oxygen. You can read about the names of compounds in Chapter Four (Ores).

Mineral streak

When minerals are rubbed on the back of a porcelain tile, a mark or streak of the mineral is rubbed on to the surface. The colour of the streak is always constant and gives information about metallic minerals. For instance, haematite gives a red streak. The test is less useful for non-metallic minerals as they nearly all give a white streak.

Rock formation

Rocks are made from minerals. Rocks can be divided into three main groups depending on the way they were formed. These are igneous rocks, sedimentary rocks and metamorphic rocks.

Igneous rocks

There are about 540 **active** volcanoes on the Earth's crust, of which about 80 are on the sea bed. Active volcanoes are those that have **erupted** in the last 80 years. Volcanoes form when molten rocks from deep inside the Earth are forced upward and through the surface. This is called an **eruption**.

When volcanoes erupt, solids, liquids and gases are hurled out of an opening called a **vent**. In some volcanoes ash formed from rock fragments is ejected under high pressure. This is followed by **lava** (liquid rock). Lava is formed from molten rock called **magma**. The gases are mainly water vapour, steam and gases containing sulphur like sulphur dioxide. It's the pressure of these gases that propels the ash into the air.

▶ *Using the photos on this page write about the effects of volcanic eruption on people's lives.*

◤ An **extinct** or dead volcano produced these rock formations in the Giant's Causeway in Antrim. Uniform cooling produced this column-like formation in the ancient lava flow.

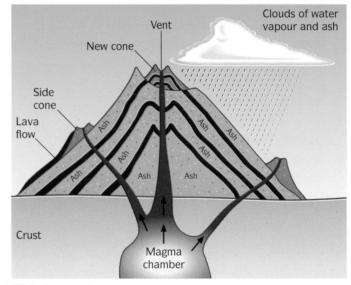

Clouds of water vapour and ash
Vent
New cone
Side cone
Lava flow
Ash
Crust
Magma chamber

◤ Inside a volcano.

◤ When Mount Etna erupted in Italy, in 1971, people watched the lava slowly flow through their homes and crops.

◤ This shows lava flow entering the sea near Heimaey, an island south of Iceland. Volunteers sprayed millions of gallons of seawater onto the lava to cool it down and to prevent the harbour from becoming blocked.

Looking at the way lava flows

Plan and carry out an investigation into the way lava flows. You might like to base your investigation around the idea shown in the diagram below.

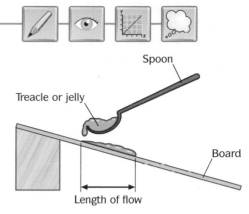

You might be able to predict how lava will flow using this model of the side of a volcano.

Magma

Igneous rocks have one thing in common. They were all once magma. When a volcano erupts, magma forces its way upwards. If it reaches the surface it is called lava. On cooling, the liquid magma forms interlocking crystals of minerals. The size of the crystals depends on the rate of cooling. Some magma forces its way between rocks in the Earth's crust. This magma cools slowly and forms large, well-formed crystals like granite and gabbro. Magma that flows out over the sides of the volcano as lava cools quickly forming small crystals, like pumice and basalt.

Basalt is an igneous rock made when magma pours onto the surface from a volcano. It cools quickly and so has small crystals that can only be seen using a microscope. Rocks like basalt are called **extrusive rocks**.

Granite is an igneous rock made by slow cooling. It is formed when magma is forced in between other rocks in the Earth's crust. Granite is called an **intrusive rock**.

Making rock crystals

Molten rock cools and forms crystals. The size of the crystals depends on whether this happens deep underground or nearer the Earth's surface. You may be given a worksheet to help you make rock crystals.

Sedimentary rocks

Sedimentary rocks are 'second hand rocks'. They are all formed from deposits of material that have come from other rocks or living things. Rocks on the exposed surface of the Earth are slowly broken down or **weathered**. The rock fragments produced in this way are washed away into rivers and into the sea where they collect in layers of **sediment**. Pressure and temperature then squeeze and harden these layers into rocks. Sometimes the sediment is cemented together by compounds that were dissolved in the water. As these rocks are formed in layers, younger sedimentary rocks are usually found on top of older rocks. Examples of sedimentary rocks are limestone, sandstone, shale or mudstone.

Sedimentary rock often contains small fragments bound together or cemented by another mineral into solid rock. They sometimes contain fossils formed from shells or the remains of other living things.

Investigating sedimentary rocks

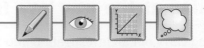

Certain conditions are needed to turn rock fragments into solid rock. You may be given a worksheet to help you make and find out more about sedimentary rocks.

Physical weathering

Changes in temperature play a large part in the weathering of rocks. For example, water enters cracks in rocks and, in cold conditions, freezes making the crack bigger. On thawing, water seeps further into the crack. The next time the water freezes, the crack gets even bigger until a fragment breaks away. Piles of small rock fragments called **scree** are formed.

Physical weathering also happens when the roots of trees and other plants grow down into cracks and split rocks slowly over the years.

▶ *Why does freezing water in a crack make the crack bigger?*

Chemical weathering

Water containing dissolved carbon dioxide is a dilute solution of carbonic acid. It reacts with some of the minerals in rocks. The products of the reaction are **clay minerals** and solutions containing ions such as sodium, calcium, potassium and magnesium. These solutions form other rocks or make their way to the sea. The finely divided clay minerals are transported away to be deposited as the sticky mud or clay sediments found in estuaries and in rivers.

Weakly acidic rainwater also reacts with limestone and chalk forming soluble calcium hydrogencarbonate which is carried away in solution.

$$CaCO_3(s) + H_2O(l) + CO_2(g) \rightarrow Ca(HCO_3)_2(aq)$$

Physical and chemical weathering have been described separately but they are both going on all the time. Other living things also play a part. Burrowing animals dig into the ground. We walk on paths, dig mines to get minerals and sink wells to get oil. All these processes break up rocks and minerals.

Transportation and erosion

The rock fragments and solutions produced by weathering are often moved or **transported** to another site before they are converted into sedimentary rocks. Transportation occurs by one or more of the following methods:

- by gravity
- in water by rivers and streams
- in water by the sea
- by ice in glaciers
- by wind

▶ *Give an example of how each of the above methods are involved in moving rock fragments from one place to the other.*

▶ *Explain how wind plays a part in eroding rocks and transporting rock fragments.*

◢ Hot days and cold nights cause minerals to expand and contract day after day. In the end the outside layers crack up and peel away.

◢ When rainwater containing dissolved calcium hydrogencarbonate drips through and onto rocks, insoluble calcium carbonate is reformed and **stalactites** and **stalagmites** grow.

During transportation, rock particles can cause **erosion**. Erosion always involves movement, while weathering does not. The fragments knock and rub against each other and against larger rocks breaking away corners and edges and smoothing out surfaces. The fragments become smaller and rounder as they move further and further from their source. They wear away or **erode** the rocks in the river beds, caves and valleys through which they pass.

During transportation a kind of sorting process occurs. The rock fragments are not all deposited in the same place. Larger fragments will be deposited in one place and small pieces in another. The sediment mixture is separated out into different types of particles which produce different sedimentary rocks.

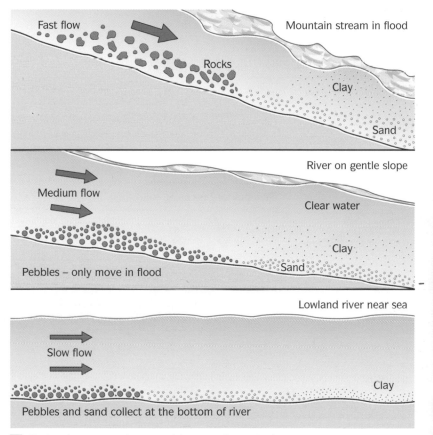

During transportation, particles may be sorted.

Wind can cause erosion.

▶ *A river delta is a large area of sand banks and mud flats at the place where the river enters the sea. How do you think deltas form?*

Metamorphic rocks

Deep in the Earth high temperatures and pressures cause rocks to change without melting. The texture and structure of the rock changes. It recrystallises forming new substances called **metamorphic** rocks. Because the rocks are under pressure the new minerals often rearrange in parallel layers or bands. Sedimentary rocks are formed at low temperatures and pressures. When conditions change they are the most likely rocks to become metamorphic rocks. Under stress slate is formed from mudstone or shale. Metamorphic rocks such as schist and gneiss are formed from slate at higher temperatures and pressure.

Limestone (above) is the source of the metamorphic rock, marble (below). Note how increased pressure and temperature has altered the rock.

CHEMISTRY

The rock cycle

Igneous rock fragments form sedimentary rocks. Sedimentary rocks form metamorphic rocks. If temperature and pressure underground get too high, metamorphic rocks melt, become magma and on cooling become igneous rocks. The materials in rocks are changing and reforming all the time. They go through a series of events that repeat – a cycle called the **rock cycle**.

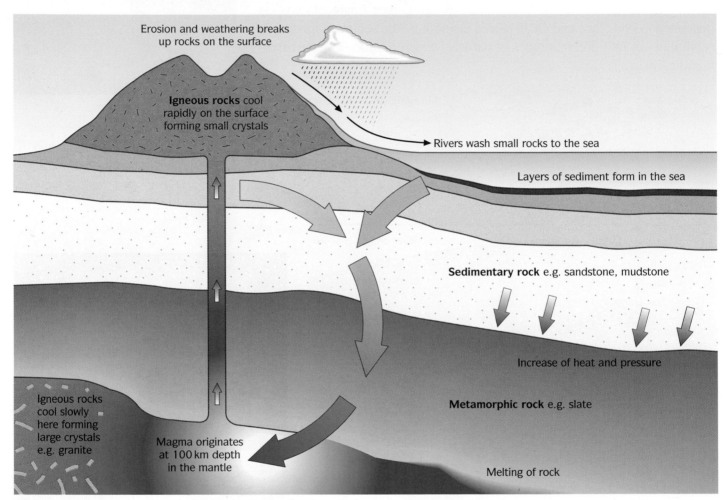

Erosion and weathering breaks up rocks on the surface

Igneous rocks cool rapidly on the surface forming small crystals

Rivers wash small rocks to the sea

Layers of sediment form in the sea

Sedimentary rock e.g. sandstone, mudstone

Increase of heat and pressure

Metamorphic rock e.g. slate

Igneous rocks cool slowly here forming large crystals e.g. granite

Magma originates at 100 km depth in the mantle

Melting of rock

The rock cycle shows the relationships between the three main types of rocks. Over time each type can change into another.

Sand

Most sand grains are composed of the mineral quartz. Quartz is abundant on the surface of the Earth. Desert sand grains are well-rounded, so the sand grains on the right probably do not come from a desert region. The ragged surface shows that the sand grains have struck each other when carried by the wind. Sand grains on the beach are transported by breaking waves and tidal currents. Sand grains can be carried by rivers and glaciers as well. Sand is a very common sediment on the surface of the Earth today and was also common in the past.

This shows sand grains magnified using a microscope.

Quartz

▶ *Look at the pie chart on the right. This shows the abundance of elements in the Earth's crust. What are the two most common elements?*

▶ *In what ratio are silicon and oxygen in the Earth's crust?*

The ratio of the two most common elements is approximately silicon:oxygen = Si:O = 1:2. So it's hardly unexpected that a chemical with the formula SiO_2 should be common in the Earth's crust. Quartz is silcon dioxide, SiO_2

The mineral quartz is sometimes referred to as silicon dioxide and sometimes as silica. They are the same thing. The formula tells you the ratio of atoms in the substance. In quartz the atoms are joined together by covalent bonds and the arrangement of the atoms produces beautiful crystals. You can read more about covalent bonds in Chapter Fourteen (Structure and bonding).

Quartz is not only found in grains of sand. It is also abundant in igneous and metamorphic rocks and in other sedimentary rocks. Quartz is a very stable mineral and so it is often left behind when other less stable minerals are weathered.

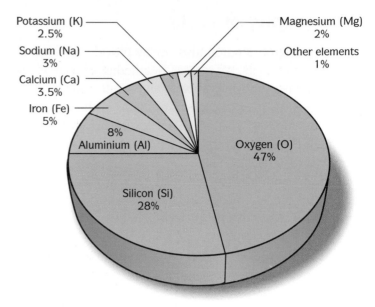

△ This shows the abundance of elements in the Earth's crust.

Potassium (K) 2.5%
Sodium (Na) 3%
Calcium (Ca) 3.5%
Iron (Fe) 5%
8% Aluminium (Al)
Silicon (Si) 28%
Oxygen (O) 47%
Magnesium (Mg) 2%
Other elements 1%

△ Crystals of quartz show hexagonal prisms topped by a hexagonal pyramid.

Looking at the evidence

While it is easy to carry out experiments on sediments in the lab, it is difficult to plan tests that reflect the origin of igneous and metamorphic rocks. This is because they are formed at such high temperatures and pressures. We have to look at evidence in the rocks themselves to find out how they were formed.

The origins of rocks

Things going on all around us today provide evidence about the origins of rocks. We can see weathering, erosion in mountains, sediment moving in rivers and winds and volcanic lava flows cooling. There is indirect evidence in the **rock record**. Scientists look at rocks and their texture. From the size and shape of the crystals they can tell which minerals cooled first and how fast they cooled.

In sedimentary rocks scientists look at the evidence from the fossils present. Plants and animals which became trapped in the rock when it formed provide clues about the original location. For instance, the presence of shells probably indicates that the rock formed at the bottom of the sea.

By looking at the shape of the grains in the rock, it is possible to tell roughly how far the grains were transported. Consider the evidence in the pictures below and on the next page and read about how they can be interpreted.

In the magma chamber crystals of these minerals grew slowly to their present shape. Granite contains crystals of many different minerals.

Interpretation

This rock originated as a magma. The olivine crystals grew first. The partly crystalline magma was then pushed up into cracks high in the crust. The crystals around the olivine grew faster (they are smaller). When the magma emerged at the Earth's surface as lava, the pressure fell and gas bubbles came out of the solution. Quartz then formed in the bubbles.

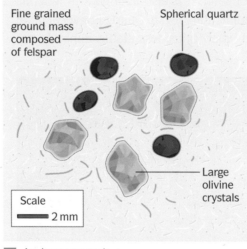

Fine grained ground mass composed of felspar

Spherical quartz

Large olivine crystals

Scale
 2 mm

An igneous rock.

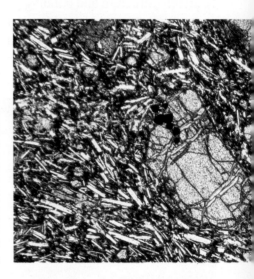

Interpretation

This rock was probably originally a sedimentary mud rock that became buried. The mica crystals grew at right angles to the direction of the pressure. A mineral called garnet also grew, probably at a higher temperature, and pushed the mica aside.

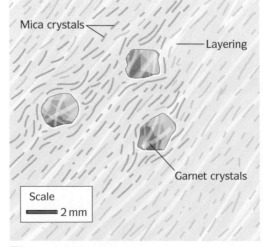

Mica crystals

Layering

Garnet crystals

Scale
2 mm

A metamorphic rock.

Interpretation

The roundness of the sand grains indicates that the particles originated either in a wind-blown desert or on a beach. The presence of shell fragments confirms the beach environment. The cement was precipitated around the grains from groundwater when the sand was buried.

▸ *What happens to a fizzy drink when pressure is released by opening the can? Relate this to what happens when magma erupts from volcanoes.*

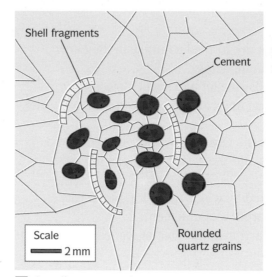

A sedimentary rock.

In the British Isles all three types of rock can be seen in relation to one another in the Grampians of Scotland. The interpretation of the rock record in this part of Scotland is as follows.

Interpretation

Sedimentary rocks were laid down in the sea. Evidence of this can be found in the metamorphic rocks which formed from these sedimentary rocks.

▸ *What type of evidence would show that the sedimentary rocks were laid down by the sea?*

The sedimentary rocks were pushed up and folded into a mountain chain by a closure of an ancient ocean by plate tectonics. You can read more about plate tectonics in Chapter Seven (The Earth).

The sedimentary rocks were buried so deep that some of them became 'cooked' (subjected to high temperatures and pressures) and changed into metamorphic rocks.

At greater depth some rocks became partly molten and rose up into the crust forming a **magma chamber**. This magma crystallised to form the igneous rock, granite.

▸ *What is a magma chamber?*

The metamorphic rocks and igneous rocks originated deep underground, but erosion and movement in the mountains caused the whole crust to lift up. As a result these rocks eventually became exposed at the surface.

Granite, gneiss and schist are the source rocks for the sedimentary rocks in the Midland Valley of Scotland.

These sedimentary rocks were laid down by ancient rivers which eroded the Grampian mountains in the past.

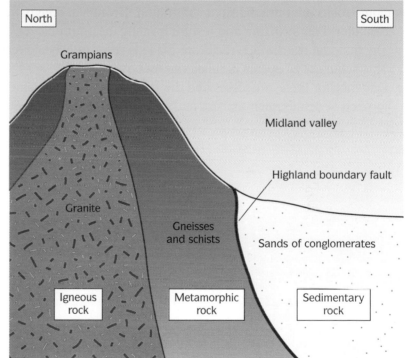

▸ *Explain how granite rock could be the source of sedimentary rock many kilometres away.*

▸ *Explain the term 'eroded' in the last sentence on the left.*

▸ *Copy the diagram above. Label it and put in arrows showing how the rocks moved through a cycle over millions of years.*

Summary

- Minerals are solid chemicals that are formed naturally in the Earth.
- Rocks are made from one or more minerals.
- Weathering breaks rock down into smaller and smaller pieces.
- Rocks are weathered by expansion and contraction, by freezing of water and by chemicals in rainwater.
- Erosion involves movement. It is the wearing away of river beds and valleys by mobile rock fragments and the wearing away of the rock fragments themselves.
- Rock fragments can be transported by water, wind, ice and gravity.
- Faster running water can carry larger rock fragments.
- Rocks are classified as sedimentary, metamorphic or igneous, depending on how they were formed.
- Igneous rocks form as molten magma cools.
- The faster the magma cools the smaller the crystal size.
- Weathering and erosion build up deep sediments on land and sea.
- Pressure on the layers turns the sediments into rocks. The rock fragments are cemented together.
- Younger sedimentary rocks usually lie on top of older sedimentary rocks.
- Some rocks are buried deep underground. Heating and high pressure can alter their structure and texture forming metamorphic rocks.
- The material from which rocks are made is constantly being recycled. This sequence of events is called the rock cycle.
- Evidence for these processes and the rock cycle can be obtained by looking at details such the size and form of the crystals in the rock.

Revision Questions

1 Use the following phrases and examples to make a table with three columns, headed igneous rock, sedimentary rock and metamorphic rock.

Formed from cooling magma	Formed by increasing temperature and pressure
Contains fossils	Cemented together
Has grains or layers	Formed by deposition of rock fragments and fossils
No layers or fossils	Made of crystals
No layers or fossils	Marble
Quartz	Basalt
Slate	Limestone
Sandstone	Granite

2 Which of these words fit with the statements below?
   i marble   *iii* granite   *v* clay
   ii concrete   *iv* limestone

   a A metamorphic rock.
   b Changes into marble when subjected to high temperatures and pressures.
   c Contains large crystals.
   d Manufactured by people.
   e These are carbonates.

3 Fragments can break away from rock faces.
   a Describe four ways in which this happens.
   b What are these piles of fragments called?
   c What is likely to happen to these fragments?

4 The layers of sediment in the beaker drawn in the next column represent a river bed. Clay is deposited by still water, sand is deposited in moderate conditions and floods deposit pebbles.
   a Make a drawing of the sediment in each layer.
   b Describe the thickness of each layer and the size and shape of the fragments.
   c Was each layer deposited by still, slow or fast water? If you can, say whether the fragments have travelled far or not.

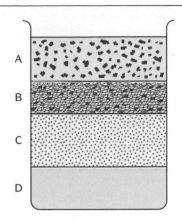

5 Clay changes into different types of rock as the temperature and pressure change. The deeper it is buried the greater the pressure upon it.

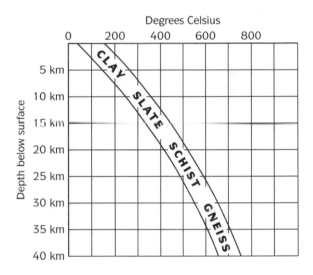

Look at the graph. Then copy the table below, filling in the names of rocks formed under certain conditions.

Type of rock	Name of rock
A sedimentary rock	
A metamorphic rock formed at shallow depths and low temperatures	
A metamorphic rock formed at medium depths and temperatures	
A metamorphic rock formed at great depths and very high temperatures	

6

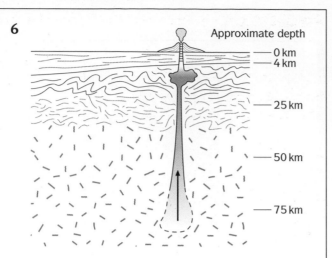

Approximate depth
- 0 km
- 4 km
- 25 km
- 50 km
- 75 km

Read the sentences below. Copy the diagram. Add the sentences to the diagram to explain how volcanoes produce molten lava.

- Magma contains dissolved gases including a lot of steam.
- The Earth's crust and mantle are mostly solid.
- Only a little of the mantle rock melts, but the high pressure squeezes the molten bits out of the rock so that they come together to make larger masses of magma.
- Magma is molten rock in the mantle underneath the crust of the Earth.
- Magma forms between 30 km and 100 km underground in regions where the temperature reaches 1000 °C.
- The sudden release of gases provides the power of an eruption.
- Lowering the pressure lets dissolved gases come out of the solution. The gases and steam in magma take up about 1000 times more space when they come out of solution.
- The pressure gets less as molten magma rises towards the surface of the Earth.

7 This drawing shows part the Earth's crust where magma has been forced between other rocks.

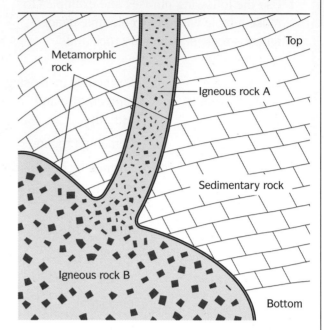

Metamorphic rock

Top

Igneous rock A

Sedimentary rock

Igneous rock B

Bottom

a Make a copy of the diagram and mark on it:
- The two types of rock which have been formed from cooled magma.
- Where the magma has cooled more slowly and where it has cooled faster.
- Where the crystals will be smallest and where will they be largest.

b Explain why metamorphic rock has formed around the igneous rocks. How can you tell that the sedimentary rock is the oldest rock on the rock face?

8 How do scientists get evidence about the origin of rocks? Give as many ways as you can.

The Earth

Long ago, earthquakes were thought to be signs that the gods were having a bad day. In Japan people thought that there was a monster catfish imprisoned under their islands. In Greece they thought the upheavals were caused by the anger of the sea god Poseidon. Nowadays we have more scientific explanations for earthquakes but we are still some way from fully understanding them or knowing exactly when they are going to occur.

Review

Before going any further read this page and attempt the tasks. Write the answers in your notes.

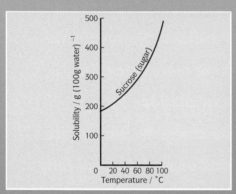

△ Sugar dissolves in tea. If you keep adding more and more sugar, in the end no more will dissolve and solid sugar collects in the bottom of the cup.

△ This graph shows the solubility of sugar at different temperatures.

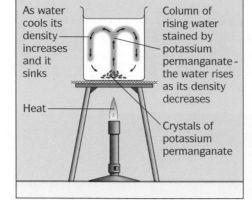

As water cools its density increases and it sinks

Column of rising water stained by potassium permanganate - the water rises as its density decreases

Heat

Crystals of potassium permanganate

△ The density of water falls when it is heated and so the water rises. As the water cools its density increases again so it sinks.

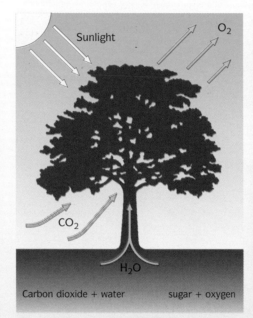

Sunlight

O_2

CO_2

H_2O

Carbon dioxide + water   sugar + oxygen

△ During photosynthesis green plants use energy from the Sun to convert carbon dioxide and water into sugar and oxygen.

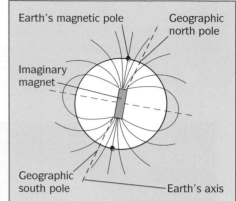

Earth's magnetic pole   Geographic north pole

Imaginary magnet

Geographic south pole   Earth's axis

△ This is a sketch of the magnetic field around the Earth. It acts as though there is a giant bar magnet inside the Earth.

△ Living things, including humans, obtain energy by respiration. In cells, in a reaction with oxygen, glucose is broken down and energy is transferred for use in growth, reproduction and keeping alive. This is an aerobic process as it uses up oxygen.

CHECK SEVEN

1 What are convection currents and why do they occur in heated liquids?

2 Using the example of sugar in a cup of tea, explain the meaning of the terms solvent, solute and solution.

3 How much sugar will dissolve in 100 cm³ water at 40 °C and at 80 °C?

4 How does the solubility of sugar alter as the temperature is raised?

5 What would happen if you cooled a solution containing 400 g sugar in 100 cm³ water from 90 °C to 60 °C?

6 The Earth's North and South poles swap over every few thousand years. Make a sketch showing the Earth's new magnetic field if this happened.

7 Write word equations to represent:
   a photosynthesis
   b aerobic respiration.

Earthquakes

Every so often the Earth shakes and rattles. Sometimes these movements or **tremors** are slight and do no damage. On other occasions the surface of the Earth is ripped apart causing the collapse of buildings and houses and resulting in many deaths. Over the years scientists have come to a better understanding of the forces that shape the Earth's surface and of the earthquakes they produce. The Earth is constantly changing, though most of us are not aware of it. Then, every so often, forces inside the Earth become strong enough to break up large masses of rock and make them move. This upheaval is an **earthquake**. These can devastate large cities. The forces that cause earthquakes have, over millions of years, created the shapes of mountains and ocean floors.

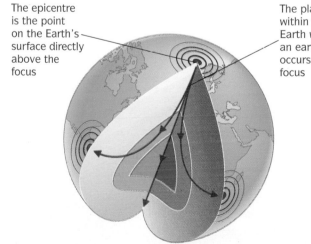

▲ An earthquake in the Japanese city of Kobe killed 4500 people and left many others homeless. The cost in rebuilding and lost industrial output could be as high as £90 billion.

Seismometers

Earthquakes make the ground move up and down and from side to side. These movements can be detected using a **seismometer**. The diagram below right shows you how a simple seismometer works. The base of the seismometer is firmly fixed onto the Earth. During a tremor the heavy weight with its pointer stays still with any slight movement being absorbed by the spring. The rotating drum and chart are free to shake with the Earth. As the drum moves the pattern of the shock waves is recorded on the chart.

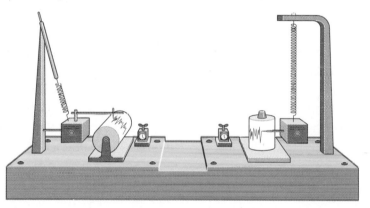

▲ This is a simplified diagram of a sensitive seismometer. The traces are recorded on charts on rotating drums.

Epicentre

Earthquakes are generated at points within 750 km of the Earth's surface. Energy is released and spreads out travelling through the Earth as **shock waves**. The point on the surface directly above the place where the earthquake started is called the **epicentre** and it is here that the movements are felt most strongly. There are different ways of classifying the strength of earthquakes.

The epicentre is the point on the Earth's surface directly above the focus

The place within the Earth where an earthquake occurs is the focus

▲ The earthquake is usually strongest at the epicentre.

CHEMISTRY

Richter scale

The energy associated with an earthquake can be measured on the Richter scale. This measures the amount of energy generated and the resulting movement of the Earth on a scale of 0–9. The scale does not measure how much damage is caused. A tremor that measures 1 on the Richter scale is very weak whereas a disturbance that measures 9 on the scale would make waves on the Earth's surface. This would have disastrous effects.

Mercalli scale

This scale is based on effects of earthquakes that can be seen and felt by people.

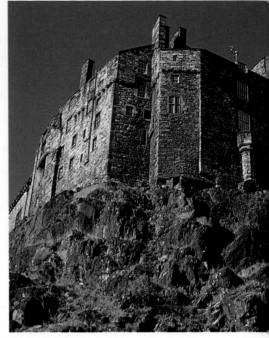

The Mercalli scale

1 Not felt by people
2 Just noticeable if you are still
3 Like vibrations from a passing lorry
4 Loose objects rattle
5 Some sleeping people are woken up, doors swing open or close
6 Trees sway, loose objects fall and break
7 Walls crack and plaster falls, difficult to stay standing

8 Cars crash, houses crack, chimneys fall
9 Ground cracks, underground pipes break, houses might fall
10 Ground badly cracked, many buildings destroyed, landslides
11 Few houses standing, bridges destroyed
12 Total destruction, objects thrown into the air, ground rises and falls in visible waves

⬔ The global seismic monitoring system in Edinburgh picks up about 30 thousand tremors a year, but few cause destruction on a serious scale.

Earthquakes and volcanoes

Looking at the map you can see that there is a pattern. There are long thin continuous bands or belts of places where earthquakes occur. These belts are found along high mountain ranges like the Andes, the Himalayas and the Alps. Beneath the oceans belts of earthquake zones are found in the middle of the seas or they pass through chains of volcanic islands such as the Caribbean and the Philippines. Surveys show that these ocean belts pass through underwater mountains that are much larger than any mountains on the land.

▶ *Look at the map below. What patterns can you see in the locations of earthquakes and volcanoes? Use an atlas to help you comment if you are unsure of the names of the continents and oceans.*

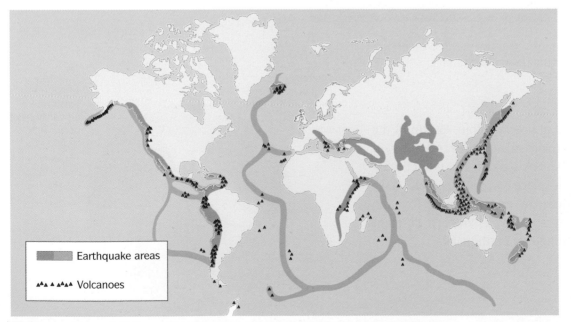

Earthquake areas

▴▴ ▴ ▴▴ Volcanoes

⬔ The locations of all the earthquakes and volcanic eruptions can be plotted on a map of the world.

Plates

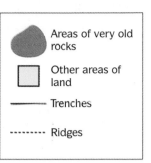

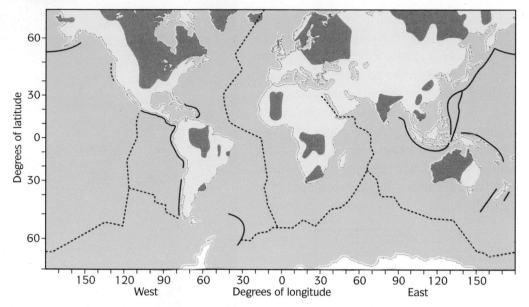

🔺 This map shows the pattern of oceanic ridges, trenches and areas of very old rock (known to be over 1000 million years old).

Oceanic **ridges** are mountain ranges under the sea. The ridges are lines of mountains rising out of the ocean floor to heights of between two and five kilometres. **Trenches** are deep long valleys on the ocean floor where the sea can be up to nine kilometres deep.

You can see from the maps that most earthquakes and volcanoes occur on or near ocean ridges and trenches, or near mountain ranges. If you join all these locations together you can see that the Earth's surface is divided up into separate large areas called **plates**.

So, the Earth's surface is not a continuous skin. It consists of plates that are solid slabs of crust with the upper part of the mantle, about 100 km thick. There are six large plates as well as many small ones. Earthquakes and volcanoes occur most often along the edges or **margins** of these massive slabs.

▶ *What pattern can you see in the ridges, trenches and very old rock on the surface of the Earth?*

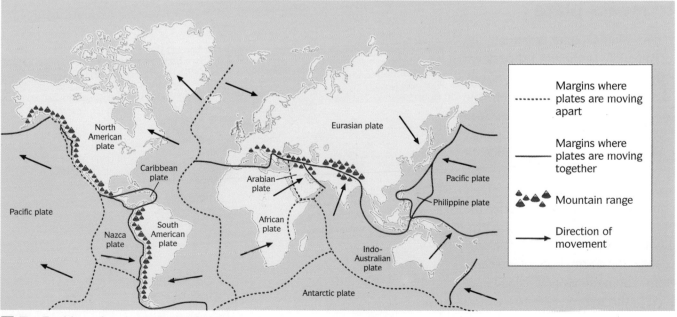

🔺 The Earth's surface is made up of plates.

Moving plates

Evidence from rocks and satellites tells us that plates move at the rate of about five centimetres a year. They move very slowly carrying their continents and oceans with them. For example, Liverpool and New York are moving apart at the rate of about one centimetre a year. Plates move past one another and they may get jammed. Pressure builds up and when they eventually move the edges are deformed (change shape). The land around is shaken up. Even a small movement can cause severe earthquakes. When the edges of plates move relative to one another the result is called a **fault**. When plates move into one another the rocks get pushed together and can become deformed, **folded** or even turned upside down. Folding can result in gentle slopes or in mountain chains like the Rockies and the Alps.

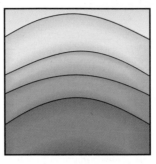
Syncline

Anticline

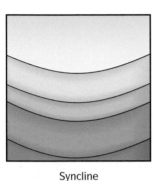 When sediments are squeezed together the rock gets deformed. Upfolds are called **anticlines**. Downfolds are called **synclines**.

The San Andreas fault in California is a plate boundary that is hundreds of miles long.

Folding of rocks

You may be given a worksheet to help you find out how the structure of mountain ranges is affected by different amounts of earth movement. The folding and lifting of rocks can result in steep mountains or gentle slopes.

Plate meets plate

When two plates come together, the edge of one plate is forced to slide down under the other. This movement of one plate down under another and into the mantle below is called **subduction**. When two oceanic plates move together under the sea, subduction produces a deep trench in the ocean floor. Melting eventually occurs where the two plates meet due to the heat released by the Earth's core. Pockets of magma are produced which, when they reach the surface, cause the formation of volcanic mountains. Sometimes new islands are produced in the sea.

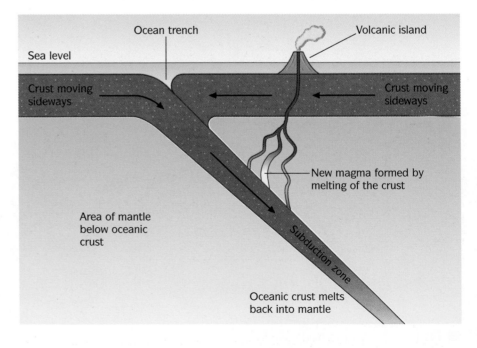
Ocean trench
Volcanic island
Sea level
Crust moving sideways
Crust moving sideways
New magma formed by melting of the crust
Area of mantle below oceanic crust
Subduction zone
Oceanic crust melts back into mantle

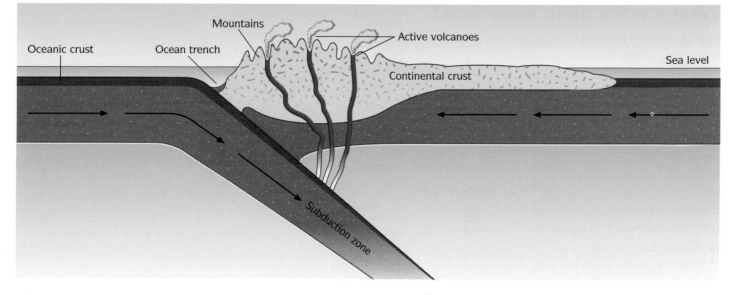

When an oceanic plate meets a continental plate, the denser oceanic crust moves down and the continental crust is forced upwards forming mountain ranges and producing massive earthquakes. At the same time, magma may rise upwards through the continental plate producing volcanoes.

Margins moving towards one another where crust is destroyed or modified are called **destructive plate margins**. You can usually recognise them by the presence of an ocean trench.

▶ *Look again at the maps on page 97. Give an example of an area where oceanic crust is being subducted, or pushed under continental crust.*

Plates moving apart

If some plates are pushing into one another, others must be moving apart. Under the oceans, plates move slowly apart. This happens along the oceanic ridges, including the mid-Atlantic ridge. Magma wells up from below, forming new rock and filling up the space. Material is deposited on the edges of the plates forming new oceanic crust. In this way, the seafloor gets spread out and continents gets pushed further apart. Margins where new crust is being made are called **constructive plate margins**.

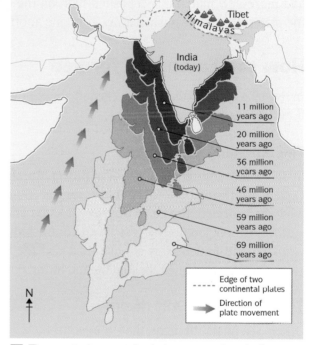

🔺 The greatest mountain chains are produced when a continental plate meets another continental plate. The Tibetan mountain range, the Himalayas, is the result of a collision 40 million years ago between the continental plates carrying Asia and India.

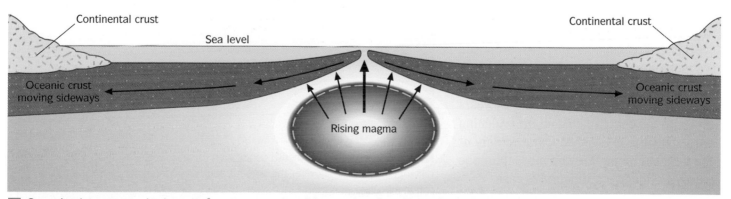

🔺 Oceanic plates move slowly away from one another. Magma rises from below forming new rock.

CHEMISTRY

What causes plate movement?

The reasons for plate movement are not fully understood.

Some people think that it is due to the slow movement of partially molten rock beneath the plates. Heat could produce convection currents similar to those in a beaker of heated water. As the upper mantle is partly liquid heat energy could be transferred from the upper layers to produce convection currents. It could cause the upward movement of magma under the ocean ridges and also the downward movement of the oceanic crust in subduction zones.

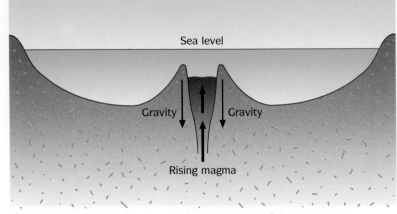

🔺 According to one theory, gravity may cause plate movement.

Another newer theory is that movement of the plates is driven by gravity. Material moving upwards between ocean ridges deposits itself in layers. More and more new material is deposited high on the edges of the ridge. Perhaps the plates are simply pushed away from one another by a gravitational force.

How the Earth was formed

In the 1920s two main theories existed about how the Earth was formed and how mountain building occurred.

The Shrinking Earth theory

In the nineteenth century the **Shrinking Earth theory** was proposed to explain the formation of mountain ranges. Some scientists thought that, when first formed, the Earth was very hot. On cooling, a skin formed on the surface. On cooling further, the Earth contracted and so the surface became wrinkled and folded. This shrinking caused the movement observed in the crust and also explained the folding and lifting of the Earth's crust.

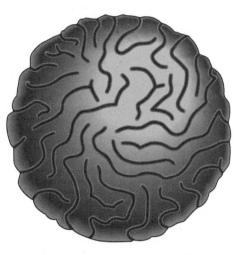

🔺 In the Shrinking Earth theory the continents and oceans are fixed.

The Continental Drift theory

Other scientists thought that the continents of the world had once been joined together. For some reason they broke up into large pieces and slowly drifted apart.

Over the years, the way the continents fit together like bits of a jig-saw puzzle has been pointed out by many people.

At the beginning of this century, Alfred Wegner, a German meteorologist, proposed a supercontinent that he called Pangaea. It was made from all the known continents and began to break up millions of years ago with the oceans filling up the widening gaps. This theory seemed extraordinary at the time but he put forward more than one piece of evidence to support his case.

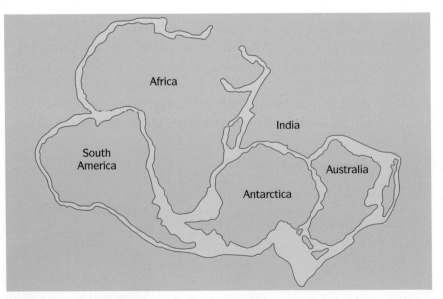

🔺 At the end of the nineteenth century an Austrian scientist called Eduard Suess put together a map showing the present southern continents combined into a giant continent called Gondwanaland.

Wegner's evidence

- There is a jig-saw fit of land masses on either side of the Atlantic Ocean and a match between rock types in Africa and South America.
- Fossil remains of *Mesosaurus*, a small aquatic reptile, are found in Africa and South America.
- Coal, which usually forms in hot, swampy conditions, is found at the Antarctic.
- There is evidence that areas, now near the Equator, were once covered with an ice sheet.

In the years that followed, much attention was paid to these ideas. Wegner was not a geologist and had based his ideas on the observations of others. Scientists presented evidence for and against his theory in ways which would best support their own investigations and arguments. No one could quite see how solid rock could flow or where the energy could come from to move around such massive continents. In the end, people did not support his theory.

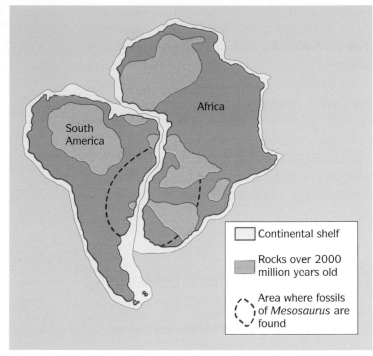

Continental shelf

Rocks over 2000 million years old

Area where fossils of *Mesosaurus* are found

🔺 Similar rocks are found in Africa and South America.

Talking about Alfred Wegner

You may be given a worksheet to help you plan a presentation on Alfred Wegner's work.

▸ *Why are scientists today able to exchange ideas more easily? How does this affect scientific research?*

In 1928 a great British geologist, called Arthur Holmes, suggested that convection currents might provide the energy to move continents. He suggested that heat from the Earth's core moved the molten mantle around with the continents on top. He thought that continents could be dragged apart when the currents flowed down and that the ocean floor could be built up where convection currents dragged material upwards. This theory is not unlike our modern ideas. At the time Holmes pointed out that his theory was based on his own views. Although the theory matched the known facts, results of scientific investigators were needed to prove it.

It was not until after World War II that convincing evidence emerged. It originated from data collected by geologists studying the seabed in the mid-Atlantic. They discovered a deep crack-like valley or **rift** running down its centre. New oceanic crust was being made when lava poured up through the centre of these cracks on to both sides of the plate. They found, using their knowledge of radioactive dating, that no oceanic crust was older than 200 million years and that the youngest rock was near the ridge. They also realised that ocean crust was newer than mountain crust, a fact that they had not considered before. You can read more about radioactive dating in Physics, Chapter Fifteen.

▸ *Explain why this last finding supported Holmes' theories.*

Worldwide magnetic surveys of rocks provided more confirmation of Wegner's and Holme's ideas. When lava solidifies, the new rock inherits magnetic properties depending on the direction of the Earth's magnetic field at the time. Because the Earth's magnetic field reverses periodically the magnetism of the newly formed rock keeps changing. Magnetic surveys have shown a pattern of magnetic stripes on the seabed. New rock is formed on both sides of the ridge and the pattern on either side matches perfectly.

▶ *How could you explain the fact that the width of these magnetic bands differs?*

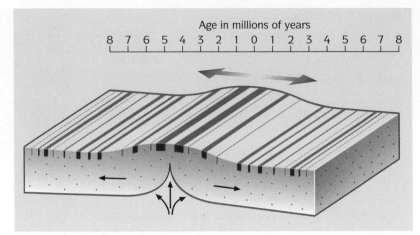

Age in millions of years

🔺 The magnetic pattern on either side of the ridge is symmetrical.

The theory of plate tectonics

The theory of plate tectonics, which is based on Wegner's and Holme's ideas, was accepted by about 1970. We now believe that the Earth's crust is cracked into a number of plates which move at speeds of a few centimetres a year. This movement is a result of convection currents within the Earth's upper mantle. The theory has been accepted because it links together older ideas about continental drift, the distribution of mountains and rocks and the location of earthquakes and volcanoes, with what we know about the way the Earth works internally and the way rocks are created. The same ideas can be used to explain all the processes that act at the surface of the Earth such as the ocean tides, and short and long term weather changes. But the theory of plate tectonics still does not explain everything. Some mountain ranges like the Eastern Highlands of Australia can not be explained by plate tectonics. Scientists also believe that the oceanic crust is being made at a faster rate than it is being destroyed by subduction into the mantle. Maybe the Earth is expanding. This could also explain how the plates move. Obviously there is still some hypothesising and investigating to be done. Maybe the theory will be modified in your lifetime.

Atmosphere on Earth

Most planets have atmospheres containing hydrogen, nitrogen in the compound ammonia, and carbon in the compound methane. The Earth is different. Its atmosphere is mainly nitrogen and oxygen with small amounts of carbon dioxide. Nitrogen in compounds is found in the atmospheres of other planets, but nitrogen the element, and oxygen, are unique to Earth's.

Origin of the atmosphere

The Earth is assumed to have formed from the same material that formed the Sun. How and when the atmosphere began to form is difficult to decide. It is thought that about 4500 million years ago the atmosphere contained hydrogen and helium which were removed by the gravitational pull of the Sun. Today's atmosphere is certainly different from that of the past. You may be wondering how the composition of gases has changed and from where the

Gas	% by volume in dry air
Nitrogen	79.03
Oxygen	20.99
Argon	0.93
Carbon dioxide	0.03
Neon, helium, krypton and xenon	0.002
Hydrogen	0.001

🔺 The composition of gases in dry air has been about the same for 200 million years. The amount of water vapour varies from place to place.

atoms and molecules that are present now came. It is generally thought that gases, produced by heat and chemical reactions, were released from inside the Earth.

Scientists trying to find out more about how our atmosphere was formed have studied the gases in volcanic eruptions. They noticed that over the centuries eruptions have been frequent and they wondered if volcanic gases have mixed with and changed the atmosphere. They assumed that the composition of volcanic gases would not have changed much over the years. Their results showed that enormous volumes of gas are produced by volcanoes. The most common gas was steam (water vapour), followed by nitrogen and carbon dioxide. They did not, however, find any oxygen. Life as we know it today would have been impossible in an atmosphere of volcanic gases. Of the world's surface, 70 per cent is covered by water, most of it seawater (97 per cent).

Calculations based on scientific measurements have confirmed that over 400 million years volcanic gases could account for enough water vapour to condense and fill the oceans and enough nitrogen to account for the level of that gas in today's atmosphere.

🔺 Mount Fuji is a famous volcano in Japan.

Making oxygen

Oxygen may have been produced by the breakdown of water to hydrogen and oxygen by ultraviolet radiation. However oxygen formed this way would quickly react with other gases or metals like iron.

The production of significant amounts of oxygen probably only came after blue-green algae had evolved. Like all green plants which carry out photosynthesis, algae use energy from sunlight to convert carbon dioxide and water into sugars. Oxygen is a by-product that is released into the atmosphere. You can read about photosynthesis in Biology, Chapter Twelve.

Maintaining a balance

Oxygen reacts with most other elements. It reacts with other substances during burning and rusting. It reacts with hydrogen forming water. It also dissolves in water. All these processes remove oxygen from the atmosphere. In spite of this, oxygen levels continued to rise due to photosynthesis. Then new life forms developed that could combine oxygen with carbon from their food, making energy for their own use. They respired aerobically. You can read about aerobic respiration in Biology, Chapter Five. Aerobic respiration, together with biological decay, which also removes oxygen from the atmosphere, balances the build-up of oxygen from photosynthesis.

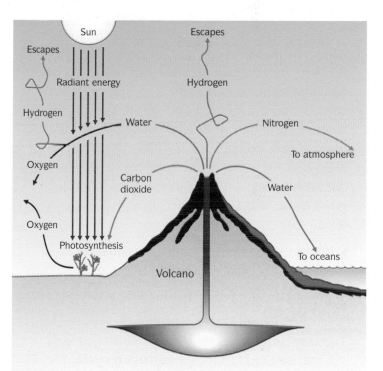
🔺 Eruptions of volcanoes contributed enormous amounts of water, carbon dioxide and other gases to the atmosphere as it evolved. Sunlight broke some water into hydrogen and oxygen. Photosynthesis by plants removed carbon dioxide and released oxygen into the atmosphere.

The Earth is 140 million km from the Sun. If it were only 10 million km nearer, the higher temperature would have prevented water vapour from condensing into the oceans.

Maintaining water in the oceans and water vapour in the atmosphere depends on the temperature. The temperature on any planet depends on its distance from the Sun. The levels of water and water vapour on Earth depend on the alternate evaporation and condensation, described as the **water cycle**. The average temperature throughout the year allows this cycle to be kept in balance.

▶ *Copy and label the diagram on the right to show what is happening at each stage.*

Carbon dioxide

During the Earth's first billion years, its atmosphere is thought to have been mainly carbon dioxide. Today only 0.03 per cent of the atmosphere is carbon dioxide. Much of it was removed by reacting with calcium, hydrogen and oxygen to form limestone and coal and oil, which lie buried under the Earth's crust. The small amount of carbon dioxide left is essential for photosynthesis. Today, although carbon dioxide is still removed by reaction with seawater, we are responsible for returning large amounts of it to the atmosphere by our unrestricted use of coal and oil as fuels. This, together with the destruction of tropical rainforests, may account for a build up of carbon dioxide in the atmosphere sufficient to influence our weather and climate. You can read about the greenhouse effect in Chapter Twelve (Energy in reactions).

▶ *How does our increased use of coal and oil influence the carbon cycle?*

Nitrogen

The constant uptake and release of nitrogen from the atmosphere is called the **nitrogen cycle**. You can read about the nitrogen cycle in Biology, Chapter Thirteen. There are about 4×10^{15} tonnes of nitrogen in the atmosphere. Large amounts are 'fixed' chemically by people, using the Haber process, and about the same amount is **fixed** by biological processes. (Fixing means incorporating in compounds with other elements.) Fortunately for us the natural processes returning it to the atmosphere, keep nitrogen at a constant level. You can read about the Haber process in Chapter Thirteen (Using reactions).

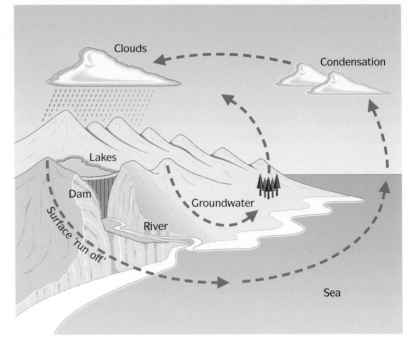

⬛ Our supplies of fresh water depend on the water cycle.

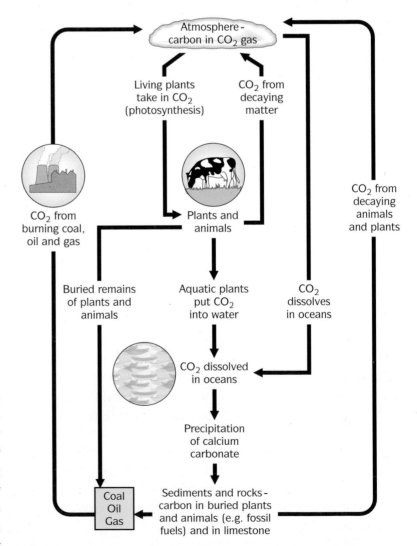

⬛ The carbon dioxide in the atmosphere is constantly being used and reused. This sequence of events is called the **carbon cycle**.

Seawater

Oceans are huge reservoirs of salts that flow in and out from the Earth's crust. Dissolved salts in seawater come from the weathering of rocks on land. Particles are transported to the sea by rivers. Seawater contains 3.45 per cent of salts, the most abundant being sodium chloride. The concentration of salts in the oceans remains remarkably constant as water circulation evens out the effects of dilution by freshwater rivers and evaporation by the Sun.

▶ *What could cause an increase or a decrease in the salt content of sea water?*

The only major variations in salt level can be seen in seas that are partly or wholly surrounded by land. For example, in the Red Sea there is excessive evaporation and the average salt level is between four and five per cent. In the Baltic Sea, where there is a large inflow of freshwater from rivers, the salt level is between one and two per cent.

Seawater is not just concentrated river water. The main ions in river water are calcium and hydrogencarbonate. In seawater the main positive ions, such as sodium and magnesium, come with river water from the land. The main negative ions, chloride and sulphate, come from submarine volcanoes. Seawater contains only very low levels of calcium and hydrogencarbonate ions and silica as these are removed by organisms to make their shells and skeletons.

▲ Rivers bring dissolved salts and rock particles from the land into the oceans.

▲ The salt level in the Dead Sea can be up to 32 per cent.

Ion	Seawater concentration (mol × 10⁻²)	River water concentration (mol × 10⁻²)
Na^+	47.0	0.027
K^+	1.0	0.006
Ca^{2+}	1.0	0.038
Mg^{2+}	5.4	0.017
Cl^-	55.0	0.022
SO_4^{2-}	3.8	0.012
HCO_3^-	0.2	0.096

▲ Scientists have compared the average composition of seawater and river water.

▶ *Which two ions are most common in:*
  a *seawater*
  b *river water?*
  How can you account for this difference?

Evaporites

Changes in climate sometimes cause water to evaporate from areas that were once covered by a shallow sea. The sedimentary rocks left after the evaporation of water are called **evaporites**. These salt deposits are useful sources of chemicals like sodium chloride, calcium sulphate, magnesium chloride and magnesium sulphate.

▲ This salt deposit is in Iran. The bands show the salt deposited in a year.

CHEMISTRY

The various salts found in seawater have different solubilities. So when normal seawater is evaporated the salts are precipitated in a definite order.

Mineral	Ions precipitated	per cent of water evaporated for precipitation
Dolomite	Ca^{2+}, Mg^{2+}, HCO_3^-	50
Gypsum	Ca^{2+}, SO_4^{2-}	80
Rock salt	Na^+, Cl^-	90
Sylvine	K^+, Mg^{2+}, Cl^-	when water has almost all gone

Summary

- Scientists think that the surface of the Earth was once one large land mass because the edges of continents have shapes that fit together reasonably well. The continents also have similar patterns of rocks and fossils.
- The Earth's surface has split up into large plates which are thought to be moving slowly away from or into one another. This theory of plate movement is called plate tectonics.
- Plates can be made from oceanic or continental crust.
- Plates can slide past one another producing faults.
- Plates can be compressed together causing folding and uplifting of rock.
- Convection currents within the Earth's mantle are thought to provide the forces which move the plates.
- When plates meet, the edge of one is pushed down (or subducted) underneath the other. The edge of the other is forced upwards.
- Earthquakes, volcanoes and mountain ranges occur where plates meet.
- Some plates move away from one another, which explains why continents have drifted apart. Magma moves upwards, filling the gap and producing new rock.
- The magnetic pattern of rocks on either side of oceanic ridges helps to support the theory of plate tectonics.
- Plate movement plays a part in the way rocks are recycled. Continental rocks are uplifted. Rocks may be subducted and then melt forming magma.
- Today the Earth's atmosphere contains about 79 per cent nitrogen, 20 per cent oxygen and small amounts of various other gases, including carbon dioxide.
- The composition of the atmosphere remains roughly constant and is maintained by the carbon cycle and the nitrogen cycle. You should know the main steps in these cycles.
- The present atmosphere has evolved and been formed by the Earth itself.
- Volcanic activity released the gases that formed the original atmosphere and the water vapour that formed the oceans.
- When early micro-organisms and plants developed, photosynthesis played a major part in the development of the atmosphere.
- The dissolved salts in river water are the result of rock erosion.
- The dissolved salts in the sea come from river water and underwater volcanoes.

Revision Questions

1 Make a poster with drawings or cut-out pictures to illustrate the Mercalli scale.

2 What is the composition of the atmosphere around the Earth? Use other chapters in this book and any other available resources to make a chart showing how the various gases in the air are used, either as they are or as raw materials by the chemical industry.

3 You have been asked to give a talk to a Year 9 class to convince them that an atmosphere exists around the Earth. You might like to include, for example, a demonstration and explanation of why, if all the air is pumped out of a metal can, the sides cave in. Give details of the examples and slides you would use to illustrate your talk.

4

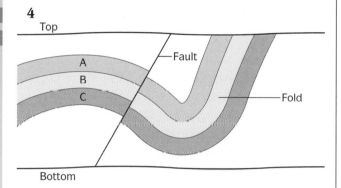

This diagram shows a cross section of a rock face.

  a Which of the rocks labelled A, B and C is likely to be the oldest? Give a reason for your choice.
  b How can you account for the shape of these rocks?
  c In the diagram which is older, the fault or the folds? Explain your answer.

5 100 million years ago the atmosphere contained much more carbon dioxide than it does now. Since then, in the oceans, a reaction has taken place between dissolved carbon dioxide and calcium ions. Calcium carbonate or limestone was formed.

  a 100 million years ago, the sea contained a higher concentration of calcium ions than it does now. Suggest why this should be so.

  b How would the temperature of the seawater influence the formation of limestone?
  c You have been given a rock to study, and you think it may be limestone. What test could you use to support your ideas?
  d How is limestone changed into marble?
  e What percentage of the atmosphere is carbon dioxide today?
  f How is carbon dioxide released into the atmosphere?
  g Lately it seems that the concentration of CO_2 in the atmosphere is increasing. Give two reasons why this might be so.

6

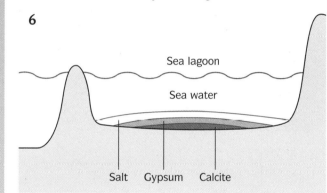

Seawater can be trapped in large pools called lagoons.

  a What will happen to the water in the lagoon on a hot summer's day?
  b Explain why, after a long period of time, minerals form around the edges of the lagoon.
  c Why do the minerals form in layers?

7

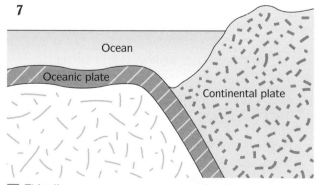

This diagram represents an oceanic plate meeting a continental plate.

Copy the diagram at the bottom of the previous page.

a Draw an arrow showing the direction of movement of the oceanic plate.

b Label the ocean trench and the subduction zone.

c Mark on the diagram where earthquakes and volcanic eruptions are most likely to occur.

d Label the *destructive* plate margin and explain why it is given this name.

e What is a *constructive* plate margin? Include a labelled diagram in your answer.

8

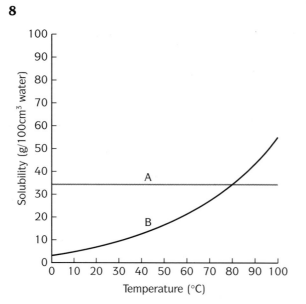

▲ This diagram shows how the solubility of two salts varies with temperature.

a Which of A and B is more soluble in water at 100 °C?

b At what temperature are A and B equally soluble in water?

c A mixture of 30 g of A and 30 g of B is added to 100 g water at 100 °C and stirred.

   i Will all the solid dissolve in water?

   ii The solution is cooled to 20 °C. What will happen?

9 Imagine you are a scientist living earlier this century. Prepare an illustrated article for a magazine in support of Wegner's theory of continental drift.

10 Write a letter to Alfred Wegner supporting the Shrinking Earth theory and including the main doubts regarding his ideas about continental drift.

11 What convincing evidence supporting Wegner's ideas came to light in the years following World War II? Why do you think his theories were disregarded for many years?

12 You have been asked to write a page to be included in a revision guide for GCSE on the the origin of the gases in the atmosphere today. It will be divided into sections with the following headings.

In the beginning
Carbon dioxide
Oxygen
Nitrogen

Your guide should include ideas for any helpful diagrams or photographs.

13 You have received a letter from your Japanese pen pal asking if you know why there are so many volcanoes and frequent earthquakes in the Japanese islands. Write a letter back, basing your explanation on what you have studied in this chapter. Use the map below to help you.

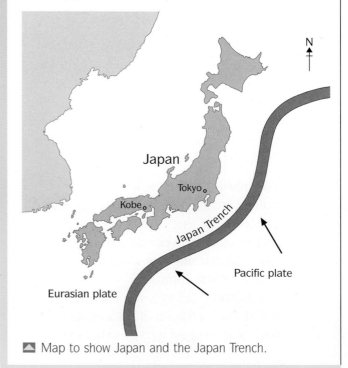

▲ Map to show Japan and the Japan Trench.

The periodic table

■ Putting the elements in order

H	Li	Be	B	C	N	O
F	Na	Mg	Al	Si	P	S
Cl	K	Ca	Cr	Ti	Mn	Fe

Mo

Pb

Bi

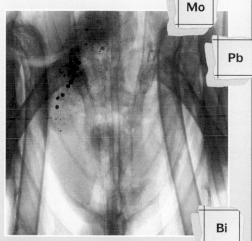

Lead shot is poisonous. Wildfowl poisoning from spent lead shot and fishing weights is now a serious problem. This X-ray shows lead weights swallowed by a swan. Non-toxic shot containing bismuth or molybdenum which have similar properties to lead is being tested.

Ni
Pd
Pt

Cl	Br	I

C

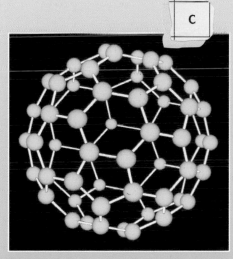

Cool stars like Red giants throw vast quantities of carbon molecules and dust into space. Until recently carbon was known to exist as diamond and graphite only. Now a third form containing 60 carbon atoms joined in a structure similar to a panelled football has been found. It is called Buckminsterfullerene.

C
Si
Ge
Sn
Pb

Li	Na	K

Fe	Co	Ni

N	P	As	Sb	Bi

Scientists trying to find a pattern among the elements had to cope with a few problems. To start with, some of the so-called elements were really compounds. The data for the relative atomic masses of elements was often incomplete and inaccurate and, to add to their difficulties, they had not realised that not all the elements had been discovered.

Ge

Si

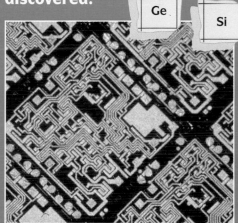

Silicon and germanium are semiconductors and are used to make transistors and microchips.

Rb	Sr	Y	Zr	Nb	Mo	*
Ag	Cd	In	Su	Sb	Te	I

Ru	Rh	Pd

Review

Before going any further read this page and attempt the tasks. Write the answers in your notes.

The Periodic Table

H																	He
Li	Be											B	C	N	O	F	Ne
Na	Mg											Al	Si	P	S	Cl	Av
K	Ca	Sc	Ti	V	Cr	Mn	Fe	Co	Ni	Cu	Zn	Ga	Ge	As	Se	Br	Kr
Rb	Sr	Y	Zr	Nb	Mo	Tc	Ru	Rh	Pd	Ag	Cd	In	Sn	Sb	Te	I	Xe
Cs	Ba	La	Hf	Ta	W	Re	Os	Ir	Pt	Au	Hg	Tl	Pb	Bi	Po	At	Rn

CHECK EIGHT

What element is:
a diamond?
b used in match heads?
c used as a disinfectant?
d used to galvanise other metals?
e often chosen for its lightness?
f used to make jewellery?
g part of a compound used to make photographic emulsions?
h highly flammable?
i used to make fertilisers?
j in an X-ray opaque compound?
k used to fill light bulbs?
l thought to have poisoned Mozart?
m used to fill weather balloons?
n a metal found in the chlorophyll molecule?
o sometimes added to toothpaste?

Patterns among the elements

You are going to look at work which might have been done by some famous scientists when they were students. Evaluate their work and answer the questions.

Name: Johann Döbereiner
Date: 1817

Plan

I am planning to try to put the elements in groups according to their properties. I am going to try this because I have already noticed one big group of elements that are all metals.

Observations

I have put together two groups of three elements where the property of the middle element is a kind of average of the other two.

The first group of three contains lithium, sodium and potassium. Looking at the property of relative atomic mass, A_r:

Lithium $A_r = 7$ Potassium $A_r = 39$

Average $A_r = \dfrac{39 + 7}{2} = 23$

Sodium $A_r = 23$

Features of Li, Na and K	Observation
Appearance	Shiny, soft metals
Melting point and boiling point	Low for metals
Density	Low, can float on water
With water	React vigorously with fizzing
With oxygen	React in a ratio of 2:1 to give Li_2O, Na_2O and K_2O.

Another group of three contains chlorine, bromine and iodine.

Analysis

Elements seem to fall into groups of three depending on their properties. I am going to call these groups triads.

Teacher's comment

Very good so far. Why not include the properties of chlorine, bromine and iodine to prove they support your theory? Also did you find any groups of elements that didn't fit in with your theory? What suggestions have you for further work?

▶ *Look at the properties of chlorine, bromine and iodine on page 117. Do they fit in with Döbereiner's ideas?*

Plan

I know that different elements have different relative atomic masses. I am going to arrange the elements in order of relative atomic mass and see if I notice any patterns in their properties.

Observations:

I put the elements in a list of increasing relative atomic mass and noticed that the same properties recurred every eighth element. I decided to arrange the elements in a grid starting a new row every eighth element.

1	2	3	4	5	6	7
H	Li	Be	B	C	N	O
F	Na	Mg	Al	Si	P	S
Cl	K	Ca	Cr	Ti	Mn	Fe

Analysis

This seems to work quite well for the first four vertical groups. The properties of the elements in each vertical group are very similar. For groups 5 to 7 I see that there are two non-metals and a metal in each and the properties of these elements are very different. Nonetheless, my arrangement puts some metals in groups. I am going to call each row an octave and call this the Law of Octaves.

Evaluation

I must have found part of a way of classifying the elements even although not all elements fitted into my scheme. I think the values for relative atomic mass for some of the elements are not very accurate which might explain why some of them are out of order.

▶ *What do you think Newland's teacher would have said about this work? Write a comment.*

Plan

Name: Lothar Meyer

Date: 1870

Because I am looking for a pattern in the properties of the elements, I am going to measure the volume of the atoms of each element and then draw a line graph. I will show the atomic volume on the y-axis and the relative atomic mass of each element on the x-axis. I am going to do this for the first 60 elements.

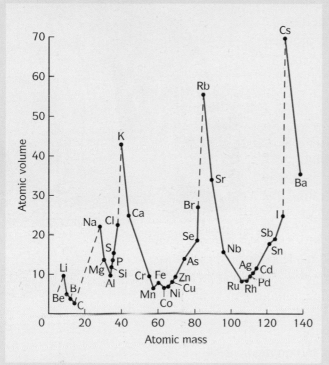

My graph shows atomic volume against relative atomic mass.

Analysis

The elements with similar properties fall on the graph at similar points. For example lithium, sodium, potassium and rubidium fall on the peaks. However, when I look at the peaks on the graph I notice that the rows contained different numbers of elements. The first row seems to contain two elements, the next two rows contain eight, and then the rows seem to get longer. Maybe when the elements are arranged into a grid, the rows will have different lengths.

Evaluation

If I had more time I would measure other properties of the atoms and see if the pattern is the same.

▶ *Write a comment on this plan and the way these results are recorded.*

Plan

I am going to arrange all the elements in order of relative atomic mass. I am then going to arrange the elements into a grid putting elements with similar properties underneath one another.

Name: Dimitri Mendeléev
Date: 1869

Observation

When I carried out my plan I found that some elements were clearly in the wrong row because their properties did not fit in. I suddenly realised that some elements probably have not yet been discovered. So I arranged the elements, still in order of relative atomic mass with similar properties underneath one another.

Analysis

This arrangement works well because elements with similar properties are in vertical groups. There is also a repeating pattern from row to row, so I am suggesting that new elements will be found later to fit into the spaces.

I then realised that you could predict the properties of each element from the element above and below it in the group, so I made some predictions for one of the missing elements.

I predict the missing element between silicon (Si) and tin (Sn) in my table will be a grey metal with:

- a density of 5.5 g/cm^3
- a relative atomic mass between that of silicon and tin (about 73.4)
- a melting point higher than tin (about 800 °C)
- an oxide with the formula XO_2, if X is the symbol of the element.

Evaluation

The one thing I do not understand is why the rows are of different lengths. I would like to try to discover why this is.

	GROUP							
	I	**II**	**III**	**IV**	**V**	**VI**	**VII**	**VIII**
Period 1	H							
Period 2	Li	Be	B	C	N	O	F	
Period 3	Na	Mg	Al	Si	P	S	Cl	
Period 4	K _Cu_	Ca _Zn_	* _*_	Ti _*_	V _As_	Cr _Se_	Mn _Br_	Fe Co Ni
Period 5	Rb _Ag_	Sr _Cd_	Y _In_	Zr _Sn_	Nb _Sb_	Mo _Te_	* _I_	Ru Rh Pd

▲ I am going to call the vertical rows **groups** and the horizontal rows **periods**. The stars show where I think there are elements yet to be discovered.

▶ *What is the name of Mendeléev's missing element X?*

▶ *Use the tables in this book to find out how accurate Mendeléev's predictions about the properties of the missing element X were.*

The periodic table today

You can see by studying the work of Döbereiner, Newland, Meyer and Mendeléev that evolution of the pattern of elements took place over many years. Today we call this pattern the **periodic table**. It was John Dalton, born in Cumbria in 1766, who first suggested that finding out the masses of atoms would be a good idea. From this work he published his Atomic Theory in 1808.

The main points of his theory were:

- Elements are made of tiny round particles called atoms.
- These atoms cannot be destroyed.
- All the atoms of one element have the same mass.

This theory was used together with the work of Newlands, Döbereiner, Meyer and Mendeléev to refine the classification of elements and to produce the periodic table. In the modern version of the periodic table (see page 247) each element is given a number, called the **atomic number**. This is shown below the symbol for the element. The mass number is shown above the symbol. Groups and periods are also given numbers.

▶ *On a copy of the periodic table mark the group numbers and period numbers. Using different colours, shade in the metals and the non-metals.*

▲ John Dalton.

Group 1 elements

7	
Li	
3	
23	
Na	
11	
39	
K	
19	
85.5	
Rb	
37	

▲ Sodium is used as a coolant in nuclear reactors. Here you can see places where cooling rods are lowered into the reactor's core.

▲ Potassium chloride provides the K in NPK fertilisers.

Sodium and potassium are **group 1** elements. You might have seen sodium and potassium in the Science Museum, but otherwise you won't have seen these elements out of school. They have to be stored in oil to prevent them reacting with the air. Their violent reactions with water have probably been demonstrated to you. Both metals are silver in appearance and quite soft and shiny when freshly cut. On exposure to air they rapidly get covered with the dull oxide.

▶ *Make a list showing similarities among the group 1 metals. Include as many features as you can.*

▶ *Explain why the group 1 elements are often called the '**alkali metals**'.*

Looking at the table below you can see that the group 1 elements have a lot in common.

Element	Reaction when burned in air	Reaction with cold water	Melting point (°C)	Boiling point (°C)	Formula of ion	Formula of chloride	Formula of oxide
Li	Burns with a red flame forming a white, alkaline oxide	Reacts forming a soluble alkali (LiOH) and hydrogen	180	1340	Li^+	LiCl	Li_2O
Na	Burns vigorously with a yellow flame, forming a white alkaline oxide	Rapid reaction giving a very soluble alkali (NaOH) and hydrogen	98	880	Na^+	NaCl	Na_2O
K	Burns vigorously with a lilac flame, forming a white alkaline oxide	Very rapid reaction forming a very soluble alkali (KOH) and hydrogen	63	760	K^+	KCl	K_2O

🔺 Some properties of the group 1 elements.

Group 1 elements:
- are metals
- react with water producing an alkaline solution and hydrogen gas

     sodium + water → sodium hydroxide + hydrogen

   $2Na(s) + 2H_2O(l) → 2NaOH(aq) + H_2(g)$

- burn in oxygen forming an oxide which dissolves in water producing an alkaline solution
- form metal ions with a charge of 1^+ (e.g. Na^+).

You should also be able to see some trends or patterns. As you look down the group, the group 1 elements:
- become more reactive
- have higher melting points and boiling points.

Looking at trends

You may be given a worksheet to help you to look for patterns and trends among **group 2** elements. This will enable you to compare this group with others in the periodic table.

Group 7 elements

You will have already seen that **group 7** contains non-metals. Also, remember that Döbereiner picked out chlorine, bromine and iodine as one of his triads. Group 7 contains the reactive elements known as the **halogens**.

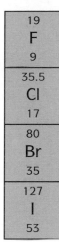

19 **F** 9
35.5 **Cl** 17
80 **Br** 35
127 **I** 53

▲ Iodine is used to make the polarising filters in sunglasses.

▲ Chlorine is used to make bleaches and sterilising solutions.

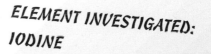

▲ Fluoride in toothpaste helps to fight tooth decay.

Looking at group 7

Susan, Rajni and Steven were asked find any patterns in the properties of the group 7 elements. They each researched the properties of one of the following elements: chlorine, bromine and iodine. Here are their individual results.

ELEMENT INVESTIGATED: CHLORINE

- pale green/yellow gas
- non-metal
- structure Cl_2 (g) (molecule)
- melting point = −101°C
- boiling point = −35°C

ELEMENT INVESTIGATED: BROMINE

- deep red/brown liquid
- structure, Br_2 (l) (molecule)
- melting point = −7°C
- boiling point = 58°C

ELEMENT INVESTIGATED: IODINE

- black lumps of solid with a slight shine
- forms a purple vapour
- structure I_2 (s) (molecule)
- melting point = 114°C
- boiling point = 183°C

▶ Devise a way to present this information that makes it easier to compare the properties of the elements.

▶ Compare these group 7 elements pointing out any trends in their properties.

Reactions of group 7 elements

Iron (on the right of this photograph) glows brightly when it reacts with chlorine.

Chlorine bleaches damp litmus paper. This is used as a test for chlorine.

Element	With dyes such as litmus	When heated with iron (Fe)
Chlorine	Bleaches instantly	Glows brightly reacting vigorously and forms FeCl$_3$
Bromine	Bleaches	Reacts and glows but not as brightly as chlorine. Forms FeBr$_3$
Iodine	Bleaches slowly	Reacts slowly, forming FeI$_3$

Comparing the chemical properties of group 7 elements.

As you can see from the table above group 7 elements react in similar ways, but there are differences. Chlorine is the most reactive and the reactivity gets less as you move down the group. Fluorine (F$_2$), a yellow gas which is above chlorine in the periodic table, is the most reactive of all.

▶ *Write word and balanced symbol equations for the reaction between iron, Fe, and chlorine gas, Cl$_2$, to form iron chloride, FeCl$_3$.*

Comparing compounds of group 7 elements

Here you are going to look for patterns in the properties of some halogen compounds. You may be given a worksheet to help you with this experiment.

Displacement reactions with group 7 elements

When chlorine is added to potassium bromide solution, it can **displace** or push out bromine. Chlorine can also displace iodine from potassium iodide.

chlorine + sodium bromide → bromine + sodium chloride

$$Cl_2(g) + 2NaBr(aq) \rightarrow Br_2(aq) + 2NaCl(aq)$$

Bromine can displace iodine but not chlorine. As a rule a more reactive group 7 element will displace a less reactive one from a solution of its salt.

▶ *Write the word and balanced symbol equations for adding chlorine to potassium iodide solution, KI(aq).*

▶ *What will happen when iodine is added to solutions of sodium chloride or sodium bromide?*

Group 0 elements

The gases in **group 0** are all **monatomic**. This means that they are found as single atoms. Compare these gases to hydrogen, H_2, and oxygen, O_2, which are **diatomic**. The group 0 elements have several names. Sometimes they are called the **rare gases** because, with the exception of radon and argon, only small amounts are found in the Earth's atmosphere. At first, no compounds containing these elements were known, so they were called **inert gases** or sometimes **noble gases** because 'they did no work'. Now some compounds of krypton, xenon and radon have been prepared by scientists.

	4
	He
	2
	20
	Ne
	10
	40
	Ar
	18
	84
	Kr
	36
	131
	Xe
	54

Element	Melting point (°C)	Boiling point (°C)	Density (gcm^{-3})
Helium	-272	-269	0.00017
Neon	-248	-246	0.00084
Argon	-189	-186	0.0016
Krypton	-157	-153	0.00346

▶ *What trend can you see in the reactivity of the noble gases as you move down the group?*

▶ *How does this trend compare with those of group 1 and 7?*

As you move down the group the noble gases become slightly more reactive and the melting and boiling points steadily increase.

🔺 Neon is widely used in advertising signs.

🔺 The gas breathed by divers is helium mixed with oxygen. Helium is also used in meteorological balloons.

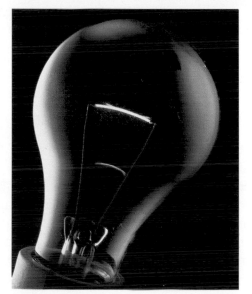
🔺 To prevent reaction of the hot metal filament with oxygen, air in light bulbs is replaced with inert argon.

CHEMISTRY

The transition elements

Transition means 'in between' and the **transition elements** are found in rows between groups 2 and 3. In the sections of the periodic table that you have studied so far, elements with similar properties have been found in vertical groups. In this block of the table, similar metal elements are found in rows called periods. Transition metals are often used to make things. You can read more about the uses of metals in Chapter Three (Metals).

Metal	Melting point (°C)	Boiling point (°C)	Density (gcm^{-3})
Copper	1084	2570	8.9
Gold	1064	3080	19.3
Iron	1540	2750	7.9
Titanium	1660	3290	4.5
Zinc	420	907	7.1

Paving stones, bricks and mortar are coloured with iron oxide pigments. Iron is a useful transition metal.

1	2											3	4	5	6	7	0
			Ti		Cr		Fe	Co	Ni	Cu	Zn						
										Ag							
								Pt	Au	Hg							

Transition metals

The shaded part of the table shows the transition elements. The more common transition elements are shown.

Properties of transition elements

- Transition elements are hard metals with high melting and boiling points and high densities.
- The elements and their compounds are used as catalysts. For instance, iron or iron oxide is used as a catalyst in the manufacture of ammonia. Nickel catalysts are used in the hydrogenation of fats to make margarine. Platinum or cheaper vanadium oxide are used to catalyse a step in the manufacture of sulphuric acid.
- Compounds containing transition metals are often coloured. For example, copper sulphate is blue, compounds containing chromium are often orange or yellow, potassium permanganate (which contains the metal manganese) is purple.

- Transition elements vary in their reactivity. Iron rusts on exposure to air and water, whereas gold objects from centuries ago have been found as good as new.

▶ *How do the properties of the transition metals compare with those of the alkali metals?*

⬛ A compound of cobalt is used to test for water. Water turns blue cobalt chloride paper pink.

Acids, alkalis and the periodic table

Metals and non-metals form compounds with oxygen and hydrogen. Metals from groups 1 and 2 form alkaline hydroxides (for example sodium hydroxide, NaOH). Non-metals form acids. For example, nitrogen forms nitric acid, HNO_3.

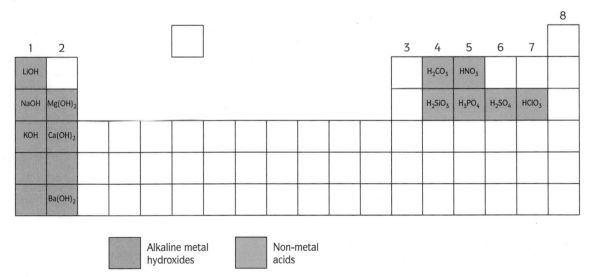

1	2												3	4	5	6	7	8
LiOH														H_2CO_3	HNO_3			
NaOH	$Mg(OH)_2$													H_2SiO_3	H_3PO_4	H_2SO_4	$HClO_3$	
KOH	$Ca(OH)_2$																	
	$Ba(OH)_2$																	

◻ Alkaline metal hydroxides ◻ Non-metal acids

⬛ You can see patterns in the compounds metal and non-metal elements form with hydrogen and oxygen.

Summary

- The periodic table groups elements with similar properties in vertical columns called groups.

- The horizontal rows are called periods. Periods are not all the same length.

- Each element is numbered in order, with a number called its atomic number. You can read more about atomic number in Chapter Nine (Atoms).

- In the periodic table, metals are found on the bottom left-hand side and non-metals on the top right-hand side.

- Group 1 contains the alkali metals. These elements have similar properties but the further down the group an element is, the more reactive it becomes. There is also a trend of decreasing melting points and boiling points.

- Group 7 contains the non-metal elements known as the halogens. These elements have similar properties, but as you move down the group these elements become less reactive and their melting and boiling points get higher.

- Group 0 contains gases called the noble gases. These elements have similar properties but as you move down the group the elements become slightly more reactive and the melting and boiling points steadily increase.

- The transition elements are a block of metal elements found, in the periodic table, between groups 2 and 3. These are hard, dense metals with similar properties that account for their wide use in everyday life.

Revision Questions

1 Write down the names, formulae and uses for three of the group 0 elements.

2 The group 0 elements are called inert gases, rare gases or noble gases. Explain why the group has been given these names.

3 Why is helium, rather than hydrogen, used to fill meteorological balloons?

4 Welding of metals is often carried out in an atmosphere of argon. Why is this used instead of air?

5 On a copy of the periodic table shade the first 54 elements, using different colours for:
   a the metals
   b the non-metals
   c solids, liquids and gases.

6 On a copy of the periodic table shade the following using different colours:
   a the alkali metals
   b the halogens
   c the noble gases
   d group 2 metals (sometimes called the alkaline earth metals).
   Put a key underneath the table.

7 Write down the names and colours of ten compounds containing:
   a group 1 and group 2 metals
   b transition metals.
   Can you see any pattern in these observations?

8

Atomic Symbols – Dalton 1807–1808			
Hydrogen	⊙	Sodium	ⵔ
Nitrogen	⊘	Copper	Ⓒ
Carbon	●	Phosphorus	⦵
Oxygen	○	Potassium	ⵕ
Sulphur	⊕	Lead	Ⓛ

🔺 This table shows symbols given to elements in about 1807.

Copy the table and show the modern symbols for the elements.

9 a Make a graph for chlorine, bromine and iodine showing their melting and boiling points on the y-axis and their relative atomic masses on the x-axis.
   b Use your graph to predict the melting and boiling points of fluorine.

10 a Draw a graph for helium, neon, argon and krypton to show melting point on the y-axis and relative atomic mass on the x-axis.
   b Use your graph to predict the melting point of xenon.

11 List the properties of the noble gases.

12 Write down the names of two elements in:
   a group 1
   b period 2
   c the transition elements
   d group 0.

13 The following pairs of elements have been placed together in certain groups of the periodic table because they have similar properties. Give two examples of these properties for each pair of elements.
   a Group 1, sodium and potassium
   b Group 2, magnesium and calcium
   c Group 7, chlorine and bromine
   d Group 0, helium and neon

14 Miss Davies is going to demonstrate the reaction of sodium with water to her class. She will drop a piece of sodium into a trough of water.
   a Predict what gas will be produced.
   Once the reaction is over Miss Davies plans to drop pieces of red and blue litmus paper into the water.
   b What will happen to the litmus paper? What would this tell you?
   c Write a word and balanced symbol equation for the reaction of sodium, Na, with water.
   d Which group 1 metal would react with water less violently than sodium? Which would react more violently?

15 You might need to consult other sections of this book to answer these questions.
   a Find out some of the uses of the group 1 elements and their compounds.
   b Find out some uses of the group 7 elements and their compounds.
   c Find out some important uses of the transition metals.

16 Make a list of the characteristic properties of the group 7 elements.

17 Notice that, according to their relative atomic masses, argon and potassium are in the wrong places in the periodic table. Why were scientists justified in swapping them over?

18 What did Lothar Meyer notice from his graph that led him to believe that the periods in the table did not all have to be the same length?

19 The scientists who developed the periodic table were not all alive at the same time. Imagine you are Mendeléev. Write a letter addressed to Newlands and Döbereiner explaining how their ideas helped you to formulate the periodic table. Include Mendeléev's most recent ideas on how the elements should be arranged.

20 Astatine (atomic number=85) is a halogen. Predict the properties of astatine using your knowledge of the properties of the other group 7 elements and their trends.

21 Rubidium (atomic number=37) is a group 1 metal. Predict the properties of rubidium using your knowledge of the properties of the other group 1 elements and their trends.

22 Transition metals are often used as catalysts. What is a catalyst? List three manufacturing processes that use transition metals as catalysts.

23 a What would you expect to see if you added chlorine dissolved in water to a colourless solution of potassium iodide?
   b Explain your answer and write the balanced symbol equation for this reaction.

Atoms

■ Particles

A team of 440 scientists from all over the world has been working to produce evidence that the top quark has been detected. Particles are hurled round a four mile ring in opposite directions. When they collide they break into smaller bits that exist only for a fraction of a second. These tiny particles cannot be seen. They can only be detected by the traces they leave. Experiments so far seem to support scientists' ideas about quarks, but more supporting data is needed before they can be sure about the sub-atomic structure of matter.

Matter is the word used to describe the materials around us. All matter is made up of the same basic particles. Protons, neutrons and electrons are just three of them. In the 1960s, a new theory that protons and neutrons were made from even tinier particles called *quarks* was developed. There are likely to be twelve types of quark and scientists now think they have detected the last of these, the top quark.

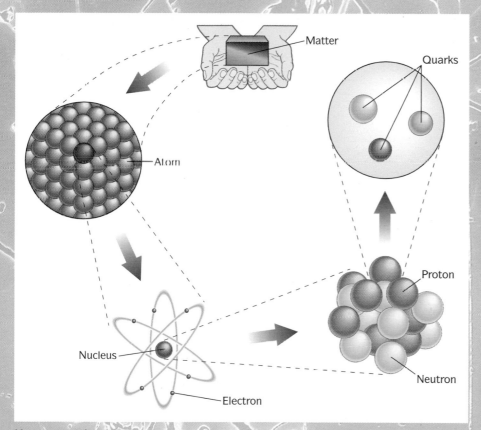

How matter is made up.

Review

Before going any further, read this page and attempt the tasks. Write the answers in your notes.

Ions

Ions are charged particles. They can be positive or negative:

Na$^+$ and Cl$^-$.

Ions can have more than one charge:

Al^{3+}, Ca^{2+}, O^{2-} and N^{3-}.

Ions can be made from groups of atoms:

OH$^-$, SO$_4^{2-}$ and NH$_4^+$.

Key

Mass number
Symbol
Atomic number

The value used for mass number is that of the most common isotope e.g. ^{35}Cl not ^{37}Cl

1 **H** 1																	4 **He** 2
7 **Li** 3	9 **Be** 4											11 **B** 5	12 **C** 6	14 **N** 7	16 **O** 8	19 **F** 9	20 **Ne** 10
23 **Na** 11	24 **Mg** 12											27 **Al** 13	28 **Si** 14	31 **P** 15	32 **S** 16	35 **Cl** 17	40 **Ar** 18
39 **K** 19	40 **Ca** 20	45 **Sc** 21	48 **Ti** 22	51 **V** 23	52 **Cr** 24	55 **Mn** 25	56 **Fe** 26	59 **Co** 27	59 **Ni** 28	64 **Cu** 29	65 **Zn** 30	70 **Ga** 31	73 **Ge** 32	75 **As** 33	79 **Se** 34	80 **Br** 35	84 **Kr** 36
85 **Rb** 37	88 **Sr** 38	89 **Y** 39	91 **Zr** 40	93 **Nb** 41	96 **Mo** 42	(99) **Tc** 43	101 **Ru** 44	103 **Rh** 45	106 **Pd** 46	108 **Ag** 47	112 **Cd** 48	115 **In** 49	119 **Sn** 50	122 **Sb** 51	128 **Te** 52	127 **I** 53	131 **Xe** 54
133 **Cs** 55	137 **Ba** 56	139 **La** 57	178 **Hf** 72	181 **Ta** 73	184 **W** 74	186 **Re** 75	190 **Os** 76	192 **Ir** 77	195 **Pt** 78	197 **Au** 79	201 **Hg** 80	204 **Tl** 81	207 **Pb** 82	209 **Bi** 83	(210) **Po** 84	(210) **At** 85	(222) **Rn** 86

CHECK NINE

1 Divide the following into four groups, headed 'elements', 'compounds', 'positively charged ions' and 'negatively charged ions'.

K, CaO, Li$^+$, H$_2$O, NH$_4^+$, NH$_3$, Cl$^-$, Fe^{3+}, Br$_2$, HNO$_3$, Mg^{2+}, HCO$_3^-$, S$_8$, S^{2-}, H$^+$

2 In the periodic table there are groups and periods. What are these?

3 What group contains:
a the alkali metals
b the halogens
c the noble gases?

4 How does the reactivity of the elements vary in group 1 and group 2?

5 How many elements are in period 1 and period 2?

Atoms

All elements are made from atoms and yet each element has its own individual properties. Diamond is shiny and hard, whereas sodium is soft. Chlorine is a poisonous gas and yet at this moment you are breathing in and out another gaseous element, nitrogen, without even noticing. The atoms in each of these elements must be different.

JJ Thomson first discovered particles inside atoms. Atoms of all the substances he studied contained these particles. He knew from their properties that they were negatively charged particles and he decided to call them **electrons**. His discoveries started the search for other particles inside the atom.

Thirty years later his son showed that beams of electrons could be spread out (**diffracted**). This was a shocking discovery, because only waves can be diffracted, not particles. One Thomson had discovered that electrons were particles and another had found that they were waves. Scientists now believe that both of these ideas are right. Inside the atoms waves and particles are the same thing.

In simple terms atoms are built up from three types of particle, called **protons**, **neutrons** and electrons. This is not the whole story – there are other sub-atomic particles, such as **quarks**. But you will find that understanding the three most important sub-atomic particles to start with, will help you to understand more about atoms and how they behave.

Sub-atomic particle	Location in the atom	Mass relative to a hydrogen atom	Charge
Proton	Nucleus	1	1$^+$ (positive)
Neutron	Nucleus	1	no charge
Electron	In space around the nucleus	Neglible (small enough to be ignored)	1$^-$ (negative)

🔺 Some properties of the three most important sub-atomic particles.

🔺 Joseph James Thomson (top) won the Nobel Prize for Physics in 1906. Later, in 1937, his son George (bottom) did the same.

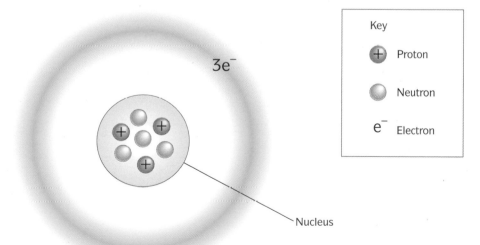

🔺 The nucleus of an atom contains protons and neutrons tightly packed together. Electrons orbit in the space around the nucleus.

Protons, neutrons and electrons

The centre of the atom, the **nucleus**, contains protons and neutrons tightly packed together. The nucleus is very dense as it contains the heavier particles and is very small compared with the size of the whole atom. The number of protons in the nucleus of any one element is given by its **atomic number**. You can find the atomic number of an element by looking on a data table or at a copy of the periodic table. For example, the atomic number of lithium is 3 and so an atom of lithium contains 3 protons.

From the same tables you can find the **mass number** of any element. This tells you the number of protons added to the number of neutrons. For lithium the mass number is 7. From this you can work out the number of neutrons in the nucleus.

> mass number = number of protons + number of neutrons
>
> So number of neutrons = mass number – number of protons
>
> For lithium, number of neutrons = (7 – 3) = 4
>
> Number of electrons = number of protons = 3

Electrons are found outside the nucleus moving around in the space surrounding it. Atoms are electrically neutral so for every positively charged proton in the nucleus there is a negatively charged electron orbiting around it. The number of electrons equals the number of protons. For lithium the number of electrons is 3.

▶ *Copy and complete this table showing the sub-atomic particles in these elements. Do the same for two elements of your own choice. Use the data tables in Chapter Sixteen (Chemistry help).*

Element	Atomic number	Mass number	Number of protons	Number of neutrons	Number of electrons
Lithium	3	7	3	4	3
Carbon					
Oxygen					
Hydrogen					

 You can use the mass number and atomic number to work out how many protons, neutrons and electrons are in each atom of an element.

| $^{7}_{3}\text{Li}$ | This is a shorthand way of writing an element showing the mass number as the superscript and the atomic number as the subscript. |

▶ *Write the shorthand symbol showing the mass number and atomic number for carbon, oxygen and hydrogen.*

Atoms with a difference

The mass of each atom is made from the protons and neutrons. Because each of these has a mass of one unit you might reasonably expect that the relative mass of each atom (A_r) would be a whole number. For example a lithium atom with 3 protons and 4 neutrons would have a **relative atomic mass** of 7. (The relative atomic mass of an element is the mass of a certain fixed number of its atoms). However, for some elements this is not the case. Look on a data table and you will see that for chlorine $A_r = 35.5$ and for copper $A_r = 63.5$. From reading about the development of the periodic table in Chapter Eight, you will have realised that making exact measurements was a problem for scientists in the past. So, it was thought that the values which were not whole numbers were inaccurate. When more reliable ways of measuring relative atomic mass were developed, this problem was solved but not in the way that scientists had expected.

▲ All atoms started with the formation of the universe about 15 000 million years ago.

Mass spectrometry

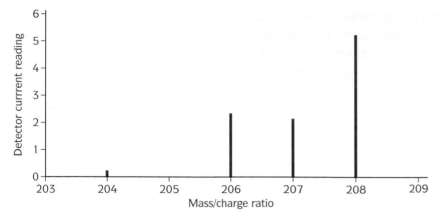

▲ This shows a mass spectrum for lead.

In 1919 the mass spectrometer was developed. Scientists were able to separate different atoms and make accurate measurements of their mass. They found that some elements contained atoms with the same number of protons, but different numbers of neutrons. These different forms of the same element with different numbers of neutrons are called **isotopes**.

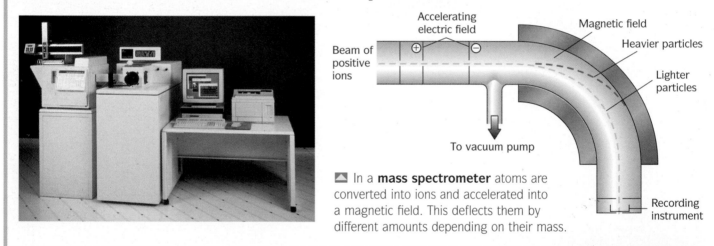

▲ In a **mass spectrometer** atoms are converted into ions and accelerated into a magnetic field. This deflects them by different amounts depending on their mass.

Isotopes

Chlorine has two main isotopes, one with a mass number of 35 (chlorine–35) and one with a mass number of 37 (chlorine–37). They each have the same number of protons and electrons, but chlorine–35 has 18 neutrons and chlorine–37 has 20 neutrons.

Isotope	Mass number	Atomic number	Number of protons	Number of neutrons	Number of electrons
$^{35}_{17}$Cl	35	17	17	18	17
$^{37}_{17}$Cl	37	17	17	20	17

▶ *Make a copy of the table above and add the following isotopes:*

$^{1}_{1}H, \, ^{2}_{1}H, \, ^{3}_{1}H, \, ^{12}_{6}C, \, ^{14}_{6}C.$

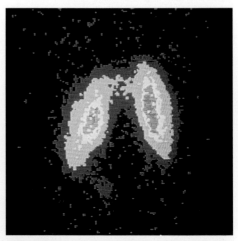

▲ A radioactive isotope of iodine, iodine–131, is used to investigate disorders of the thyroid gland.

CHEMISTRY

Relative atomic mass of isotopes

If you make some chlorine gas in the lab, you get a mixture of the isotopes of chlorine. The relative atomic mass of the atoms in the gas depends on just how much of each isotope is present. Mass spectrometer measurements tell us that chlorine is 75 per cent $^{35}_{17}Cl$ and 25 per cent $^{37}_{17}Cl$.

Average relative mass of an atom of chlorine = (75% × 35) + (25% × 37)
= 35.5

▶ *A sample of neon gas contains 10 per cent $^{22}_{10}Ne$ and 90 per cent $^{20}_{10}Ne$. What is the relative atomic mass of the neon in this sample?*

Atoms and the periodic table

For many years, scientists had problems understanding the periodic table. They did not know why certain groups of elements had similar properties which altered slowly as their relative atomic mass increased. They could not see why the rows in the periodic table had different lengths, some having only two elements and others having eight. It was not until more was known about the way electrons are arranged in atoms that these patterns and trends could be explained.

The most likely place

In 1913 a Danish physicist called Niels Bohr argued that electrons surrounding the nucleus were arranged in a series of layers called **orbits** or **shells**. Each shell could hold up to a certain number of electrons.

Scientists investigating how easy it was to remove electrons from atoms discovered that electrons were most likely to be found in these shells or orbits. The shell next to the nucleus, the first shell, could hold up to two electrons. The next electron would then be fitted into the next shell which could hold up to eight electrons. The third shell could also hold eight electrons.

▲ Niels Bohr.

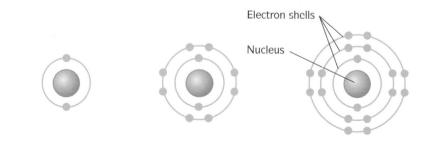

▲ Electrons are arranged like this.

▲ Electrons can move from shell to shell, taking in and giving out energy as they do so. The colours of these rockets are caused by electrons leaping back from one shell to another.

CHEMISTRY

WRITING ABOUT ELECTRONS

Electrons play a central role in science and so they are often described using a shorthand code. Sometimes they are represented by **e** and sometimes by **e⁻**. So two electrons would be 2e or 2e⁻. In diagrams of atoms sometimes they are shown as a dot like this • and sometimes by a cross x. Dot and cross electrons are not different: the symbols are used to show from which atom each electron came. There is also a shorthand way of showing how electrons are arranged in atoms. For instance, Na (2,8,1) shows that sodium has 11 electrons, 2 in the first shell, 8 in the second shell and 1 in the third shell.

▶ *Copy and complete the table below showing how electrons are arranged in shells for the first 20 elements. (Don't try to add any other elements yet as you need to learn a bit more about atoms before going further.)*

Element	Atomic number	Electrons in first shell	Electrons in second shell	Electrons in third shell	Electrons in fourth shell
Hydrogen	1	1			
Helium	2	2			
Lithium	3	2	1		

🔺 The arrangement of electrons in shells helps to explain the arrangement of elements in the periodic table.

This arrangement of electrons is reflected in the patterns of elements in the periodic table. Elements in period 1 have electrons only in the first shell. The first shell can hold only two electrons so there are only two elements in period 1. Once that is full the next electron must be accommodated in the next shell. So, elements in period 2 have electrons in the first two shells. The second shell can hold eight electrons so there are eight elements in period 2.

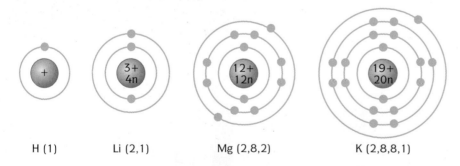

H (1)   Li (2,1)   Mg (2,8,2)   K (2,8,8,1)

🔺 These electron diagrams show how electrons are arranged in atoms of hydrogen, lithium, magnesium and potassium. This is called the **electronic structure** of the atom. The shorthand version is shown underneath.

▶ *Choose three other elements from the first 20, and for each construct an electron diagram for the electronic structure of an atom. Show the shorthand version underneath.*

Electronic structure and the periodic table

The atoms of different elements have different masses and different properties. You may be given a worksheet to help you compare the electronic structure of elements in the same group of the periodic table and to look for trends in their properties.

GROUP 1		GROUP 2		GROUP 7		GROUP 0
atom	ion	atom	ion	atom	ion	atom
Li (2,1)	Li$^+$	Be (2,2)	Be^{2+}	F (2,7)	F$^-$	He (2)
Na (2,8,1)	Na$^+$	Mg (2,8,2)	Mg^{2+}	Cl (2,8,7)	Cl$^-$	Ne (2,8)
K (2,8,8,1)	K$^+$	Ca (2,8,8,2)	Ca^{2+}			Ar (2,8,8)

▶ *What patterns can you see in the electronic structures of the elements in groups 1, 2 and 7?*

▶ *Does this pattern relate in any way to the charge on the ion for each of these atoms?*

▶ *What do the group 0 elements have in common?*

Looking at the electronic structure of the elements in groups 1, 2 and 7 shows why some elements behave in similar ways. The outer shell of each atom, within each group, contains the same number of electrons, and the atoms form ions with the same charge. For example, group 7 elements all have 7 electrons in the outer shell and form ions with one negative charge.

Group 0 is exceptional. The outer shell does not contain the same number of electrons but, for each element, the outer shell is complete.

Atoms and ions

Scientists noticed that the group 0 elements were very **stable** (very unreactive) and also that these elements have outer shells of electrons that are full. They drew some conclusions about chemical reactions.

- Only the outer shell electrons are involved when atoms react.
- Atoms often give or take electrons so that in the newly formed ion, the outer shell is full. Each ion in a compound has an electronic structure like that of the nearest group 0 element.

Metal ions

The metals in group 1 all have one electron in their outer shell. When they react this electron is removed and a charged particle called an ion is formed. In the sodium

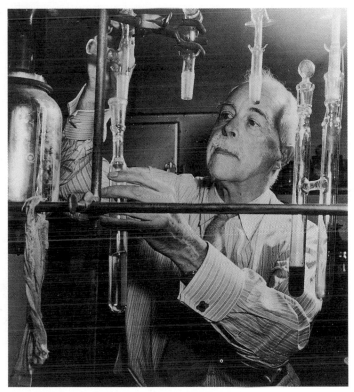

⏷ In 1916 GN Lewis first suggested that, in ions, the outer shell of electrons was full.

ion the outer shell structure is full and similar to neon, Ne (2,8). The sodium ion has 11 protons in the nucleus surrounded by 10 electrons. So, the overall charge is 1^+.

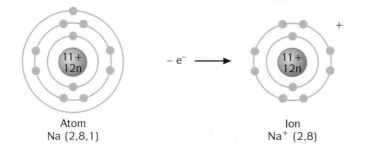

Atom
Na (2,8,1)

Ion
Na$^+$ (2,8)

▲ One electron is removed leaving an ion with one positive charge.

▶ *Draw a dot and cross diagram for the formation of a lithium ion from its atom, and of a potassium ion from its atom.*

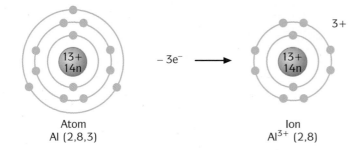

Atom
Al (2,8,3)

Ion
Al^{3+} (2,8)

▲ More than one electron can be transferred forming ions with more than one positive or negative charge.

Electronic structure and reactivity of metals

The reactivity of the group 1 metals changes as you move down the group. You can read about this in Chapter Eight (The periodic table). This trend can be explained using the electronic structure of the atoms. In an atom the electrons are held in place by the positively charged nucleus. As the total number of electrons in an atom gets larger, the electrons in the outer shell get further and further away from the nucleus. As a result they are held less firmly and are more easily removed. This accounts for the increased reactivity as you move down the group.

▶ *Draw electron diagrams showing the formation of ions for the first three group 2 metals. (Clue: more than one electron can be lost from the outer shell. Remember that the charge of the ion results from the number of electrons lost.)*

▶ *Does the reactivity of the group 2 metals vary as the atoms get bigger and bigger? Use your diagrams and what you can find out about the group 2 metals to explain your answer.*

Ions and the periodic table

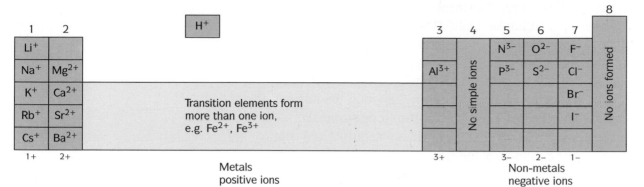

1	2								3	4	5	6	7	8
				H⁺										
Li⁺											N^{3-}	O^{2-}	F^-	
Na^+	Mg^{2+}								Al^{3+}		P^{3-}	S^{2-}	Cl^-	
K^+	Ca^{2+}			Transition elements form									Br^-	
Rb^+	Sr^{2+}			more than one ion,									I^-	
Cs^+	Ba^{2+}			e.g. Fe^{2+}, Fe^{3+}										

No simple ions (column 4). No ions formed (column 8).

1+   2+ (columns 1, 2)
Metals positive ions

3+ (column 3)   3− 2− 1− (columns 5, 6, 7)
Non-metals negative ions

▲ If you write the formulae for the simple ions of the elements into a copy of the periodic table you can see a pattern in the way they are formed. The transition element section has not been filled in because most transition elements form more than one ion.

Non-metal ions

Reactions of non-metal elements also involve the outer shell electrons but their outer shell is completed by *gaining* electrons. Again the outer shell structure of the newly formed ion is similar to that of the nearest group 0 element.

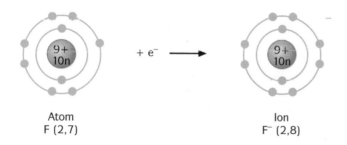

Atom
F (2,7)

+ e⁻ ⟶

Ion
F⁻ (2,8)

▲ Here the atom has gained control of an electron so now the overall charge on the ion is 1⁻ because there is one more electron than proton. The outer shell structure is similar to neon.

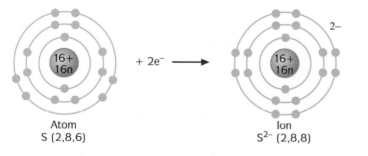

Atom
S (2,8,6)

+ 2e⁻ ⟶

Ion
S^{2-} (2,8,8)

▲ More than one electron can be gained.

▶ *Draw electron diagrams for the formation of ions from an atom of chlorine and an atom of oxygen.*

Metals react forming positive ions. The ions can have 1, 2 or 3 positive charges. For example: K^+, Ca^{2+} and Al^{3+}.

Non-metals react forming negative ions. The ions can have 1, 2 or 3 negative charges. For example: Br^-, O^{2-} and N^{3-}.

CHEMISTRY

Electronic structure and reactivity of non-metals

You may have read that the group 7 elements decrease in reactivity as you move down the group in Chapter Eight (The periodic table). Consider whether the theory of electron transfer supports this finding. At the top of the group, fluorine atoms are small. The nearer the outer shell is to the nucleus, the greater the tendency to gain and hold on to another electron to complete the outer shell. As you move down the group the number of electrons increases and the outer shell is further from the nucleus. The larger the atom, the less likely it is that the nucleus will attract and control another electron. So the reactivity of the elements get less going down the group.

Ions into atoms

You have just learned that in chemical reactions atoms change into ions. In **electrolysis**, ions can be changed into atoms (as well as the other way around). When ionic compounds are melted or dissolved in water the ions are freed and are able to move around. When an electric current is passed through, the positive ions move to the cathode (–) and the negative ions move to the anode (+). For example when an electric current is passed through molten sodium chloride, sodium ions move to the cathode. Here the positively charged ions combine with electrons that have flowed from the electric circuit, forming sodium atoms. Each ion gains the one electron it needs to form a sodium atom. You can read about electrolysis in Chapter Four (Ores).

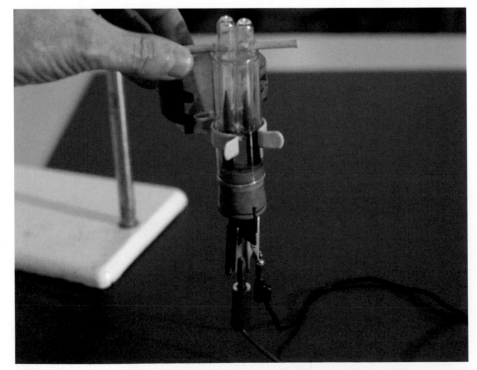

◣ You might use equipment like this to investigate electrolysis of solutions.

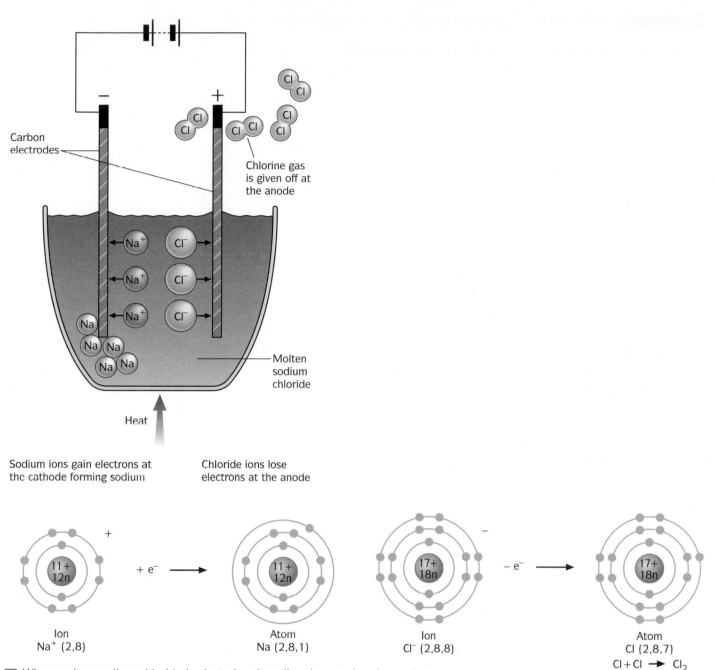

Carbon
electrodes

Chlorine gas
is given off at
the anode

Na⁺

Cl⁻

Na⁺

Cl⁻

Na⁺

Cl⁻

Na

Na Na

Na Na

Molten
sodium
chloride

Heat

Sodium ions gain electrons at
the cathode forming sodium

Chloride ions lose
electrons at the anode

Ion
Na⁺ (2,8)

$+ \; e^-$

Atom
Na (2,8,1)

Ion
Cl⁻ (2,8,8)

$- \; e^-$

Atom
Cl (2,8,7)

$Cl + Cl \longrightarrow Cl_2$

When molten sodium chloride is electrolysed, sodium ions each gain an electron from the cathode to form sodium atoms. Chloride ions move to the anode where they each give up one electron and form a chlorine atom. Chlorine atoms then pair up forming chlorine gas, Cl_2. So, energy from an electric current splits sodium chloride into its elements sodium and chlorine.

▶ *The electrolysis of molten aluminium oxide is similar to the electrolysis of molten sodium chloride. Work out what would happen to the aluminium ions and the oxide ions. Draw electron diagrams to illustrate this. (Atomic numbers: Al = 13, 0 = 8.)*

CHEMISTRY

Summary

- Protons and neutrons are found in the nucleus of an atom.
- The atomic number of an element tells you how many protons are in each atom.
- The mass number of an element tells you the sum of the protons and neutrons in each atom.
- Atoms are electrically neutral. This means that the number of electrons equals the number of protons.
- Electrons are most likely to be found in areas around the nucleus called shells or orbitals.
- Each shell holds a maximum number of electrons.
- The shell next to the nucleus can hold up to two electrons. The next electrons are accommodated in the second shell which can hold up to eight electrons. The third shell can also hold up to eight electrons.
- The outer shell of electrons of atoms of group 0 elements is full.
- When an element reacts, the ion formed has the same outer shell arrangement as the group 0 element nearest to it in the periodic table.
- When atoms react chemically only the outer shell electrons are involved.
- Metal atoms react by giving away electrons so that their outer shell is complete.
- Metal atoms react forming positively charged ions.
- Non-metal atoms react by taking in electrons to complete their outer shell.
- When non-metal atoms react to form an ion, that ion is negatively charged. You can read more about the formation of ions in Chapter Fourteen (Structure and bonding).
- Isotopes are forms of the same element whose atoms have different numbers of neutrons.
- Elements in the same group of the periodic table have similar properties because their atoms have the same number of electrons in their outer shell.
- In atoms, the further away the outer shell is from the nucleus the more easily electrons are lost and the less easily electrons are gained. This explains the patterns in reactivity of the elements within groups in the periodic table.
- In electrolysis, ions are changed into atoms at the electrodes. Electrons are supplied to ions at the cathode and taken from ions at the anode.

Revision Questions

You will need a periodic table or a table of data to complete these questions.

1 Make a drawing to show where in an atom the following are:
  a nucleus
  b protons
  c neutrons
  d electrons.

2 Choosing from proton, neutron and electron, which has:
  a no charge
  b a relative mass of 1
  c a positive charge?
  Which type of particle is found in the space around the nucleus?

3 Which element has:
  a 5 protons
  b 6 electrons
  c 7 neutrons?

4 Write the shorthand way (for example, lithium, $_3^7 Li$) of showing the atomic number and mass number of these elements:
  a helium
  b sulphur
  c beryllium.

5 Write down the number of protons, neutrons and electrons for rhodium $_{45}^{103} Rh$ and platinum $_{78}^{195} Pt$.

6 Sodium, sulphur, iodine, bromine, calcium, magnesium, potassium and oxygen. Which of this list of elements will react forming:
  a positive ions
  b ions with two negative charges?

7 a Draw electron diagrams describing how ions are formed from sodium and potassium.
  b Use these diagrams to explain why these two metals react in similar ways. Also say why potassium is more reactive than sodium.

8

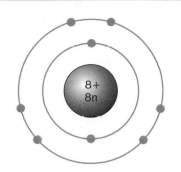

  a To which group of the periodic table does this element belong?
  b Draw an electron diagram for another element in the same group and name it.

9 Copy and complete the electron equations shown below. The first has been done for you.
  a K, (2,8,8,1) $- e^- \rightarrow$ $\underline{K^- (288)}$
  b _____ $+ 2e^- \rightarrow S^{2-}$ (2,8,8)
  c Ca (2,8,8,2) _____ $\rightarrow Ca^{2+}$ (_____)
  d F (_____) + _____ $\rightarrow F^-$ (_____)

10 How many protons, neutrons and electrons are there in:
  a a sodium atom, Na
  b a sodium ion, Na^+
  c an oxygen atom, O
  d an oxygen ion, O^{2-}?

11 Construct electron diagrams for the following pairs, and name two differences between them:
  a a chloride ion and an argon atom
  b a sodium ion and a neon atom
  c an oxygen atom and an oxide ion.

12 Carbon–12 and carbon–14 are isotopes. Explain fully the meaning of the term isotope using carbon to illustrate your answer.

13 Carbon–14 is radioactive which means that it changes slowly into carbon–12 at a known rate. How do you think this fact could be used to date material which contains carbon? If possible find out more about radio-carbon dating.

14 Write ionic equations that describe the electrolysis of each of the following molten compounds:

a sodium bromide

b calcium chloride.

15

Element	Fluorine	Chlorine	Bromine	Iodine
Formula	F_2	Cl_2		I_2
State at room temperature	Gas	Gas		Solid
Melting point (°C)	−220	−101		114
Boiling point (°C)	−188	−35		184
Reaction with heated iron	Very fast	Fast		Not very fast

a Without consulting a data table, predict the information about bromine which is needed to complete this table.

b Using data tables find the published data for the same information. How accurate were your predictions? Why were you able to make such predictions?

16 As you move down groups of elements in the periodic table, the relative atomic mass increases and the reactivity changes. Explain how the change in reactivity in the group 1 metals is different from the trend in reactivity of the group 7 halogens. Use what you know about electronic structure to explain why the trends are different.

17

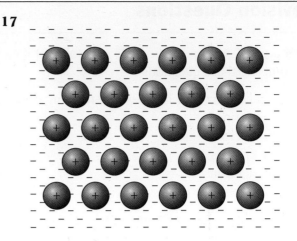

A simple model of metallic bonding shows positively charged particles in a sea of electrons.

a Why do you think that metals are good conductors of electricity?

b Use the theory of metallic bonding to explain why aluminium is a better conductor than magnesium, which is a better conductor than sodium. You can read more about the structure of metals in Chapter Fourteen (Structure and bonding).

Rates of reaction

■ Under control

silver + nitric acid → silver nitrate + nitrogen dioxide + water

$$Ag(s) + 2HNO_3(c) \rightarrow AgNO_3(aq) + 2NO_2(g) + H_2O(l)$$

This equation summarises reaction to produce silver nitrate.

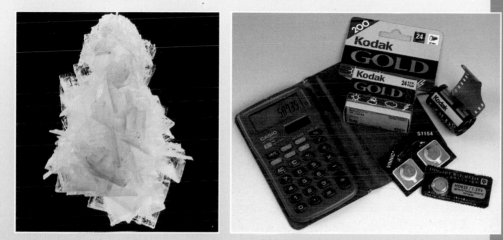

Very pure silver nitrate is used in silver plating. It is also used to make photosensitive film and the button batteries used in watches and calculators.

In industry, the rate of the reaction used to produce silver nitrate is monitored and controlled in several ways. First of all, crystalline silver is used instead of silver powder. Crystalline silver comes in larger pieces and therefore has a smaller total surface area which means the reaction with nitric acid proceeds at a steady rate. The silver is fed into the nitric acid at normal temperature and, as it is an exothermic reaction (it gives out heat energy), the mixture steadily heats itself up to 100–120°C. You can read more about exothermic reactions in Chapter Twelve (Energy in reactions).

The reaction is monitored by the amount of nitrogen dioxide gas being produced. If there is too little gas either more silver or more acid needs to be added. Otherwise the reaction will soon finish.

The rate of the reaction is controlled by the amount of concentrated nitric acid added. The temperature in the reactor is monitored. If the temperature drops, much more acid is needed. If it rises, only a small amount is added.

A close watch is also kept on the pH in the reactor. If the pH rises to 6 the reaction will stop. If it falls to 1 or below then the acid is not immediately being used up in the reaction and so either more silver or less acid is needed.

The newly made silver nitrate solution is purified and then evaporated to give fine crystals of silver nitrate.

The raw materials used to make silver nitrate are silver and concentrated nitric acid. But you cannot just add them together. Silver powder reacts very quickly and the temperature of the reactor, where the reaction takes place, would shoot up. The acid would boil over and splash. Toxic nitrogen dioxlde gas would be produced at an unmanageable rate. To produce silver nitrate safely and efficiently, the reaction rate must be carefully controlled.

Review

Before going any further, read this page and attempt the tasks. Write the answers in your notes.

▲ It only took five seconds to reduce this 24 storey block of flats to 20 000 tonnes of rubble. How could you express the rate of this reaction?

Rates

When you follow an event, whether it is a chemical reaction or your revision for an exam, you might measure what happens and how long it takes. This tells you the rate of the event. The thing you measure depends on the event. You might read your revision notes at the rate of two sections a week. The scoring rate in cricket is measured in runs per minute. Your pulse is measured in heart beats per minute.

To measure volume you might use a measuring cylinder or a burette. To measure mass you use a balance. To measure time you use a clock or watch. To measure temperature you use a thermometer or a temperature sensor.

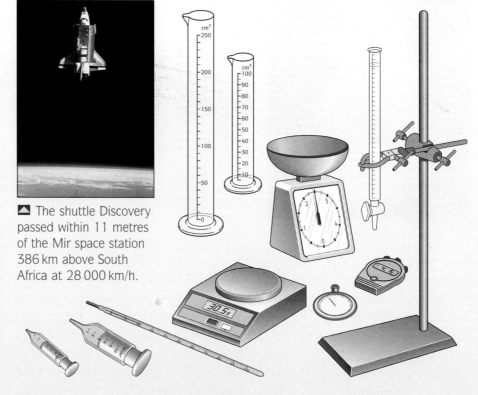

▲ The shuttle Discovery passed within 11 metres of the Mir space station 386 km above South Africa at 28 000 km/h.

▲ Apparatus for measuring.

CHECK TEN

1 From the pieces of apparatus shown above which would you use to measure out a volume of
a 50 cm^3
b 7 cm^3
c 0.5 cm^3
d 25 cm^3
when you need to know exactly how much has been added but you do not know exactly how much will be needed?

2 From the above pieces of apparatus which would you use to measure out a mass of:
a 5 kg
b 10.5 g?

3 Explain why, in some cases, you can use the classroom wall clock to time a reaction but on other occasions you need a stop watch.

4 Why is a clinical thermometer used to measure body temperature rather than a laboratory thermometer?

5 What units would you use to describe:
a the rate at which a tap is leaking
b the rate at which the water in a kettle is heating up
c the speed limit for vehicles in towns
d the rate at which cress seeds are growing?

Different rates of reaction

Different reactions happen at different speeds or **rates**. If you hold a piece of magnesium ribbon in a flame it will burn for a few seconds. If you hold a lit taper in a mixture of hydrogen and oxygen the two gases react together with a 'pop' in a fraction of a second. Rusting takes much longer. You have to leave experiments investigating the causes of rusting for several days before you can see the orange crumbly solid forming on the surface of iron. The reactions that turn the remains of plants and animals into coal and oil take millions of years.

▶ *Choose two other reactions you have seen and decide if they were fast, quite fast or slow reactions.*

Controlling rates of reaction

We are all affected to some extent by how fast reactions occur. You might have worried about how quickly fizzy drinks go flat or how quickly you need to eat an open bag of crisps before they go limp and rancid. Keeping food from going off is an example of a chemical reaction which is much easier to control nowadays. The rate at which food alters is slowed down by storing it in a refrigerator at 5 °C and the food can be kept fresh for even longer at lower temperatures in a freezer. In the kitchen you can also increase the rate of some reactions. Food can be cooked faster in pressure cookers and microwave ovens. We can control the rate at which it is cooked using the thermostat switches on hobs and ovens.

In industry, controlling rates of reaction is vital. Reactions used to manufacture substances for everyday use must be safe, fast and easily controlled. Speed is often the factor that decides whether or not a reaction can profitably be used. Controlling reactions is equally important to ensure that any new substances produced do not damage the environment.

▲ The weathering of stonework on buildings and statues can take centuries.

▲ In air sodium soon reacts with oxygen to form white sodium oxide. Storing sodium in oil controls and slows down this reaction.

▲ The poison gas tragedy in Bhopal, India, in 1984 was caused by a reaction in a pesticide factory that got out of control. Thousands of people and animals in the area were killed by a gas which escaped into the air, and just as many were severely injured.

Measuring rates of reaction

Reaction rates can be followed by measuring:
- the time from start to finish
- how much of one of the reactants is left unaffected during the reaction. For example, the mass or volume of one of the reactants can be measured (see page 146)
- how fast one of the products is made during the reaction. For example, the volume of a newly produced gas (see below) or the amount of a **precipitate** produced (see page 241) can be measured
- changes in the reaction mixture throughout the reaction. For example, the pH or the temperature, can be measured.

Measuring time

In the reaction between magnesium and dilute hydrochloric acid you could measure the time taken from the start to the finish of the reaction. This could be from when the magnesium is added to when it has all dissolved. In reactions the starting substances are called the **reactants** and the newly formed substances are called the **products**.

$$\text{reactants} \rightarrow \text{products}$$
$$\text{magnesium} + \text{hydrochloric acid} \rightarrow \text{magnesium chloride} + \text{hydrogen}$$
$$Mg(s) + 2HCl(aq) \rightarrow MgCl_2(aq) + H_2(g)$$

▶ *Look through this book and copy equations for four reactions. Show the reactants and the products for each reaction.*

Measuring mass or volume

Measuring the time from the start to the end of a reaction tells you about the overall rate of the reaction but it does not provide any information about what is happening in the course of the reaction.

Measuring what happens to the concentration of the reactants or the products throughout the reaction provides more information. In the reaction between magnesium and dilute hydrochloric acid you could measure how fast either the magnesium or the acid was used up but this would be difficult to do without interfering with the reaction. Here, as shown on the right, it is easier to measure the volume of one of the products, hydrogen gas, at regular intervals.

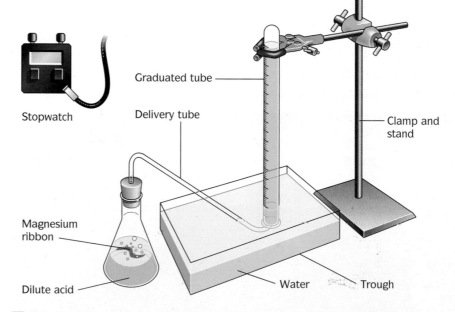

Graduated tube

Delivery tube

Clamp and stand

Stopwatch

Magnesium ribbon

Dilute acid

Water   Trough

🔺 You can follow the rate of the reaction between magnesium and acid by measuring the volume of hydrogen gas produced. In this case, the end of the reaction could be when no more gas is produced.

Time (min)	0	1	2	3	4	5	6	7	8	9	10
Volume (cm³)	0	21	38	53	67	76	80	85	85	85	85

🔺 Table of results.

CHEMISTRY

Measuring speed

The graph shows typical results, as given in the table on page 144, for the reaction of magnesium and dilute hydrochloric acid. The graph levels off after 85 cm³ of hydrogen have been collected. The reaction was complete after 7 minutes. The reaction was fastest at the beginning. You can see this from the slope of the curve which was steepest at the start and then levelled off until it was horizontal at the finish of the reaction.

▶ *What is the advantage of monitoring rates of change as a reaction takes place instead of just measuring the time taken for the whole reaction to occur?*

Controlling reaction rates

In industry time and cost are vital considerations. Under normal conditions some reactions would either not take place at all or occur so slowly that it would cost too much money to use them. Slow reactions have to be speeded up and reactions that are dangerously fast have to be slowed down. The rest of this chapter looks at some of the factors that influence reaction rate.

Surface area

To react, substances have to be in contact with one another. In some reactions a solid is added to a solution. In these cases the size of the solid pieces makes a difference to the reaction rate. The larger the total surface area of the solid, the more of it will come into contact with the other reactants and therefore the faster the rate of the reaction will be.

▶ *Work out the surface area of the cubes shown in a and b on the right.*

▶ *Put the types of sugar shown below in order of total surface area per gram, with the largest first. Which type would dissolve fastest in water?*

▶ *Why does steel wool burn when it is heated in air but a steel nail does not?*

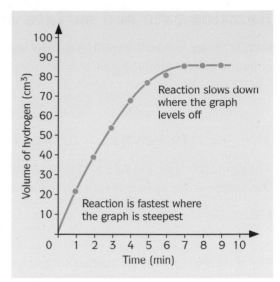

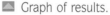
Graph of results.

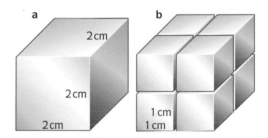
Smaller pieces mean a larger total surface area.

The total surface area of a material affects how quickly it dissolves.

Fine steel wool burns when you heat it in air.

CHEMISTRY

Reaction rate and surface area

Marble chips (calcium carbonate) react with dilute acid, as shown in the equation below, producing carbon dioxide gas and water.

$$\text{calcium carbonate} + \text{hydrochloric acid} \rightarrow \text{calcium chloride} + \text{carbon dioxide} + \text{water}$$

$$CaCO_3(s) + 2HCl(aq) \rightarrow CaCl_2(aq) + CO_2(g) + H_2O(l)$$

You can investigate the rate of this reaction by following the loss in mass of the marble chips as they react with the acid.

▶ *Why does the mass of the flask and its contents, shown on the right in b, decrease?*

The results below were obtained by two groups of students who compared the same mass of small and large marble chips to find out if the size of the pieces made any difference to the rate at which they reacted with acid. Group 1 used small chips.

▶ *Which have the largest total surface area per gram, the large or the small chips?*

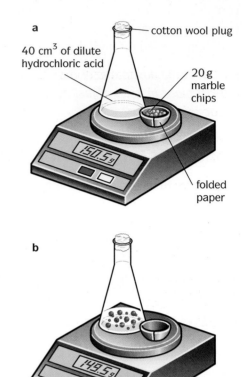

a

cotton wool plug

40 cm³ of dilute hydrochloric acid

20 g marble chips

folded paper

b

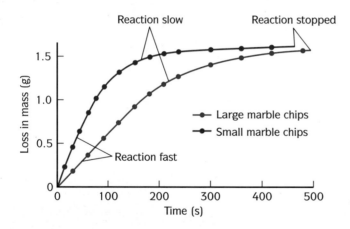

Reaction slow   Reaction stopped

Loss in mass (g)

— Large marble chips
— Small marble chips

Reaction fast

Time (s)

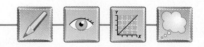

▲ When the marble chips are added to the acid, the total mass begins to fall.

Results from both groups are shown in the graph above.

▶ *Explain, using the graph above to support your answer, which reacted faster, the small or the large chips.*

▶ *Write a sentence or two explaining the effect of the surface area of a solid reactant on the rate of a reaction.*

Large and small

You may be given a worksheet to help you consider the effect of surface area on a reaction. The reaction is that of magnesium and dilute hydrochloric acid. Magnesium chloride and hydrogen are made.

Temperature

Most of us have, at one time or another, tried to speed up a reaction by increasing the temperature. Fast food like steaks or bacon are cooked at high temperatures under the grill. Chips cook quickly in heated fat, but potatoes boiled in water cook more slowly in a lower temperature of about 100°C.

You might think that more heating will always increase the rate at which reactions take place. In most cases you would be correct as scientists have found that many reaction rates are doubled by a 10°C rise in temperature. Most industrial reactions take place at raised temperatures. You can read about industrial processes in Chapter Thirteen (Using reactions).

Food cooks quickly in heated fat or oil.

Limestone heated in the hottest part of a bunsen flame breaks down forming lime and carbon dioxide.

Effect of temperature

The results shown below were obtained by a student who was investigating the effect of temperature on the rate of the reaction between magnesium and acid using the apparatus shown on page 144. For each chosen temperature, the time taken to collect 30 cm³ of hydrogen gas was measured.

▶ *What factors would have to be kept constant to ensure that this was a fair test?*

Temperature (°C)	Time to collect 30 cm³ hydrogen (s)	1/time (s)
20	90	0.011
30	65	0.015
40	50	0.020
50	40	0.025
60	32	0.031

You can see from the results in the table on page 147 that the higher the temperature gets, the shorter is the time taken to collect the same amount of gas, which shows that the rate of this reaction is higher.

The rate of any reaction is **inversely proportional** to the time taken. You can recognise this type of relationship when one set of numbers increases while the other decreases.

rate of reaction $\propto$ 1/time taken

The faster the reaction, the shorter is the time taken to collect 30 cm^3 of gas.

The reaction speeds up as the temperature is raised. The rate of reaction is proportional to the temperature.

rate of reaction $\propto$ temperature

Concentration

The **concentration** of a solution tells you how much substance (or **solute**) is dissolved in it. The more solute that is dissolved in it, the higher the concentration of the solution is. A **dilute** solution contains a small amount of solute. Bottles of orange squash contain a concentrated solution that has to be diluted with water before drinking. Scientists express the concentration of a solution in moles per litre (mol/l).

The rate at which the bubbles are produced shows how fast the lime deposit in the kettle is reacting with the descaler. The more concentrated the descaler, the faster the reaction. As the descaler is used up, the rate at which the bubbles are produced gets less until either all the deposit is dissolved or all the descaler is used up.

When you looked at the table and graph on pages 144 and 145 you may have noticed that the rate of the reaction between magnesium and acid fell off with time. In the reaction between marble chips and acid described on page 146 the same thing happened. It did not matter what size the chips were, the reaction still slowed down as time went on. This is because reaction rates are also affected by concentration. The higher the concentration of the reactants, the faster the reaction is. Once the reaction has started, the reactants get used up and, as the concentration falls, the reaction gets slower and slower. If one of the reactants is completely used up, the reaction finally stops.

▶ *Why does the amount of corrosion of stonework on buildings and statues vary in different parts of the country?*

▶ *Why should you wash your eye out with lots of water if something harmful gets in it by accident?*

Pressure

The concentration of a gas can be increased by increasing the pressure. A car engine has four cylinders. A mixture of air and fuel vapour is compressed before being ignited by the spark plug.

You can read more about the relationship between the pressure volume and temperature of a gas in Physics, Chapter Ten.

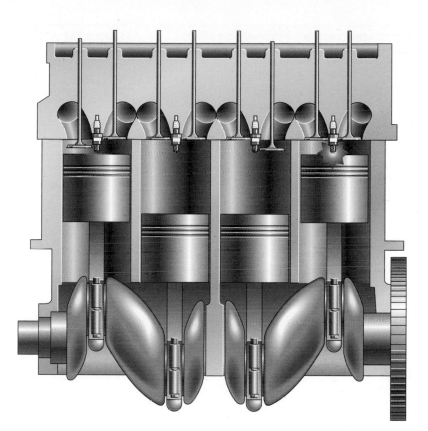

In the compression stroke in this engine, the piston moves up and compresses (squeezes) the mixture of air and petrol vapour into a smaller space.

Investigating the reaction between zinc and acid

zinc + hydrochloric acid → zinc chloride + hydrogen

$$Zn(s) + 2HCl(aq) \rightarrow ZnCl_2(aq) + H_2(g)$$

Zinc granules (1.45 g) of similar size were added to 50 cm³ of hydrochloric acid of different concentrations, as shown in the diagram below. The time taken to collect 10 cm³ of gas was measured. The results are shown in the table on the next page.

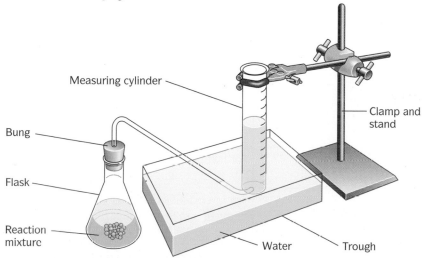

Apparatus used to investigate the effect of concentration on the reaction between zinc and acid.

Zinc reacts with acid forming hydrogen.

Acid concentration (mol/litre)	Time to collect 10 cm³ gas (s)	1/time (s) × 10⁻³
1	196	5.1
2	136	7.4
4	68	14

▸ *Draw a graph of the results in the table above, putting acid concentration (mol/litre) on the x-axis and time (s) on the y-axis.*

▸ *The student carrying out this investigation then decided to measure the rate for two more acid concentrations. The results are shown in the table below. Explain why he thought this was necessary.*

▸ *Draw graphs showing the data in the two tables. Draw one for acid concentration against time, and one for acid concentration against 1/time.*

Acid concentration (mol/litre)	Time to collect 10 cm³ gas (s)	1/time (s) × 10⁻³
0.5	295	3.38
3	91	10.9

The higher the concentration of acid, the shorter is the time taken to collect 10 cm³ gas.

The rate of the reaction is inversely proportional to the time taken. (As one number gets bigger, the other gets smaller.)

rate of reaction ∝ 1/time taken

The reaction goes faster when the concentration of acid is increased. The rate of the reaction is proportional to the concentration of acid. (As one number gets bigger, the other gets bigger.)

rate of reaction ∝ concentration

Catalysts

Catalysts are substances that speed up reactions. Without catalysts some reactions would not take place at a measurable speed. Catalysts only influence the rate at which a reaction takes place. They are not included in the reaction itself as a reactant. Catalysts manage to speed the reaction up without being used up themselves in the process. Unless they are poisoned (**inactivated**) by some by-product in the process, they remain unaffected and can be used over and over again to speed up the same reaction. You can read about **enzymes**, the catalysts in living things, in Chapter Eleven (Enzymes).

Some substances slow down reaction rates. They are called **inhibitors**.

The catalysts used in the chemical industry are often transition metals or their compounds.

▲ Some metal paints contain corrosion inhibitors.

Catalyst	Reaction
Platinum	For one of the reactions in the manufacture of nitric acid (see page 200)
Nickel	For hydrogenation in the formation of solid fats from unsaturated oils (see page 22)
Iron	For the manufacture of ammonia from nitrogen and hydrogen in the Haber Process (see page 197)
Vanadium oxide	For one of the reactions in the manufacture of sulphuric acid (see page 199)

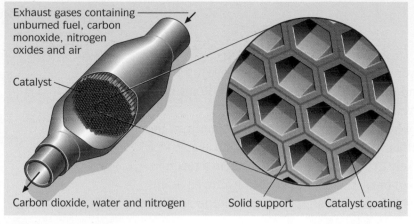

Exhaust gases containing unburned fuel, carbon monoxide, nitrogen oxides and air

Catalyst

Carbon dioxide, water and nitrogen

Solid support

Catalyst coating

The honeycomb arrangement in a catalytic converter offers a large surface area to the exhaust gases.

Nitrogen and unburned fuel escape from cars and lorries polluting the atmosphere. Recently catalytic converters have been developed and fitted to the exhaust systems of all new vehicles. In the converter the waste gases pass over a surface coated with platinum and rhodium (the catalysts) and react to form carbon dioxide, nitrogen and water.

Measuring the effectiveness of catalysts

Hydrogen peroxide slowly breaks down forming water and oxygen.

$$2H_2O_2(aq) \rightarrow 2H_2O(l) + O_2(g)$$

The breakdown of hydrogen peroxide is speeded up by oxides of metals like manganese, zinc and copper. Find out which of these oxides is the most effective catalyst. You may be given a worksheet to help you with this practical.

The collision theory

In any chemical reaction the atoms are rearranged. First bonds between particles in the reactant have to be broken and then new bonds have to be made to produce the product. Before any reaction can take place the particles have to get together, or **collide** with one another.

Collisions and reactions

hydrogen + oxygen → water

$$2H_2(g) + O_2(g) \rightarrow 2H_2O(l)$$

Before the above reaction can take place, hydrogen and oxygen molecules have to collide. The bonds between the hydrogen atoms and the bonds between the oxygen atoms have to be broken. New bonds forming water have to be made.

The millions of molecules in a mixture of hydrogen and oxygen are constantly on the move and frequently collide with one another. However, not all **collisions** result in a reaction. High-energy collisions are most likely to be 'successful' and result in a reaction. High-energy collisions have enough energy to break the bonds between hydrogen atoms and oxygen atoms. In low-energy collisions the molecules just bounce off one another and no reaction takes place.

Collisions and reaction rate

Anything that increases:
- *either* the frequency of the collisions (the number of times molecules meet one another)
- *or* the energy of the collisions
  will increase the rate of the reaction.

Temperature

When the temperature of the reaction mixture is raised, the particles move around faster and so collide more often. At the same time, the collisions have more energy. The frequency and the energy of the collisions is increased, resulting in an increased rate of 'successful' collisions and therefore an increased rate of reaction. Raising the temperature increases the frequency of high-energy collisions and so increases the rate of the reaction.

▶ *Use the collision theory to explain why cooling slows down reactions.*

Surface area

Collisions take place on the surface of solids. With a large surface area collisions are more frequent and there is a greater chance of a 'successful' collision. In reactions involving solids, powders react faster than granules, which react faster than lumps.

Concentration

As the concentration increases, the particles get closer together. In gases, increasing the pressure has the same effect of pushing the particles closer together. This produces an increased number of collisions and so the reaction rate increases.

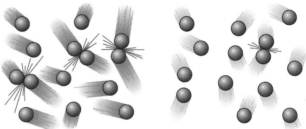

High temperature   Low temperature

▲ Temperature affects the rate at which molecules or ions react in solution.

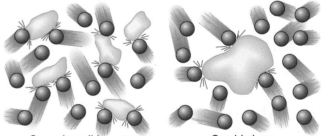

Several small lumps   One big lump

▲ Surface area affects the rate at which molecules or ions in solution react with lumps of a solid.

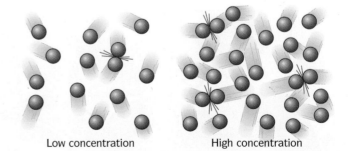

Low concentration   High concentration

▲ Concentration affects the rate at which molecules or ions react in solution.

How catalysts work

High-energy collisions are most likely to result in a successful reaction. A successful collision where the reactant forms the product can be likened to an outing by a hill walker. The walker has to climb up and over a hill, or barrier, to get from one side to the other. Successful collisions have to have enough energy to get over an energy barrier called the **activation energy**. If the activation energy barrier is high, few collisions are successful and the reaction may not occur at all.

A catalyst provides a slightly different reaction route, with a lower activation energy barrier for the reaction. Lower-energy collisions can now result in reaction and so the frequency of successful collisions increases. The catalyst speeds up the reaction by providing an easier way for the reactants to change into the products.

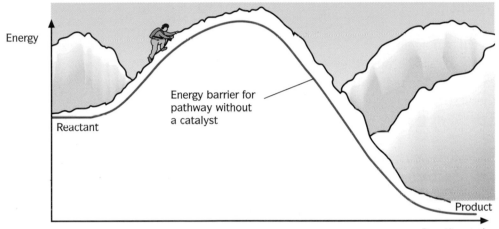

Without a catalyst, the activation energy is high.

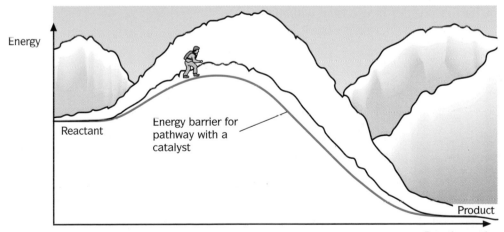

With a catalyst, the activation energy is lower.

Summary

■ Reactions can be summarised as

  reactants → products

■ The rate (speed) of a chemical reaction increases if:
  – the temperature increases
  – the concentration of the solution increases
  – the solids are in smaller pieces, so increasing their surface area
  – a catalyst is used.
■ The rate of reactions between gases can be influenced by changes in pressure.
■ Catalysts are often transition metals or their compounds.
■ Different catalysts are used for different reactions.
■ Catalysts:
  – increase the rate (speed) of the reaction
  – are not used up during the reaction
  – can catalyse the same reaction again and again.
■ Catalysts are important in industrial reactions because they:
  – reduce the time taken for the reaction and so reduce the cost
  – allow reactions to occur that otherwise would not take place at a
    measurable rate, or would react so slowly that the manufacture of the
    product would be too costly.
■ The rate of a chemical reaction can be followed by measuring how much
  of the product is made or how much of a reactant is used up.
■ Reaction rates between particles depend on:
  – the frequency of collisions
  – the energy of collisions.
■ Frequent, high-energy collsions produce fast reactions.
■ The effect of temperature, concentration and surface area on reaction
  rates can be explained using the collision theory.
■ The height of the activation energy barrier decides how easy it will be to
  get a reaction started.
■ Using a catalyst lowers the activation energy.

Revision Questions

1 Explain why:
   a flour dust sometimes explodes in mills
   b using a pressure cooker reduces the cooking time
   c a candle with a long wick burns away faster
   d jellies set faster if you dissolve them in less water.

2 Give three examples of everyday reactions that are affected by temperature.

3 Which would you expect to give faster pain relief, aspirin tablets or soluble aspirins? Explain your answer.

4 This curve represents the loss of mass when marble chips react with acid.

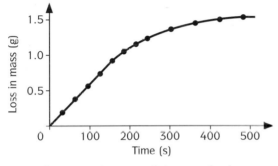

   a Make a rough copy of the graph above and mark on it where the reaction is:
   i finished
   ii fastest
   iii slowest.
   b Draw on the graph the curve you would expect to get if the same marble chips were used with acid that is half as concentrated. Although the acid is less concentrated, there is enough to react with all the marble chips.

5 Some students investigated how fast hydrogen gas was released in the reaction between magnesium and dilute hydrochloric acid. They were comparing magnesium powder with magnesium ribbon. First they used 0.1 g magnesium ribbon and then they used 0.1 g magnesium powder. Their results are shown in the next column.
   a Draw a diagram to show the apparatus you could use to get results for this experiment.

Time (mins)	Volume of hydrogen (cm³)
0	0
0.5	54
1.0	77
2.0	85
3.0	85
4.0	85
5.0	85
6.0	85
7.0	85
8.0	85

▲ Results using 0.1g of magnesium powder.

Time (mins)	Volume of hydrogen (cm³)
0	0
0.5	12
1.0	22
2.0	38
3.0	53
4.0	65
5.0	78
6.0	80
7.0	85
8.0	85

▲ Results using 0.1g of magnesium ribbon.

   b What else would you have to know to decide whether or not this was a fair way of comparing magnesium ribbon with magnesium powder?
   c Plot both sets of results on the same graph putting time (mins) on the x-axis and volume of hydrogen (cm³) on the y-axis.
   d Which reaction was faster, acid with magnesium ribbon or powder? Explain why this should be so, using the collision theory to support your answer if you can.
   e Explain why the reaction got slower and slower and finally stopped.
   f How long did the reaction of acid with magnesium powder take to complete?
   g Why was the total volume of acid used the same in both cases?

h On your graph sketch the result you would expect the students to have obtained if they had used a 0.1 g lump of magnesium metal to react with the acid.

6 A student was asked to discover the effect of concentration of sodium thiosulphate on the reaction between sodium thiosulphate and acid. When sodium thiosulphate and acid react, an opaque yellow precipitate is produced (see page 241). At room temperature she decided to mix $5\,cm^3$ of acid in a flask with different volumes of sodium thiosulphate. She then timed how long it took for a black cross drawn underneath the flask to disappear as the precipitate formed. She put her results in the table below.

Volume of acid (cm^3)	Volume of sodium thiosulphate added (cm^3)	Time taken (s)
5	50	135
5	40	137
5	30	138
5	20	140
5	10	141

a Did this investigation manage to test the effect of changing the concentration on the rate of the reaction?

b How would you improve on this student's work?

c What would you expect to find as the concentration of sodium thiosulphate was increased? Try to make your prediction quantitative. Explain your prediction using the collision theory to support your answer.

7 In some areas a scale of calcium carbonate forms inside electric kettles. Commercial preparations are used to dissolve this unwanted deposit. Plan an investigation into the effect of temperature on the rate at which scale dissolves. Write down a detailed plan including diagrams if this will make your ideas clearer.

8 A student was trying to prepare a sample of hydrogen for testing, using zinc lumps and dilute sulphuric acid. The gas was being produced but very slowly. How could he attempt to speed up the reaction? Give three suggestions.

9 When potassium chlorate is heated strongly it breaks down, forming potassium chloride and oxygen.

Three test tubes were set up as described in the table below and heated equally strongly. Every so often a glowing splint was held above the test tube to test for the production of oxygen. The time taken for oxygen to be produced was measured.

	Tube 1 potassium chlorate	Tube 2 potassium chlorate + manganese oxide	Tube 3 manganese oxide
Time taken to produce oxygen	4.5 minutes	1.5 minutes	no oxygen was produced

a Why did the potassium chlorate break down faster in Tube 2?

b Why was Tube 3 included in this experiment?

Potassium chlorate and potassium chloride are soluble in water. Manganese oxide is insoluble in water.

c How could you show that the manganese oxide:

    i was not used up in this reaction

    ii could catalyse the same reaction again?

10 Use other chapters of this book and any other resources available to describe some industrial reactions that are catalysed by metals or their compounds.

Enzymes

■ Hard working microbes

Microbes are everywhere and there are lots of them about. They, and the enzyme substances inside them, make a huge contribution to the well-being and economy of the whole world. Microbes are sometimes called micro organisms and include bacteria, fungi and viruses. This page shows a few examples of the 42 500 different microbes that exist in the UK.

This black mould fungus, *Aspergillus niger,* has been magnified 280 times. It is used to make citric acid for soft drinks, sweets and foodstuffs.

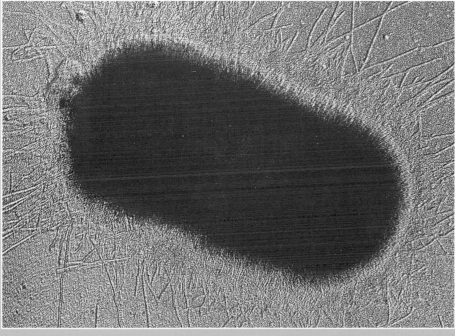

Escherichia coli, which is always present in your intestines, can provide insulin and indigo dye.

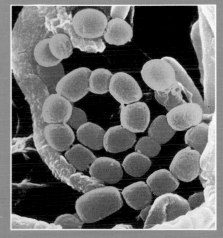

This bacteria, *Streptomyces lividans*, lives in the soil. It naturally produces antibiotic substances.

Review

Before going any further, read this page and attempt the tasks. Write the answers in your notes.

▲ Microscopic fungi cause diseases like athlete's foot, ringworm and thrush.

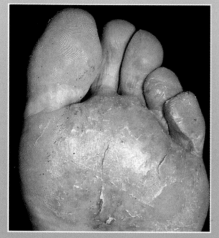

▲ At sewage farms bacteria digest sludge producing methane as a by-product.

Microbes

There are four main types of micro-organism – bacteria, viruses, fungi and protozoans. Bacteria are everywhere. Some are harmless. Others cause diseases like whooping cough and tetanus. Between 20 and 1000 bacteria would fit on a full stop.

Viruses are the smallest microbes. Viruses can only grow and breed in living tissues. They invade cells and make millions of copies of themselves. Rabies, chickenpox and AIDS are all caused by viruses. Between 2000 and 100 000 viruses would fit on a full stop.

Some fungi are microbes. (Each one is called a fungus). Some fungi are too big to be described as microbes. Mushrooms and toadstools are fungi, but are not microscopic. Yeasts are microscopic fungi. Yeast cells are larger than bacterial cells and can be seen using a school microscope.

Some types of fungi infect animals and plants causing disease. Athlete's foot, dandruff, ringworm and verrucas are all fungal infections. However not all fungi are directly harmful to humans and some play a vital part in our lives. Some fungi provide us with antibiotics. These chemicals can destroy the bacteria that cause diseases like diphtheria, food poisoning and typhoid. Other fungi are used in the food and drink industry. Beer is made by the controlled rotting of moistened barley. Soy sauce is made from rotting soya beans. Many other processes rely on special types of microscopic fungi.

Amoebae are the best known examples of protozoans. They have only one cell and are said to be unicellular. Most are harmless although some can cause serious diseases in humans, such as malaria and dysentry. You can just about see protozoans with the naked eye, but need a microscope to see them clearly.

IS YOUR BABY SAFE?

Rubella can seriously affect your unborn baby's sight and hearing.

▲ German measles (rubella) is a virus infection that can be avoided by being immunised.

CHECK ELEVEN

1 What is a microbe?

2 Write down the four most common types of microbe putting the smallest first and the largest last.

3 How can our health be affected by bacteria, fungi and viruses?

4 How are bacteria used to improve our well-being?

5 How is yeast used?

6 Why is it important to be immunised against German measles, especially if you are a woman?

Biotechnology

Today industry uses plant and animal cells, microbes and the **enzymes** (biological **catalysts**) from them to manufacture a whole range of useful products, such as vaccines, vitamins, meat substitutes, artificial snow, biodegradable plastics, insecticides, yogurts, dyes, beers and wines. You can read more about biotechnology in Biology, Chapter Nine.

Although we now recognise all these processes as biotechnology, people over the ages have used the same techniques to improve the flavour and texture of food without knowing exactly what was going on. Ancient writings show that around 6000BC yeasts were being used in what is now called Iraq to make beer. By 4000BC Egyptians had discovered how to use yeast in bread-making.

Fermentation has a long history. The oldest known fermentation process is the conversion of sugar into alcohol by yeast. The sugar is converted to alcohol and water in a whole series of chemical reactions that would be very difficult without the help of the enzymes in yeast. Yeast **ferments** the sugar using it as food to grow and multiply.

$$\text{sugar} \xrightarrow[\text{yeast}]{} \text{alcohol} + \text{carbon dioxide}$$

Fermentations can be used to make a whole range of substances other than alcoholic drinks. The manufacture of cheese, antibiotics, vinegar and yogurt all involve fermentation reactions. So does sewage treatment! Antibiotics were first made on a large scale during the Second World War. You can read more about antibiotics in Biology, Chapter Three.

▶ *Make a poster entitled 'Materials from Microbes'.*

Protein catalysts

Enzymes are protein catalysts. You can read about catalysts in Chapter Ten (Rates of reaction). They regulate and make possible everything going on inside cells. They speed up chemical reactions that would proceed only slowly at room temperature. Most cells contain about a thousand different enzymes and each catalyses one particular reaction and no other. Enzymes act on only one substance. For instance, amylase acts on carbohydrate, lipase on fat and protease on proteins. (Notice the names of enzymes often end in -ase.) The substance being acted on is called the **substrate**. Enzymes are **specific** to a particular substrate and reaction.

◭ These fermenters are being used to make penicillin G.

SALAMI

Salami is fermented minced meat. Sometimes it is beef, but mostly it is pork. Raw, minced meat, some added fat, salt and a starter culture, along with potassium nitrate to stabilise the red colour of the meat, are stuffed into casings like sausage skins. The taste and flavour of the product depends partly on the acid produced. In salami, ethanoic acid (the acid in vinegar) is produced during the fermentation and gives a tangy taste and characteristic aroma.

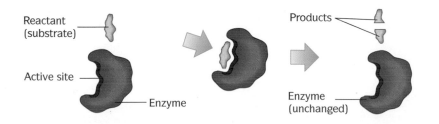

◭ Enzymes are biological catalysts. The use of a catalyst allows the reaction to take place with less energy. You can read about catalysts and activation energy barriers in Chapter Ten (Rates of reaction). This diagram shows the lock and key model of enzyme action.

CATALYSTS AND ENZYMES

A chemical conversion might need a catalyst, a raised temperature, high pressure and perhaps a certain pH. All these things make the reaction difficult and expensive to set up.

$$\text{reactant} \xrightarrow[\text{high pressure}]{\substack{\text{high temperature} \\ \text{catalyst}}} \text{product}$$

In fermentation the microbe provides the enzyme catalyst and the overall reaction usually takes place in mild conditions of temperature, pressure and pH. The microbe grows and multiplies at the same time.

$$\text{reactant} \xrightarrow[\text{microbe}]{} \text{product}$$

$$\text{sugar} \xrightarrow[\text{yeast}]{} \text{alcohol} + \text{carbon dioxide}$$

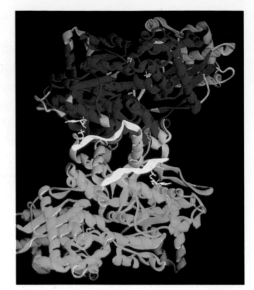

Enzyme molecules have very complex shapes.

Enzymes at work

Chemical catalysts often work well under conditions of high pressure and temperature. In contrast enzymes have evolved to function in very mild conditions in living cells. They work best at very specific pHs, that are neither too acid nor too alkaline, and at temperatures of around body temperature.

▶ *What is the best working pH for glutamate hydrogenase?*

▶ *Why do you think enzymes in the stomach must be able to work well in very acidic conditions? You can read more about digestion in Biology, Chapter Four.*

In 1900 Edward Buchner smashed open yeast cells and showed that the cell contents could ferment sugar just as well as the whole cell. He called the chemicals inside the cells enzymes (which means 'in yeast'). Later scientists developed the engineering skills to extract the enzymes from yeast in large quantities.

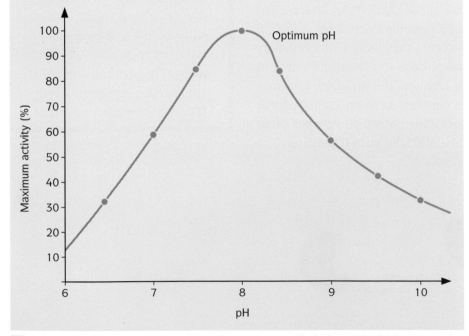

This graph shows how the activity of an enzyme called glutamate hydrogenase is affected by pH.

RENNET
Rennet is an enzyme produced in the stomachs of calves. An alternative, rennet-type enzyme is produced by certain fungi and it is estimated that about half the world production of cheese is made with these products. Cheese made with fungal rennet is sold as vegetarian cheese.

Enzymes and temperature

At low temperatures enzymes function very slowly and so the rate of reaction is correspondingly slow. As the temperature increases, the efficiency of the enzyme increases up to an **optimum temperature** for the enzyme. The optimum temperature varies from enzyme to enzyme depending on the site of enzyme action on the protein molecule.

If the temperature is further increased, enzyme activity falls off again. Enzymes are very complex molecules. Strands of protein are linked and folded into complicated shapes. Proteins are damaged (or **denatured**) by high temperatures. Heating alters the shape of the protein molecules so they can no longer function as enzymes.

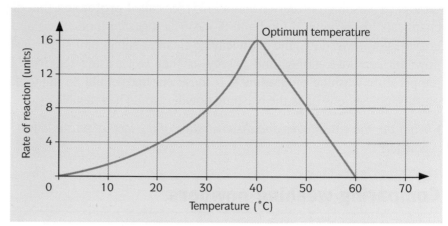

▲ At first enzyme activity increases as the temperature is raised. Above a certain temperature the reaction slows down as the enzyme is damaged.

Enzymes lower the energy barrier

Energy barriers prevent reactions from happening. Extra energy is needed to overcome the energy barrier. Then the reaction can start.

Enzymes fit on to their substrate forming a complex molecule (called a **reaction intermediate**). (See the 'lock and key' model on page 159.) This then breaks down forming the reaction product and releasing the enzyme for further use. The formation of this complex molecule allows the reaction to take place at a lower activation energy than is usual for the reaction. You can read about activation energy in Chapter Twelve (Energy in reactions).

Using enzymes

Immobilised enzymes

For many years, scientists have been trying to improve on reactions using microbes. One way of doing this is to identify the reactants and enzymes involved in a specific reaction and then reproduce it in a laboratory. Because enzymes are not broken down in the reaction they catalyse. One technique has been to fix enzymes to a surface and allow the reactants to flow over them. Enzymes trapped in this way are **immobilised**.

Some more robust enzymes can be immobilised by fixing them to beads of a special substance called sodium alginate. The resulting small beads or pellets are rich in enzyme and can be used in reactions. After use, it is easy to separate the beads with the enzyme from the reaction products.

Washday enzymes

Biological washing powders contain enzymes called **proteases** that digest chemicals like protein in food and blood. The digested food stains and the enzyme flow away down the drain leaving clean washing. Biological washing powders can save money and energy as they work using relatively low-temperature washing programmes. If these enzymes could be immobilised on, say, polystyrene balls the washing powder would be reusable.

▶ *What are the advantages and disadvantage of the idea of reusable washing powder?*

Comparing washing powders

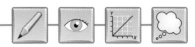

Plan and carry out an investigation to find out whether biological detergents are any better at removing stains than non-biological detergents and soap flakes. Check your plan with your teacher before you start.

Making sweet syrups from whey

Whey, a by-product from cheese-making, contains lactose. An enzyme called **lactase** is used to split lactose (milk sugar) into simpler, sweeter sugars. Lactase is immobilised on little beads packed into a column and whey is poured through. It takes only about ten minutes to convert the whey into a sweet solution that can be concentrated into syrup and used to make foods like cakes and toffees.

▶ *List the advantages of immobilising enzymes like lactase on small beads.*

▲ Whey syrup is used to make these cakes.

Soft-centred chocolates

You might have wondered how soft centres get into chocolates. Hard sugar centres and an enzyme from yeast called **invertase** are coated with chocolate. Inside the sweet, invertase goes to work splitting the sugar in the hard centre into two sugars, glucose and fructose. Inside the chocolate coating, small sugar crystals form in a syrupy solution of glucose and fructose.

▲ Making soft centres depends on an enzyme from yeast.

Fruit juice

Pectins help to bind the cellulose fibres in plant cell walls and can be used to thicken jam. In fruit juice manufacture, however, pectins cause problems. They make the juice cloudy and thick and also make juice extraction more difficult. The enzyme **pectinase** is added to the fruit pulp, and begins to break down the pectin before squeezing. The resulting juice is clearer and, because it is more easily squeezed out of the pulp, there is more of it.

◣ Fruit juice production uses enzymes.

Cloth manufacture

◣ Cotton thread is made stronger by coating it with starch. After the thread is woven into fabric, this starch is removed by treating the cloth with **amylase**. The enzyme breaks down the starch into sugars, which can then be washed from the fabric.

Dairy microbes

Milk is not only a good food for people, it is also a good food for microbes, particularly bacteria. **Pasteurisation** kills off most harmful bacteria in milk and reduces the number of bacteria that make it go bad. The only way to kill off all the bacteria is to treat the milk in a special way but this tends to alter the taste. The process is called **ultra heat treatment** and the milk is called **UHT milk**.

▶ *Milk is the raw material for dairy products. Make a list of dairy products found on supermarket shelves.*

Making cheese

In cheese-making, bacteria are added to pasteurised milk at 30°C. These souring bacteria ferment the milk converting the sugar lactose into lactic acid. The milk curdles and thickens as more acid is produced. An enzyme called rennet is added to the soured milk.

Rennet breaks down the protein in milk forming solid lumps called **curd**. Curd contains most of the butterfat and calcium from the milk. A liquid called whey is also produced but it is drained off. Whey is used to make animal feed or sweet syrups for making cakes and confectionary. Salt is added to the curd which is then squeezed dry and left to ripen and mature. Rennet continues to alter the cheese protein during ripening, producing and developing the characteristic flavour. A soft cheese is made if the whey is allowed to run out. Whey is removed from hard cheese using a cheese press.

The type of cheese made depends on the bacteria used to sour the milk, the amount of whey that is squeezed from the curd and the length of time allowed for ripening.

Little Miss Muffet sat on a tuffet
Eating her curds and whey
Along came a spider and sat down beside her

HIYA, GREEDY GUTS

BEAT IT, SPIDER!

Making yogurt

Getting milk to stay fresh has always been a problem. If untreated milk is left at room temperature, the number of bacteria growing in it soars from 10 000 to 25 000 000 per cm^3 in 24 hours. Turning milk into yogurt is one way of preserving it.

Yogurt can be made from any type of milk. Cows', goats' or buffaloes' milk can be used to make the smooth, light food that you spoon out of a carton. If skimmed milk is used the yogurt will have a very low fat content. The milk is warmed and a bacterial 'starter' is added. As the bacteria grow they convert lactose (milk sugar) into lactic acid.

$$\text{lactose (milk sugar)} \xrightarrow[\text{bacteria}]{} \text{lactic acid}$$

As the acid is produced, the pH falls, keeping the yogurt fresh by stopping other bacteria growing in it. The acid also thickens the yogurt and gives it its characteristic taste. Cooling the yogurt to 20°C slows lactic acid production once the desired thickness and taste have been obtained. Flavours and often pieces of fruit are then added before the yogurt is cooled to 5°C and packed into cartons. Yogurt has a shelf life of about three weeks compared to a few days for milk itself. Set yogurt is made by adding the fruit pieces before, rather than after, fermentation of the milk.

FROMAGE FRAIS

Fromage frais is made from skimmed milk in a similar way to yoghurt but adding different bacteria. Whey is then removed from the fermented milk and cream is added to give the desired, higher fat content.

Experimenting with yogurt production

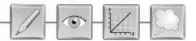

You may be given a worksheet to help you find out about how yogurt is made. You can compare different kinds of yogurt and you can also use a dye to study the bacteria within the yogurt.

pH change

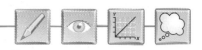

A student mixed some live yogurt with milk in a flask, and left the flask in a water bath for 12 hours. At two-hourly intervals he took samples and measured the pH. After 12 hours he put the milk mixture in the fridge.

Time (hours)	0	2	4	6	8	10	12
pH	5.0	4.5	4.0	3.5	3.0	2.5	2.0

▶ *Present the results in the table in a more informative way.*

▶ *What effect do yogurt bacteria have on milk?*
  Explain why this happens.

▶ *What would you have to know about these measurements before you could carry out more work on this yogurt and this milk?*

Making beer

◩ Brewers produce a whole range of beers and lagers. Their skill and experience produces the type and flavour of beer preferred by the customer.

Traditional ale was made from from high-protein grains which, although it made the beer more nutritious, also made it look more like porridge. Modern brewing processes use low-protein grains to ensure the clarity of the beer.

Beer is made from grain which contains starch. In the UK, barley is most commonly used. First the starch must be converted into sugar before fermentation.

starch ——————————→ sugar
  enzyme amylase

The raw materials for making beer are barley, hops (for bitterness), yeast (to ferment the sugars) and water.

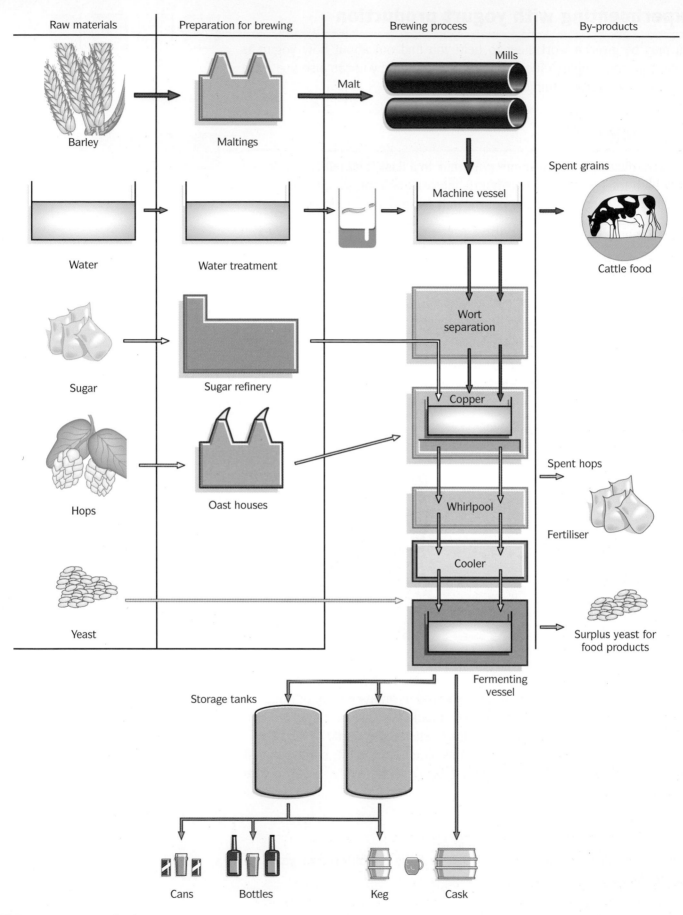

Raw materials	Preparation for brewing	Brewing process	By-products

Barley

Maltings

Malt

Mills

Water

Water treatment

Machine vessel

Spent grains

Cattle food

Sugar

Sugar refinery

Wort separation

Hops

Oast houses

Copper

Spent hops

Fertiliser

Whirlpool

Cooler

Yeast

Fermenting vessel

Surplus yeast for food products

Storage tanks

Cans   Bottles   Keg   Cask

▲ The stages in brewing beer.

1) **Malting**

Barley grains contain enzymes called **amylases** but they are only produced when the grain **germinates**. To make this happen, barley grains are kept in warm, damp conditions until rootlets appear. The malted barley or **malt** is then dried and stored until needed. The higher the drying temperature, the darker the malt and the beer made from it.

2) **Milling and mashing**

Next malt is crushed and mixed with warm water. Amylase action, which starts during germination, converts starch into sugar. The mixture is then filtered to give a clear sugary solution called **wort**.

3) **Boiling**

Wort is boiled with hops in large vessels called **coppers** to give the characteristic bitter flavour and to stop enzyme action.

4) **Fermentation**

The wort is then cooled and run into fermentation vessels where yeast is added. Yeast feeds on the sugar, producing ethanol and carbon dioxide. The yeast grows and multiplies.

$$\text{sugar} \xrightarrow{\text{yeast}} \text{ethanol (alcohol)} + \text{carbon dioxide}$$

$$C_6H_{12}O_6 \xrightarrow{\hspace{2cm}} 2C_2H_6O + 2CO_2$$

5) **Conditioning**

Yeast is removed, either by allowing it to sink to the bottom with other solids, or by filtration, and the beer is stored to allow it to mature.

Brewing vinegar

🔺 Pickles are vegetables, like beetroots and gherkins, preserved in vinegar. Vinegar can be made from beer, wine or cider.

Vinegars are made from fermented fruits and cereals. The vinegar made from beer is called malt vinegar. You can read above how beer is made from malted barley, using yeast. The process used in vinegar-making gives a poor tasting beer that is about 6 per cent alcohol. The beer is fermented again using another kind of bacteria that need a good supply of oxygen to grow (**aerobic** bacteria). The beer is trickled down towers containing wood shavings which are covered with growing bacteria. Air is continually bubbled into the liquid.

ethanol (alcohol) $\xrightarrow{\text{bacteria}}$ ethanoic acid (vinegar) + water

$$C_2H_6O + O_2 \xrightarrow{\hspace{3cm}} CH_3COOH + H_2O$$

Baking

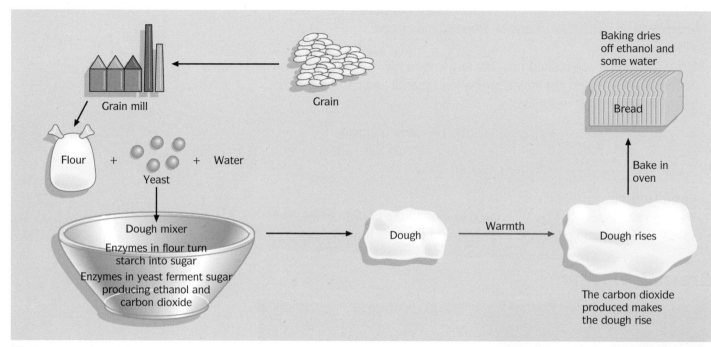

The stages in making bread.

To make bread, flour, water, salt and yeast are added together to make a dough. The addition of salt makes the dough elastic. In the flour, enzymes called amylases break down starch forming sugar. Some flours contain a low level of enzyme and so bakers add extra amylase to the dough to ensure a high level of sugar.

starch $\xrightarrow{\text{amylase}}$ sugar

After mixing, the dough is left in a warm place to rise. Yeast uses the newly formed sugars as food, fermenting them to ethanol and carbon dioxide gas. This gas gets trapped as bubbles in the dough, making it light and fluffy. After further mixing the dough is cut into loaf shaped pieces and baked at temperatures of about 220 °C. This kills the yeast and fixes holes in the bread giving it a light texture. Baking also drives off ethanol, carbon dioxide and some moisture.

sugar $\xrightarrow{\text{yeast}}$ ethanol + carbon dioxide

▶ *What gives bread dough its characteristic smell?*

 Grain used by millers to make flour for bread must have a high protein content, otherwise it will not make the tasty, springy, crumbly bread most people like.

Chemical raising agents

Baking powder is a mixture of sodium hydrogencarbonate and tartaric acid. It is used in baking to produce carbon dioxide and make sponge cakes rise. You could use baking powder to replace yeast in bread-making but the taste and texture of bread made with yeast is much better, so bakers generally use yeast. You can read more about baking powder in Chapter Five (Acids and bases).

Using yeast in baking

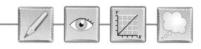

Bakers add yeast to flour and sugar to make dough. The enzymes in yeast ferment producing carbon dioxide gas and alcohol. You may be able to use a worksheet to test how bread rises. Remember not to eat any bread that you make in the lab.

Summary

- Microbes can, with a few exceptions, only be seen with the aid of a microscope.
- Bacteria, viruses, fungi and protozoans are four common types of microbe.
- Some microbes are damaging to our health.
- Many microbes are useful as they produce enzymes which convert chemicals into other substances.
- Microbes carry out reactions in mild conditions of temperature and pH.
- Enzymes are biological catalysts.
- Enzymes speed up reactions without themselves being used up.
- Each enzyme speeds up one particular reaction. It is said to be specific for that reaction.
- Enzymes are protein molecules, and so are damaged by high temperatures. Each enzyme works best at one particular temperature called the optimum temperature.
- You should know how microbes and enzymes are used in the dairy, baking and brewing industries.

Revision Questions

1 A student set up the following experiment to find out about 'homebrew' beer.

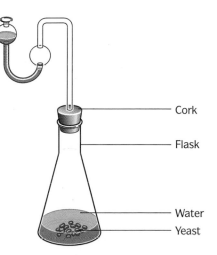

- Cork
- Flask
- Water
- Yeast

   a What was missing from the student's experiment?
   b If the missing substance was added, and the bottle left in a warm place, what do you think would happen?
   c Complete this word equation for the process.

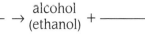 $\longrightarrow$ alcohol (ethanol) $+$ _____

   d What is the scientific name for the process?

2 a Give the names of some dairy products made using microbes.
   b Give the name of a dairy product flavoured using microbes.

3 Give the name of a product which is:
   a made by enzymes
   b contains enzymes.

4 a Why was yoghurt made from milk, in the first place?
   b Outline the main steps in yoghurt production including what happens to the pH and why this is useful.
   c Carry out a survey into the main yoghurt flavours preferred by your family and friends. Present the results of your survey in an attractive and informative way.
   d Give a difference between yoghurt and fromage frais.

5 Complete the sentences using the key words provided below.

Enzymes are _____ catalysts made by living _____ . They help to _____ reactions. Some enzyme break down _____ substances into _____ chemicals.

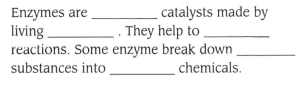

| complex simple biological |
| cells speed up |

6 Find some uses of the enzyme amylase. Find the names of some other enzymes and their uses.

7 a What could be added to milk to make it curdle?
   b Describe what is meant by curd and whey.
   c What is the difference in the manufacture of hard and soft cheese?
   d What was the first source of the enzyme rennet?
   e Why is some cheese called 'vegetarian cheese'?

8 What raw materials are used to make different vinegars? Look in the supermarket and try to find some less common varieties of vinegar. What foods are often preserved by pickling?

9 Use the following words to explain how bread is made:

| dough grain yeast amylase |
| sugar carbon dioxide starch |

10 There has recently been an increase in the use of 'immobilised' enzymes. What does the term 'immobilised' mean? What are the two main advantages of this technique?

11 Using the diagram and information in this chapter, make a flow diagram showing the main steps in brewing beer. Make sure you provide the answers to the following questions.
   a What are the raw materials used in brewing beer?
   b Why must barley be malted (converted to malt) before brewing can begin?

c What enzyme is involved in making the wort?

d Why are hops added to the wort?

e Why is wort cooled before the yeast is added?

f Write word and balanced symbol equations for the reaction inside the fermenter.

g What are the by-products of brewing beer?

12 a Make a flow diagram showing the three main stages in converting malted grain into vinegar. Include as much detail about each stage as you can.

b What are the main uses of vinegar?

c Why is vinegar a good preservative?

13 Every enzyme has an optimum temperature.

a What is meant by 'optimum temperature'?

b Use the data below to draw a graph. Mark on it the optimum temperature of this enzyme, which converts starch into glucose syrup.

Temperature (°C)	Glucose produced (mg/min)
0	0.2
10	0.4
20	0.9
30	1.6
40	2.1
50	0.3
60	0.0

c Why does enzyme activity fall off above a certain temperature?

d How do enzymes differ from chemical catalysts?

e Name two enzymes involved in brewing, baking, making cheese or washing powders.

14 Disposal of whey has always been a problem in the cheese industry. Disposal by dumping has led to some serious incidences of pollution. How is whey used today?

15 A large industrial fermenter may contain thousands of gallons of microbes and media. (Media is the solution containing everything the microbes need to grow and all the reaction ingredients.) It is essential to get the conditions correct for maximum production.

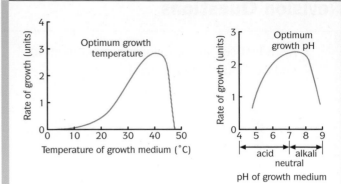

▲ These graphs show the preliminary results of an investigation into the properties of an enzyme.

a What is meant by the optimum temperature for an enzyme?

b What is meant by the optimum pH for an enzyme?

c For the enzyme used in this investigation what are the optimum temperature and optimum pH?

d In quantitive terms what would be the effect of using this enzyme at pH 6?

e What would happen if the temperature was kept at 20°C?

16 An enzyme called galactosidase can be obtained from certain microbes. The properties of the enzyme obtained from different sources are shown in the table.

Source of enzyme	Optimum pH	Optimum temperature (°C)
A	3.0–4.0	55
B	4.8	46
C	6.9–7.5	45
D	6.5	50

a From which source would you extract enzyme to break down:
  i whey, pH 4–6
  ii milk, pH 6.3–6.8?

b What else would you have to consider when selecting enzymes for these functions?

Energy in reactions

Hot and cold reactions

The cold packs in first-aid kits have two sections. One contains a white solid called ammonium nitrate. The second, thinner section contains water. To make the pack go cold, you burst the bag containing the water. The solid then dissolves in the water and this produces a cold solution. The actual temperature of the solution depends on the amount of water and ammonium nitrate in the bag but even on a hot day the temperature of the pack can fall to about 0 °C.

ammonium nitrate solid + water → ammonium nitrate solution

$$NH_4NO_3(s) \text{ with water} \rightarrow NH_4NO_3(aq)$$

Other packs can produce instant warmth. Your hands can get very cold skiing or watching sport in freezing conditions, even if you wear warm gloves. One way to keep them warm is to use a hot pack. Hot packs contain a perforated sachet, like a large teabag, sealed in a plastic cover. The sachet holds finely powdered iron and sodium chloride. You take the sachet out of the plastic cover and shake it to mix the contents with the air. A fast reaction takes place and heat is given out. The reaction is the same as the one that produces rust, but it takes place much faster because the sodium chloride acts as a catalyst, so the finely powdered iron can react quickly with the oxygen.

$$\text{iron} + \text{oxygen} \xrightarrow{\text{sodium chloride catalyst}} \text{iron oxide}$$

$$4Fe(s) + 3O_2(g) \xrightarrow{\text{NaCl catalyst}} 2Fe_2O_3(s)$$

You will learn more about the science of hot and cold pack reactions in this chapter.

If you have ever sprained your ankle or banged your head it is likely you have been told to put an ice pack on it. If you are at home, you can wrap a packet of frozen peas in a teatowel and hold it on the damaged ankle or sore head. Away from home this is not so easy, but many first-aid kits do contain packs that can change their temperature and become cold if required.

A cold pack uses a chemical reaction to take down the swelling around an injury, by taking in the heat energy.

Hot and cold packs are efficient and convenient ways of providing heat energy, or taking heat energy away.

When you are standing around in the cold, the heat energy given out by the chemical reaction in a hot pack is very welcome.

Review

Before going any further, read this page and attempt the tasks. Write the answers in your notes.

Using energy transfer

Energy is measured in joules (J) and kilojoules (kJ). One joule is not a lot of energy. It takes 100 kilojoule of energy to heat a litre of water by about 25 °C. A teenage boy needs about 12 million joule of energy a day from food to be able to go about his everyday life.

▲ Opening and closing the air hole controls a Bunsen flame. Energy transfer from fuels can be controlled and used.

One kilojoule = one thousand joule

1 kJ = 1000 J

▲ Flame is a sign that a chemical reaction is taking place.

HEAT OXYGEN FUEL

▲ Burning is a chemical reaction. The fire triangle shows what is needed for burning to occur. Often heating is needed to get burning started.

CHECK TWELVE

1 Use the fire triangle to explain why the following can be used to put out a fire:
   a putting a damp tea-towel on burning fat in a chip pan
   b cutting down trees in front of an advancing forest fire
   c hosing a bonfire with water.

2 Explain how opening and closing the air hole controls the heat you get from a Bunsen burner.

3 Carry out a risk assessment for using a Bunsen burner.

4 How is energy transfer controlled when:
   a North Sea gas is burned on a cooker hob
   b petrol is burned in a car engine
   c coal is burned on a coal fire?

5 What chemical reaction is taking place when a candle burns?

6 How many joule are in:
   a 1.5 kJ
   b 0.75 kJ?

7 Find from the label how many joule are in a serving of three of your favourite foods.

Energy transfer

From an early age most of us take the transfer of energy from chemicals for granted. Licking an ice lollipop on a hot day cools your tongue. Drinking a mug of hot chocolate or tea after being out on a cold, winter day provides comfort and warmth. We turn up the heating when a room feels chilly, and turn up the gas on the hob to try to get food cooked faster.

We constantly depend on transferring energy from chemicals. Energy is transferred when food reacts with oxygen and other chemicals, to help us grow, keep warm and go about our everyday lives. We burn fuels like oil, gas and coal to transfer energy to cook food, to heat water for washing and to warm our homes. You can read more about energy transfer in the Physics book.

In the chemical industry much effort is devoted to transferring energy to and from chemicals as cheaply and quickly as possible.

In the 1920s 70 billion matches were made in a week. A match head contains fuel and substances containing oxygen tightly packed together. Heat from friction sets off the reaction.

Fuels

Fuels are chemicals that transfer energy to the surroundings when they react with another substance, usually oxygen. The reaction between fuel and oxygen is slow at room temperature. It needs a supply of heat to get it started.

$$\text{fuel} + \begin{array}{c}\text{oxygen (or a chemical}\\\text{to supply oxygen)}\end{array} + \begin{array}{c}\text{energy to get the}\\\text{reaction going}\end{array} \rightarrow \begin{array}{c}\text{waste}\\\text{products}\end{array} + \text{energy}$$

Cars and other vehicles burn petrol or diesel. Central heating systems burn oil or natural gas. Power stations burn fuels, often coal, to produce steam to drive turbines and generate the electricity that comes into our homes at the flick of a switch. Chemical reactions producing heat energy from **fuels** in this way are known as **combustion** reactions.

Good fuels

Any chemical that releases energy when it burns in oxygen could be classed as a fuel but it is not necessarily a good fuel. In choosing fuels there are a number of considerations.

- Burning the fuel must transfer a lot of energy.
- The fuel must burn safely at a controllable rate.
- It must be possible to store the fuel safely.
- The new chemicals created by the reaction, the waste products, must be safe and not pollute the environment.
- The fuel must be cost efficient and convenient.

▶ *What different fuels do your family use during a year? Make a list and, for each fuel, include what it is used for and why it was chosen.*

Wood, peat and dried animal dung are all used as fuels. Today the most commonly used fuels in industrialised countries are coal, gas, diesel and petrol.

▶ *Show the data in the table first as a pie chart and then as a bar chart. Which in your opinion shows the data more clearly?*

This plastic explosive is Semtex. The power of an explosion comes from all the energy being released all at once.

Energy sources	Per cent of total energy provided
Coal	35
Oil	35
Gas	24
Nuclear	5
Hydro (water)	1

Sources of energy used in the UK in 1990.

Waste products from burning fuels

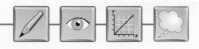

The fuel used in this investigation is ethanol (C_2H_6O). The apparatus used is shown in the diagram below. After a short time the limewater turns milky and a colourless liquid collects in the cooled test tube. In time enough was collected to measure its boiling point which was 100 °C. If you were carrying out this experiment, you would have to be extremely careful because ethanol is flammable.

▶ *What are the two waste products of burning ethanol in air?*

▶ *What colour would the indicator be after burning the ethanol?*

▶ *What chemical test could be used to identify the liquid in the cooled tube?*

▶ *Complete this word equation for the reaction and, if you can, write the balanced symbol equation.*

  ethanol + oxygen → _____ *+* _____

▶ *How could you show that the two products of this reaction came from the burning fuel and not from the air being drawn through the apparatus by the pump?*

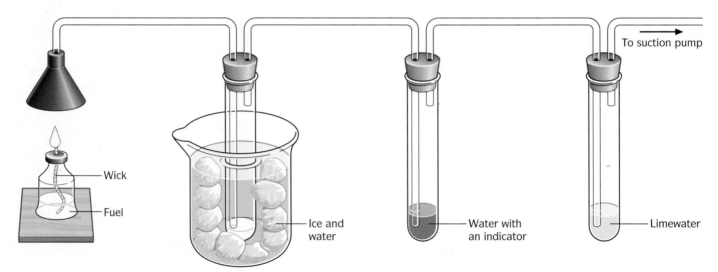

🔺 Apparatus used to investigate the waste products of burning ethanol.

Fossil fuels were created over millions of years by the decay and compression of living things, especially plants. So they contain the same elements as living things. They are made mainly from carbon, hydrogen and oxygen, with some sulphur and nitrogen.

Energy from the Sun was trapped by plants millions of years ago and stored in chemicals. Burning coal, gas and oil releases this energy for our use today.

Burning chemicals react with oxygen forming **oxides** of their elements. You can read about this in Chapter Three (Metals). For example, sulphur burns with a blue flame to form the choking gas, sulphur dioxide. Fossil fuels are compounds of carbon, hydrogen and oxygen. Ethanol is a compound of the same three elements, which is often used as a fuel. So, when they are burned, all fuels produce the same waste products – carbon dioxide and water (hydrogen oxide). These gases are released into the atmosphere.

Fuels in industry

Energy transferred from burning fuels is often used in industrial processes.

- In fractional distillation crude oil first has to be heated before passing the vapour into the fractionating column.
- Large amounts of electricity have to generated to dissolve aluminium oxide in molten cryolite and electrolyse it to produce aluminium.
- In the manufacture of plastic containers, the polythene granules have to be melted before reshaping.
- Cracking hydrocarbons takes place at high temperatures in the presence of a catalyst.
- In the manufacture of sodium hydroxide from brine, electrical energy is used to separate the elements in salt (sodium chloride).
- Lime is manufactured by heating limestone strongly in a kiln.

You can read about these processes in other chapters.

Investigating heat transfer

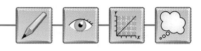

Devise an experiment to find out which transfers more heat – ethanol, C_2H_6O, or methanol, CH_4O – when burned in air.

Check your plan with your teacher before you carry it out. Remember to say what safety precautions you need to take when handling flammable substances.

Energy transfer and changes in state

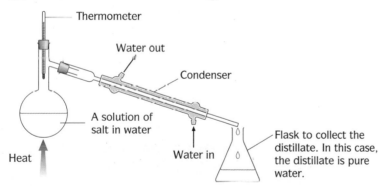

▲ In this distillation apparatus, energy is transferred to the cold water in the condenser from the steam. The water molecules in the steam move closer together and condense to form a liquid.

The theory that matter is made from moving particles can be used to explain how substances change from one state to another when heated or cooled.

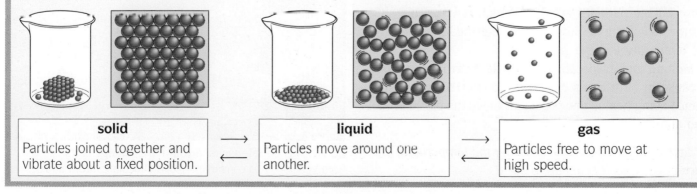

solid	**liquid**	**gas**
Particles joined together and vibrate about a fixed position.	Particles move around one another.	Particles free to move at high speed.

Melting and evaporating

When heated, an impure solid softens and then melts forming a liquid. Pure solids will melt suddenly. In heated solids the particles vibrate but still remain held together. At first, the energy being supplied makes the particles vibrate more and raises the temperature. At the melting point, the temperature remains the same, even though heating continues. This is because the energy supplied is being used to overcome the forces holding the particles together, freeing them from their solid structure. Once all the particles are free to move (all the solid has melted) further heating causes the temperature to go up again. In some substances, like metals, the forces holding the particles together are very strong and so the melting point is very high.

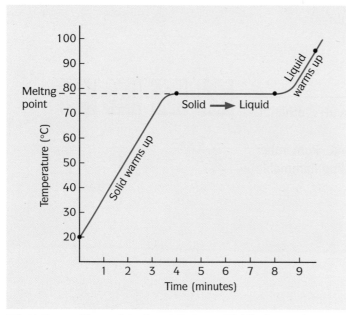

At the melting point of naphthalene, 78 °C, the temperature remains constant until all the naphthalene has melted.

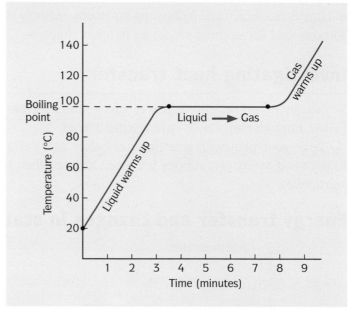

At the boiling point of water, 100 °C, the temperature stays constant until all the liquid has changed into a gas.

When a liquid is heated, its particles move around faster and the temperature rises. Some particles have enough energy to escape (evaporate) and become a gas. When the boiling point is reached, the energy being transferred is used to separate the liquid particles from each other. If heating continues, all the liquid changes into a gas. While this is happening the temperature stays the same even though heat energy is still being supplied. Once all the particles are free, which is when the substance has changed into a gas, further heating will raise the temperature of the gas.

Melting and evaporating are **endothermic** processes because in both cases energy is transferred to the substance being heated and is used to move the particles further apart.

▶ *Make a sketch of a graph showing the temperature of ice at −5 °C as it heats up to 20 °C.*

When chocolate melts in your hand, energy is transferred from your body to convert the solid chocolate into a liquid.

Condensing and solidifying

When a gas cools, the changes described on the previous page are reversed. When the substance cools down it condenses from a gas to a liquid and then solidifies. Energy in the form of heat is transferred to the surroundings during these changes, as the particles move closer together and slow down. Because heat is transferred from the substance to the surroundings, condensing and solidifying are called **exothermic** processes.

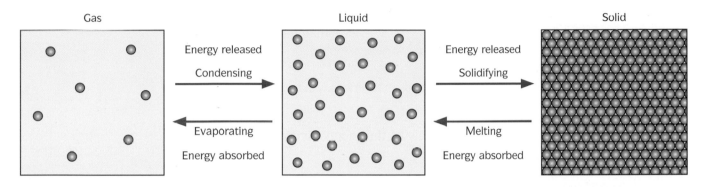

Gas		Liquid		Solid
	Energy released		Energy released	
	Condensing →		Solidifying →	
	← Evaporating		← Melting	
	Energy absorbed		Energy absorbed	

Looking at energy transfers

Chemical reactions involve energy transfers. You may be given a worksheet to help you to try out some chemical reactions to find out whether the reaction gives out energy or takes in energy from its surroundings. You can read more about the importance of energy transfers in the Physics book.

Exothermic reactions

You might have studied neutralisation in Chapter Five (Acids and bases). If so, you might have measured the rise in temperature of the solution when an acid is added to an alkali. You might have noticed that the container becomes slightly warm to the touch. You will have realised that energy can be transferred in reactions other than burning. In some chemical reactions called exothermic reactions there is a rise in temperature.

▲ In exothermic reactions energy is transferred to the surroundings.

When, for example, sodium hydroxide solution is added to hydrochloric acid, sodium chloride and water are formed. The temperature of the solution rises and energy is transferred to the surroundings. After some time the contents of the beaker return to room temperature but overall energy has been transferred away from the solution, so this is called an exothermic reaction.

▲ A temperature sensor being used to investigate a neutralisation reaction.

Energy level diagrams

Energy transfers can be shown in diagrams called **energy level diagrams**.

reactants:

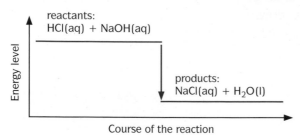

This is an exothermic reaction. Energy has been transferred to the surroundings.

The products are at a lower energy level than the reactants.

▲ The energy level diagram for the neutralisation of sodium hydroxide with hydrochloric acid.

Energy level diagrams can be drawn to scale showing the energy transferred in kilojoules per mole (kJ/mol).

Exothermic reaction	Energy transferred (kJ/mol)
Methane + oxygen → water + carbon dioxide	890
Hydrochloric acid + sodium hydroxide → sodium chloride + water	58
Sulphur dioxide + oxygen → sulphur trioxide	197
Glucose + oxygen → carbon dioxide + water	2808

▲ Energy transferred in some exothermic reactions.

▶ *Draw energy level diagrams to scale for three of the exothermic reactions listed in the table above.*

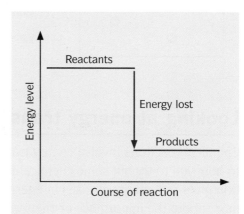

▲ In general, the energy level diagram for an exothermic reaction takes this form.

Endothermic reactions

In some reactions energy is absorbed from the surroundings as the products are formed. A sign that this is happening is if the test tube or beaker containing the reactants feels cold. Reactions in which the temperature falls and energy is absorbed from the surroundings are called **endothermic reactions**.

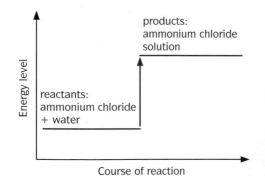

This is an endothermic reaction. Energy has been transferred to the solution.

The products are at a higher energy level than the reactants.

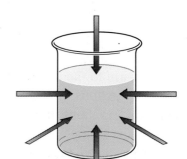

▲ In endothermic reactions energy is absorbed.

▲ The energy level diagram for dissolving solid ammonium chloride in water.

Photosynthesis is the most important endothermic reaction in the world. In forming carbohydrates from carbon dioxide and water, energy from the Sun is absorbed.

All electrolysis reactions are endothermic.

When either potassium nitrate or ammonium chloride are dissolved in water, the temperature of the solution falls. Eventually energy is transferred to the solution from the surroundings, raising the temperature back to room temperature.

Endothermic reactions can also be shown by energy level diagrams. Here the products are at a higher energy level than the reactants.

Endothermic reaction	Energy taken in (kJ/mol)
Calcium carbonate → calcium oxide + water	130
Ammonium chloride → ammonia + hydrogen chloride	176

Energy transferred in some endothermic reactions.

▶ *Draw an energy level diagram to scale for one of the endothermic reactions listed in the table above.*

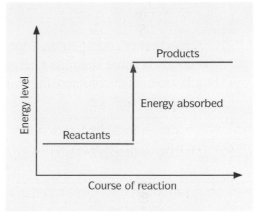

This shows the general form of an energy level diagram for an endothermic reaction.

Breaking and making bonds

When melting and evaporation take place, heating supplies the energy needed to separate the particles and move them further apart. In chemical reactions the forces or bonds within the particles have to be overcome before a reaction can take place. For example, when methane burns in oxygen, bonds in the methane and oxygen molecules have to be broken. Then new bonds in the carbon dioxide and water molecules must be made. Overall it is an exothermic reaction.

methane + oxygen → carbon dioxide + water

$$CH_4(g) + 2O_2(g) \rightarrow CO_2(g) + 2H_2O(l)$$

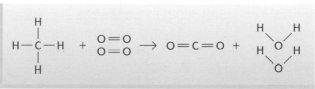

Explaining energy changes in reactions

The bonds within molecules are strong. To get a reaction started energy must be supplied to break these bonds. First, four carbon–hydrogen bonds in the methane molecule and two oxygen molecules must be broken.

Energy is released when new bonds are made. Here, two carbon–oxygen bonds and four new hydrogen–oxygen bonds are made.

The overall energy change in a reaction depends on the difference between the energy needed to break the bonds and the energy released when the new bonds are made. Burning methane in oxygen is an exothermic reaction so the energy needed to break the bonds is less than that released when the new bonds are made. You can follow this on an energy level diagram. Notice that the products, carbon dioxide and water, are at a lower energy level than the reactants, methane and oxygen, and so energy is released in this reaction overall.

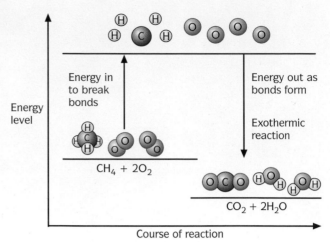

▲ Energy level diagram for burning methane in oxygen.

A reaction is endothermic if the energy needed to break the bonds is more than the energy released when the new bonds are made. Decomposing water into its elements is an endothermic reaction.

water → hydrogen + oxygen

$2H_2O(l) \rightarrow 2H_2(g) + O_2(g)$

$$ \begin{array}{ccc} H & & H \\ & \searrow \quad \nearrow & \\ H & O & H \\ & \downarrow & \\ & O & \end{array} \rightarrow \begin{array}{c} H-H \\ H-H \end{array} + O=O $$

Four oxygen–hydrogen bonds are broken and two hydrogen–hydrogen bonds and one oxygen–oxygen bond is made. The energy needed to break the bonds is more than the energy released in the formation of the new bonds so energy is absorbed in this reaction overall. The products are at a higher energy level than the reactants.

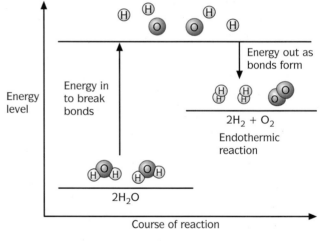

▲ Energy level diagram for decomposing water.

Bond energy

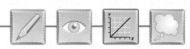

Many reactions need an energy input to get them going. You may be given a worksheet and tables of data showing the quantity of energy needed to make or break 1 mole of different bonds to help you calculate the overall energy transfer in given reactions.

Energy released by burning

Clive and Ewa investigated burning fuels. They wanted to discover if the structure of the fuel had any effect on the energy released when it was burned.

The fuels they tested included methane, ethane, propane, pentane and hexane.

▸ *What prediction (or hypothesis) would you make before planning and carrying out this investigation?*

Here are their results.

Name	Formula	Energy released on burning (kJ/mol)
Methane	CH_4	890
Ethane	C_2H_6	1650
Propane	C_3H_8	2250
Butane	C_4H_{10}	2850
Pentane	C_5H_{12}	3500
Hexane	C_6H_{14}	4200

▸ *Show Clive and Ewa's results in a clearer way, using a graph or a chart.*

▸ *Analyse these results remembering what you know about bond-making and bond-breaking in chemical reactions.*

Activation energy

Chemical reactions are only possible when particles get together. It is no good if it is just a glancing blow. For reactions to happen, collisions must occur at a high enough energy level to break bonds and get the reaction started. Bonds between atoms have to be broken before the atoms can be rearranged and joined up into new compounds. The course of a chemical reaction can be described using energy level diagrams like the ones below.

Collisions must have a minimum amount of energy, called the **activation energy**, before a reaction can take place. This is like an energy barrier that has to be got over before a reaction can happen. If the activation energy is high a reaction is less likely. Reactions that get easily started are those with a low activation energy.

Catalysts and enzymes

Reactions are speeded up in the presence of catalysts and enzymes. They seem to be able to lower the activation energy. Many more collisions are successful because the energy barrier has been lowered and so the rate of the reaction increases.

▸ *What effect does using an enzyme or a catalyst have on the activation energy for a reaction?*

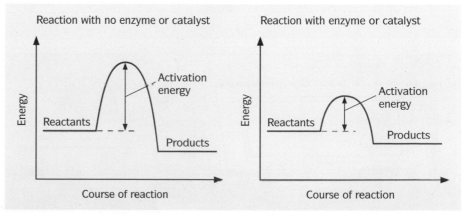

Energy level diagrams for a reaction with and without a catalyst or enzyme.

CHEMISTRY

The problem with burning hydrocarbons

The greenhouse effect

Burning hydrocarbons like fossil fuels releases tonnes of carbon dioxide into the atmosphere. Some people think that the increased level of carbon dioxide is one of the factors causing global warming.

Over recent years there has been much speculation as to whether or not the temperature of the Earth is changing. If the temperature is rising, one of the factors that may be causing it is often referred to as the **greenhouse effect**. In a greenhouse, radiation from the Sun passes through the glass and heats up the contents. The heated objects inside give out longer wave radiation, which cannot pass back out through the glass and so the temperature inside the greenhouse rises above the temperature outside.

The mixture of gases we call the atmosphere acts as a kind of greenhouse around the Earth. Methane and carbon dioxide are sometimes called **greenhouse gases** because they prevent energy transfer back into space by absorbing radiation. You can read more about greenhouse gases in Biology, Chapter Thirteen.

Some of the radiation from the Sun is reflected by the Earth and its atmosphere. Some radiation passes through the Earth's atmosphere. Radiation of certain wave lengths cannot easily pass back through the gases in the atmosphere and so it is trapped, warming the Earth to a temperature of about 15 °C. (The average temperature on the Moon, which has no atmosphere, is –18 °C.)

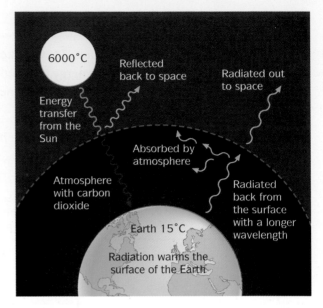

6000 °C

Energy transfer from the Sun

Reflected back to space

Radiated out to space

Absorbed by atmosphere

Atmosphere with carbon dioxide

Radiated back from the surface with a longer wavelength

Earth 15 °C

Radiation warms the surface of the Earth

Variations in the Earth's temperature

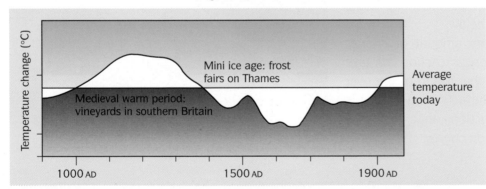

Temperature change (°C)

Mini ice age: frost fairs on Thames

Medieval warm period: vineyards in southern Britain

Average temperature today

1000 AD   1500 AD   1900 AD

The change in average temperature of the Earth over the past one thousand years.

Burning fossil fuels releases many waste products which can have devastating effects on our health and the environment.

The temperature of the Earth has varied naturally over hundreds of years. Scientists have predicted changes before and in the 1970s they forecast a mini-ice age in the near future. What we have to worry about is whether these changes are natural and just part of long-term variations or whether they have been caused by human activities.

Carbon dioxide

One of the gases in the atmosphere which absorb radiation is carbon dioxide. Over the years the amount of this gas in the atmosphere has slowly increased. At the same time people have used more fuels like oil, coal and gas which give off carbon dioxide when they burn. Around 1900, scientists suggested that increased waste gases in the atmosphere created by burning fuel was the cause of global warming, but nobody took much notice.

Year	Carbon dioxide (parts per million of air)
1740	280
1760	280
1820	280
1850	290
1915	300
1930	305
1950	310
1965	315
1975	330
1985	350

🔺 This table shows the changing carbon dioxide concentration in the atmosphere over 245 years.

Today it is thought that the warming that has been observed so far could be a result of the building up of carbon dioxide and other greenhouse gases like methane, oxides of nitrogen, ozone and CFCs. However, in spite of much investigation, scientists have so far been unable to prove this.

The Earth's ability to adjust

The Earth is a remarkably stable place. Life has gone on for about 3.5 billion years in spite of the effects of human activity during the last small fraction of this time. The composition of the soil, oceans and atmosphere has remained similar through time by a process of continual removal and replacement. Some scientists believe that the Earth can, in time, adjust itself in response to changes.

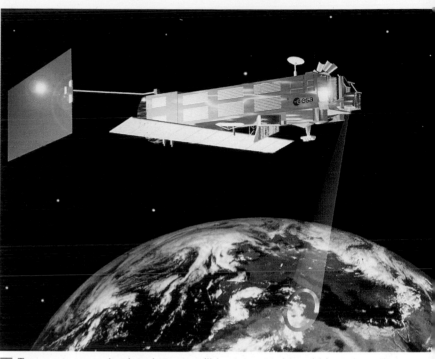

🔺 Temperatures on land and at sea will be measured to within fractions of a degree by equipment on Europe's ENVISAT-1 Satellite in 1998.

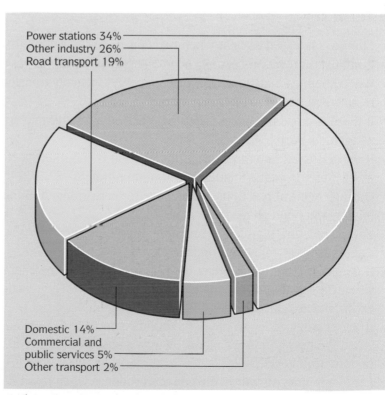

Power stations 34%
Other industry 26%
Road transport 19%

Domestic 14%
Commercial and public services 5%
Other transport 2%

🔺 This pie chart shows the different sources of carbon dioxide in the atmosphere in the UK in 1990.

CHEMISTRY

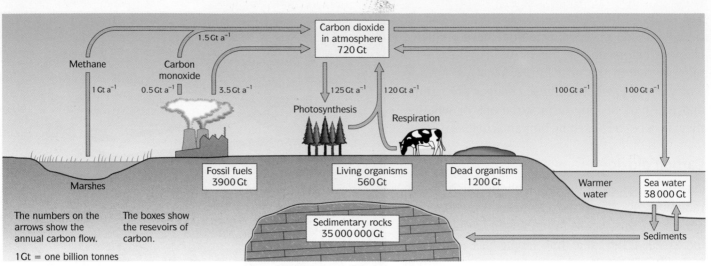

The numbers on the arrows show the annual carbon flow.

The boxes show the reservoirs of carbon.

1 Gt = one billion tonnes

The sea, atmosphere, rocks, organisms (both living and dead) and fossil fuels are all large stores or **reservoirs** of carbon. Scientists say that the reservoirs are balanced in a steady state. The **carbon cycle** is the process of uptake and release of carbon compounds that keeps the reservoirs balanced. You can read more about the carbon cycle in Chapter Seven (The Earth).

▶ *Which carbon reservoir is most likely to be influenced by the activities of humans?*

Deciding on appropriate action

There are a number of options for dealing with the problems caused by burning fuels. For example, we could take immediate steps to reduce the greenhouse gases going into the atmosphere by reducing the amount of fuel we burn, or we could wait for more definite scientific evidence before making any decisions.

▶ *Since 1900 the average temperature on Earth has risen by 0.5 °C. What effect will this have in the future if the temperature continues to rise?*

Summary

- Energy is released as heat when fuels burn. This is a combustion reaction.
- Combustion reactions usually need a supply of energy to get them started.
- When chemical reactions take place, energy is usually transferred. This results in a rise or fall in temperature.
- If there is a rise in temperature, the reaction is exothermic, for example when fuels burn.
- If there is a fall in temperature, the reaction is endothermic, for example when water is added to solid ammonium nitrate.
- During chemical reactions atoms have to be rearranged. Bonds have to be broken and bonds have to be made.
- Energy must be supplied to break the bonds.
- Energy is released when bonds are made.
- If the energy needed to break the bonds is less than the energy released when the new bonds are made, energy is released. The reaction is an exothermic reaction.
- If the energy needed to break the bonds is more than the energy released when the new bonds are made, energy is absorbed. The reaction is an endothermic reaction.
- Large amounts of carbon dioxide are produced when fossil fuels are burned. Opinions of scientists are divided regarding the possible effects of this on the environment.

Revision Questions

1 What is a fuel? What fuels are used in the following?
   a road transport lorrics
   b cars
   c camping stoves
   d living things
   e cigarette lighters

2 Energy is often needed to get reactions going. How are the following reactions started?
   a a safety match
   b a firework
   c petrol vapour in a car engine

3 What are the two main waste products formed when fossil fuels burn? Name a test you could use to identify each of these products.

4 What is crude oil? How is it formed?

5 What can you tell about a reaction if it can be described as:
   a exothermic
   b endothermic?
   Give one example of each type of reaction.

6 Most electricity is generated in power stations by burning fossil fuels. Describe two ways in which this could cause problems in the environment.

7 A sample of solid stearic acid was heated slowly in a water bath until all the solid had melted. The temperature was noted at regular intervals and the results are shown below.

Time (mins)	0	1	2	3	4	5	6	7	8	9	10	11	12
Temperature (°C)	19	28	41	48	53	55	55	55	55	62	66	71	74

   a Draw a graph showing temperature (°C) on the x-axis and time (mins) on the y-axis.
   b From the graph, what is the melting point of stearic acid?
   c Why is energy needed to melt a solid?

8 Are the following reactions or changes exothermic or endothermic?
   a magnesium ribbon with oxygen
   b respiration of glucose in living things
   c sherbet when it is moistened in your mouth
   d perfume evaporating from your skin
   e making lime from marble chips
   f neutralising an acid with an alkali

9 Copy the diagrams below. Complete each of them to show what happens in an exothermic and an endothermic reaction.
   Use the terms reactant, product, exothermic and endothermic. You will have to use some of these terms more than once.

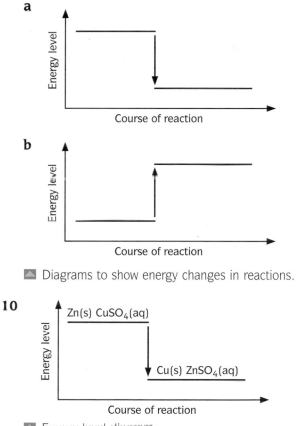

   Diagrams to show energy changes in reactions.

10

   Energy level diagram.

   a Write down the word and symbol equations for the reaction described above.
   b Is the reaction exothermic or endothermic? How can you tell from the diagram?
   c What would you expect to feel if these reactants were mixed together in a test tube you were holding in your hand?

CHEMISTRY

11

Compose a news item for inclusion in next week's edition of the paper in response to this letter. Use the information on page 184 'The problem with burning hydrocarbons' and other sources you are able to find.

12 Read the first page of this chapter.

   a Which of the packs described depends on a reaction that is:
     i exothermic
     ii endothermic?

   b Construct energy level diagrams for the reactions in the hot pack and the cold pack.

   c Give two reasons why rusting is speeded up in the hot pack.

   d You have decided to set up a small firm making hot packs. What would be the best amounts of iron and sodium chloride to put into the packs? Write a detailed plan of how you could investigate this before going into production.

13 The reaction between:

   ■ hydrogen and chlorine is exothermic

hydrogen + chlorine → hydrogen chloride

   ■ nitrogen and hydrogen is endothermic

nitrogen + hydrogen → ammonia (NH_3)

   a Write the balanced equation for each reaction.

   b If you can use an atomic modelling kit, make models of the reactants in each equation.

   c Write down how many and what type of bond is broken in each reaction.

   d Write down how many and what type of bond is made to make the products in each reaction.

   e Construct an energy level diagram for each of the reactions, similar to those for burning methane and decomposing water on page 182.

14 Copy and use the diagrams below to explain activation energy and how the presence of enzymes or catalysts alters it.

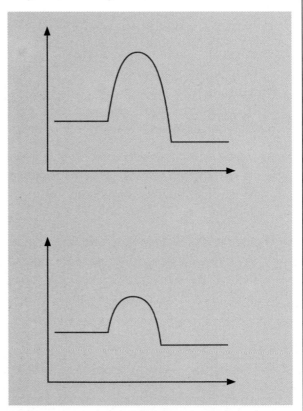

▲ Diagrams to help explain how catalysts and enzymes speed up the rates of reactions.

Using reactions

■ Manufactured goods

Manufactured goods are made from many different materials and are created by different processes.

All these manufacturing processes involve chemical reactions that have to be controlled and monitored at every stage.

Nowadays good quality china is cheaper and it is not so easily broken as in the past. Added chemicals disperse the clay evenly in water and prevent faults and bubbles. The process is more energy-efficient and so, in general, china dishes cost less.

The granules inside this nappy are biodegradable and non-toxic and yet they can absorb up to 500 times their mass of water.

Much of what is around you is manufactured. For example, think about all the things you used when you got up this morning. Toothpaste, the tube and the cap that keeps the paste fresh, are all manufactured.

So are the fabrics that make your shirts and the sheets on your bed, and so are the dyes that form the patterns on them.

Chemicals are added to personal care products to make them creamier and smoother. It makes them easier to apply and people like thick preparations. They feel they are getting value for money.

Review

Before going any further, read this page and attempt the tasks. Write the answers in your notes.

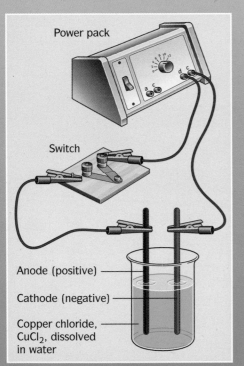

When a current is passed through a solution, it is called electrolysis.

Labels in diagram:
- Power pack
- Switch
- Anode (positive)
- Cathode (negative)
- Copper chloride, $CuCl_2$, dissolved in water

Solutions

When a solid dissolves into a liquid, such as water, a solution is made. Some compounds made from a metal and a non-metal contain two types of charged particles called ions. Metal ions are positively charged and non-metals are negatively charged. Sodium chloride, NaCl, is made from Na^+ ions and Cl^- ions.

When sodium chloride dissolves in water, the sodium ions and the chloride ions become free to move around in the solution.

Factors that influence reaction rate are:
- concentration
- temperature
- surface area
- catalyst.

Electrolysis

When an electric current flows in the circuit in the diagram, electrons (e^-) drift round the circuit from the positive electrode to the negative electrode. Positive ions move to the cathode and negative ions move to the anode. Here they are converted into atoms.

CHECK THIRTEEN

1 Sodium hydroxide, NaOH, is made from the ions Na^+ and OH^-. Make a drawing which shows what happens to these ions when solid sodium hydroxide is dissolved in water.

2 Look at the diagram showing the electrolysis of copper chloride.
  a In this symbol which is the positive terminal?
  b How do electrons flow round the circuit?
  c Which ions move to the negative electrode, Cu^{2+} ions or Cl^- ions?

d Copy and complete this equation for the formation of copper atoms:

$$Cu^{2+} + \_\_\_\_ \rightarrow Cu$$

e Copy and complete these equations for the formation of chlorine atoms and molecules:

$$Cl^- - \_\_\_\_ \rightarrow Cl \qquad Cl + Cl \rightarrow \_\_\_\_$$

f What is the source of the energy used to split copper chloride into its elements?

3 Write down four factors that influence the rate of a reaction and for each include an example.

Making chemicals from salt

Salt production

Without salt and other seasoning our food would taste bland. We also need a certain amount of salt in our diets to stay healthy. The oldest way of getting salt is by evaporation of seawater. Around the time the Domesday Book was written, in the eleventh century, there were many salt pans in the UK, mainly around the Essex coast.

▶ *How could you get some pure salt from sandy seawater?*

Nowadays we use millions of tonnes of salt a year. In Cheshire there are vast underground deposits of salt. Some of it is dug out of the ground but most salt is brought to the surface by **solution mining**. Water is pumped underground and the salt dissolves in it, forming a solution called **brine**. Brine is pumped up to the surface as it is needed. Only the valves and pipes are visible on the land above the salt.

▲ In Sicily salt is harvested from natural brine. The Sun evaporates the water leaving behind salt crystals.

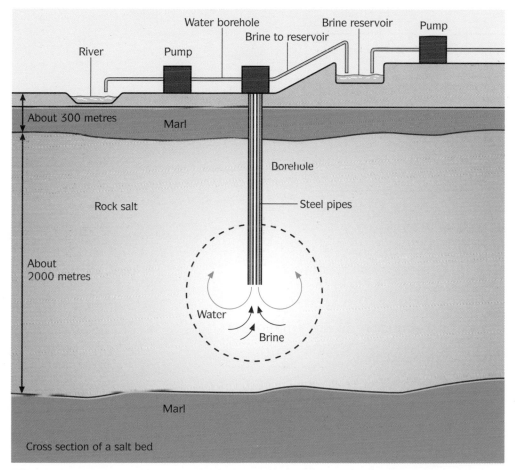

▲ Salt dissolved in water is pumped up from underground. The remaining cavities are sometimes used to store natural gas.

Salt as a raw material

Some salt is used in cooking and preserving. Some is scattered on icy road surfaces to make driving safer in winter. By far the most important use of salt is as a raw material used to make other chemicals.

The chlor-alkali process

Brine is a solution of salt (sodium chloride, NaCl) and water (H_2O). Electrolysis is used to convert these two compounds to sodium hydroxide, chlorine and hydrogen. This process is named after some of its products – chlorine and the alkali, sodium hydroxide.

Electrolysis of brine

Water pumped into salt deposits dissolves other salts besides sodium chloride. Raw brine pumped up from underground cavities contains dissolved calcium and magnesium compounds as well as salt. After these unwanted substances have been removed, an electric current is passed through the purified brine in an electrolysis cell as shown below.

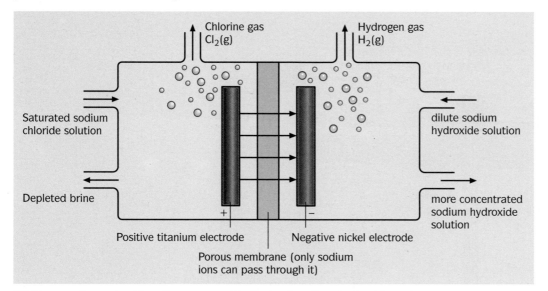

▲ The membrane in this cell separates chlorine and sodium hydroxide and prevents them reacting together.

$$\text{sodium chloride} + \text{water} \xrightarrow{\text{electrolysis}} \text{sodium hydroxide} + \text{chlorine} + \text{hydrogen}$$

▶ *Write a balanced symbol equation for the above reaction.*

Hydrogen is made at the negative electrode:

$$H^+ + e^- \rightarrow H \qquad H + H \rightarrow H_2$$

Chlorine is made at the positive electrode:

$$Cl^- - e^- \rightarrow Cl \qquad Cl + Cl \rightarrow Cl_2$$

The solution left in the electrolysis cell contains sodium ions, Na^+, and hydroxide ions, OH^-. This is a solution of sodium hydroxide, NaOH, which can be run out of the cell.

Electrolysis of solutions

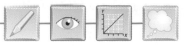

You may be given a worksheet to help you find out more about the effect of passing an electric current through brine (sodium chloride) and other solutions.

Salt in our everyday lives

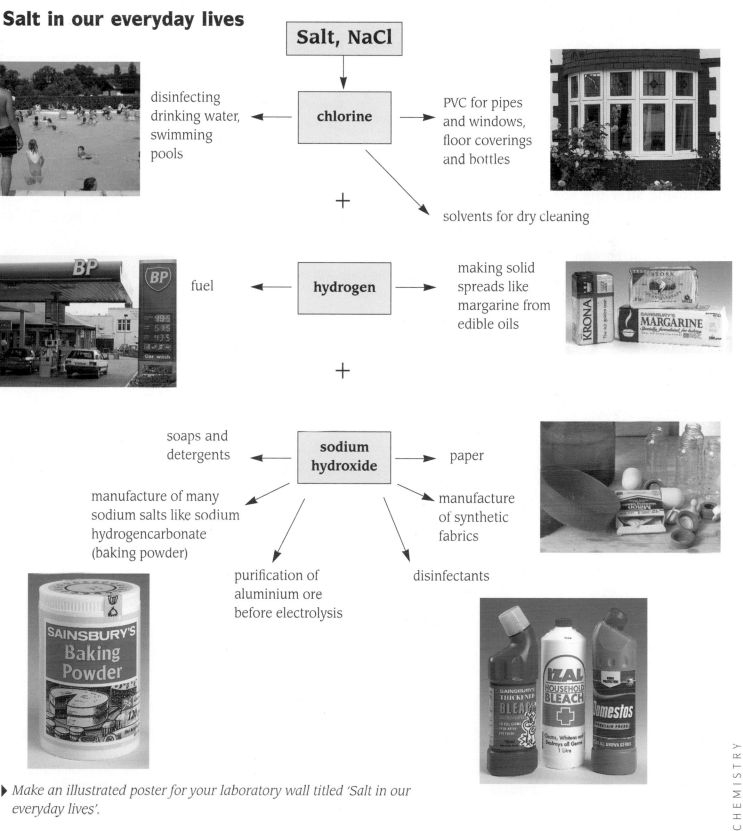

Salt, NaCl

chlorine

disinfecting drinking water, swimming pools

PVC for pipes and windows, floor coverings and bottles

solvents for dry cleaning

+

hydrogen

fuel

making solid spreads like margarine from edible oils

+

sodium hydroxide

soaps and detergents

paper

manufacture of many sodium salts like sodium hydrogencarbonate (baking powder)

manufacture of synthetic fabrics

purification of aluminium ore before electrolysis

disinfectants

▶ *Make an illustrated poster for your laboratory wall titled 'Salt in our everyday lives'.*

CHEMISTRY

Fertilisers

Plant nutrients

Like all living things plants need food and are healthiest if they have a balanced diet. Besides water, air and light, plants need thirteen different elements called **nutrients**. Of these, nitrogen is one of the most important. It is essential for the development of the stems and leaves, and it is needed to ensure good growth and colour of grass and leafy vegetables.

Plants have to able to get these nutrients:

- from a solution of substances dissolved in soil water
- at the right time in their development
- in balanced amounts.

Relatively large amounts needed	Trace amounts needed
Nitrogen N	Chlorine Cl
Phosphorus P	Iron Fe
Potassium K	Manganese Mn
Sulphur S	Zinc Zn
Magnesium Mg	Copper Cu
Calcium Ca	Boron B
	Molybdenum Mo

 Plants need all these substances. Some plants also need sodium, cobalt, vanadium, silicon and nickel.

Looking after the soil

Soil normally contains everything plants need. However, as crops grow, they remove nutrients from the soil, so in time, they have to be replaced. If crops are grown on the same soil and harvested year after year, they will use up all the nutrients and both the size and the quality of the crop will decrease. Farmers and growers try to avoid this in a number of ways.

 A crop like clover or peas can take nitrogen from the air and convert it into nitrogen compounds for its own use. Plants like this are called **nitrogen fixers.** (You may have read about these in Biology, Chapter Thirteen.) Some of this nitrogen ends up in the soil.

 Every so often a field is set aside and left **fallow**. It not used for crop growing. Weeds and other plants flourish and are ploughed back into the soil.

 Natural fertilisers like compost and manure are spread on the soil. These are called **organic** fertilisers because they are made by living things.

 Synthetic fertilisers, containing the necessary nutrients, are spread on the soil. Synthetic fertilisers, called **inorganic** fertilisers, mainly contain nitrogen, phosphorus and potassium – NPK.

Organic and inorganic

Fertilisers are chemicals that make plants grow well. Organic and inorganic fertilisers are both used to improve crop yield but they are different in a number of ways.

Organic fertilisers are natural products from animals and plants. When they are spread on the soil these fertilisers rot away, slowly releasing their nutrients for use by the growing crops. They also improve the texture of the soil by making it crumbly and trapping air. Organic fertilisers are less likely to be washed away by rain than inorganic fertilisers but they are more expensive. It would be difficult, and some people think it would be impossible, to produce enough food to feed the increasing world population using only organic fertilisers. This is because large amounts are needed and it is difficult to control the effect. Organic fertilisers are considered in more detail in the Biology book.

The nutrients in **inorganic fertilisers** are known and can be mixed precisely. Soil analysis and experience of growing particular crops show which fertiliser, and how much of it, should be added for the best effect. Nutrients are released quickly and so the fertiliser can be applied exactly when it is needed. Inorganic fertilisers can be solutions that are sprayed directly on crops, or pellets and granules which release the nutrients more slowly.

Farmers add nitrogen to crops to give a good yield and quality. Adding fertiliser raises the protein content of the grain. This has got to be above 11 per cent or millers won't buy it to make flour. Below that protein level the flour bakes into bread that won't rise and give the open crumbly quality bakers want. This is not possible without fertilisers.

Measuring the effects of fertilisers

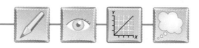

When you carry out an investigation you might add notes on what you would do if you had more time to complete it. At Rothamsted in Hertfordshire an investigation has been going on for over 150 years. Scientists have been monitoring the effect of fertilisers on the yields, or amounts, of wheat and potatoes grown on the same plots year after year. Their results for 1990–94 are shown below. The table shows the mean, or average, yield of wheat and potatoes per hectare (ha), grown continuously within a crop rotation for that five-year period. They were treated either with organic fertilisers or various different artificial fertilisers.

Plot number	Fertiliser treatment* (symbols for the elements present are given)	Mean yield of wheat for 1990–1994 (tonnes/ha)	Mean yield of potatoes for 1990–1994 (tonnes/ha)
1	organic	6.25	32.4
2	none	0.89	6.2
3	PKMg	1.22	12.2
4	N1 PKMg	3.60	17.4
5	N2 PKMg	5.49	21.1
6	N3 PKMg	6.76	24.9
7	N4 PKMg	6.94	27.9
8	N5 PKMg	7.69	28.9
9	N6 PKMg	7.76	30.7
10	N2 P	3.46	7.0

* Nitrogen dressings in N1, N2, N3, N4, N5 and N6 supply 48, 96, 144, 192, 240 and 288 kg/ha of nitrogen respectively. (Source: IACR Rothamsted)

▲ Rothamsted Experimental Station.

▶ *Analyse and comment on the results in the table, especially on the effects of artificial fertilisers and the amount of nitrogen added to the soil.*

▶ *Comment on the fact that plot 2 has had no fertiliser for over 150 years.*

CHEMISTRY

Results show that an essential part of fertilisers is nitrogen. Most plants cannot take nitrogen from the air. They need a source of nitrogen in which it is already combined with other elements. This is sometimes referred to as 'fixed nitrogen'. Plants can absorb solutions of nitrogen containing salts through their roots. **Nitrates (NO_3^-)** or **ammonium (NH_4^+)** salts are the chemicals most commonly used for this purpose as they are water soluble. **Nitrogenous fertilisers** dissolve in rainwater and can readily be taken up through plant roots. You can read more about fertilisers in Biology, Chapter Thirteen.

Fertilisers and the environment

Fertilisers have to be water soluble to get into plant roots but this means that these compounds can easily dissolve in rainwater. Solutions containing nitrate and ammonium ions can find their way into rivers, streams and lakes and, in time, into our supplies of drinking water. Drinking water containing high levels of nitrates is thought to be a possible cause of cancer of the bowel. It is also thought to be harmful to babies, especially in the first two months of life.

Making fertilisers

Reversible reactions

Scientists became more interested in making nitrogen compounds when they realised that plants grow better when they are added to the soil. The air around us is 80% nitrogen gas and so this seemed an ideal starting material from which to make nitrogen compounds. However, nitrogen is very **inert**. It doesn't easily react with any other elements or compounds.

Fritz Haber started experimenting with nitrogen a hundred years ago. He wanted to react it with hydrogen to make a gas called ammonia, NH_3, as a first step in producing artificial fertilisers as well as explosives and a wide range of other chemicals containing nitrogen.

nitrogen + hydrogen → ammonia

$$N_2(g) + 3H_2(g) \rightarrow 2NH_3(g)$$

Making this reaction take place proved very difficult, as you will learn in the next section. In addition, it is a **reversible reaction**. Not only can hydrogen and nitrogen combine with one another to make ammonia, but ammonia can break down again forming nitrogen and hydrogen.

ammonia → nitrogen + hydrogen

$$2NH_3(g) \rightarrow N_2(g) + 3H_2(g)$$

The reaction can go backwards and forwards depending on the conditions and the chemicals present. To show this, the two equations can be combined and written with this sign ⇌ to show that it's a reversible reaction.

nitrogen + hydrogen ⇌ ammonia

$$N_2(g) + 3H_2(g) \rightleftharpoons 2NH_3(g)$$

AMMONIA

Ammonia is a very reactive gas.

You can detect its very distinctive pungent smell from some household cleaners.

It dissolves in water forming an alkaline solution.

ammonia + water → ammonium ion + hydroxide ion

$$NH_3(g) + H_2O(l) \rightarrow NH_4^+(aq) + OH^-(aq)$$

A very familiar reversible process is freezing water. Ice cubes can be melted and refrozen as often as you like. Sometimes conditions affecting the change are written above and below the reversible sign as shown below.

$$H_2O(l) \underset{heat}{\overset{cool}{\rightleftharpoons}} H_2O(s)$$

▶ *Red litmus can change to blue and back again. How could you make this reversible change occur? Write a word equation for this change showing conditions affecting the change above and below the reversible sign.*

Not all reactions are reversible. Have you ever tried to get a raw egg back from a boiled one? It just can't be done. Another **irreversible** reaction is burning natural gas in air. If we could get the methane back again after using it to heat our houses, our gas bills would be much lower.

Reversible reactions

Altering the conditions can make some reactions go backwards as well as forwards. You may be given a worksheet to help you look at some reactions that can go both ways.

The Haber Process

The German chemist Fritz Haber (1868–1934) finally found a way of making ammonia from two gases – nitrogen from the air, and hydrogen.

He didn't have much luck at first. At ordinary pressure hardly any ammonia was made. At room temperature some ammonia was made but the reaction took a long time. After nine years of trying he found the conditions that were needed to make the gas. Using high temperature and pressure and using a platinum catalyst he managed to make ammonia. Even then the yield was low. If all of the hydrogen and nitrogen had been converted to ammonia the yield would have been 100 per cent. Even using the the most ideal conditions, only 8 per cent of the nitrogen and hydrogen he started with were converted to ammonia. Haber's work formed the basis of ammonia making all over the world. In 1990 world production of ammonia using what came to be known as the **Haber Process** was in the region of 100 million tonnes per year.

▶ *How did Haber try to increase the rate of the reaction between nitrogen and hydrogen?*

▶ *What is meant when a student says that she got a 50 per cent yield in a reaction? Use the words reactant and product in your answer.*

The Haber Process today

In a single ammonia plant 900 tonnes of ammonia, NH_3, might be made each day. The raw materials are air, methane and water. Air provides the nitrogen. Methane and water react together to provide hydrogen. The manufacturing process makes nitrogen and hydrogen combine to make ammonia. During the reaction all the other unwanted atoms of carbon, oxygen and the noble gases from the air have to be removed.

▲ ICI's ammonia plant at Severnside.

CHEMISTRY

To make hydrogen gas, methane and steam are passed through narrow tubes containing a nickel catalyst. This stage needs a lot of energy. Pure steam and methane are put in under pressure at one end and heated to 800 °C.

methane + steam $\rightleftharpoons$ carbon monoxide + hydrogen

$CH_4(g) + H_2O(g) \rightleftharpoons CO(g) + 3H_2(g)$

The hot gases are mixed with air, which provides nitrogen, and are exploded together. The heat released in this exothermic reaction is used to make the steam used in the first stage of the process.

nitrogen + hydrogen + oxygen $\rightarrow$ steam + nitrogen

$N_2(g) + 2H_2 + O_2(g) \rightarrow 2H_2O(g) + N_2(g)$

carbon monoxide + steam $\rightarrow$ carbon dioxide + hydrogen

$CO(g) + H_2O(g) \rightarrow CO_2(g) + H_2(g)$

Any remaining methane is burned in oxygen leaving an impure mixture that is mainly hydrogen and nitrogen.

Waste compounds containing oxygen will poison the iron catalyst used in the next stage. To prevent this happening any carbon monoxide, carbon dioxide and water left over has to be removed from the mixture of gases. The carbon monoxide, which could be an environmental nuisance, is converted into a saleable commodity, carbon dioxide.

▶ *Find out some uses of carbon dioxide.*

After a few more stages, a 1:3 mixture of nitrogen and hydrogen is left:

$N_2(g) + 3H_2(g) \rightleftharpoons 2NH_3(g) + heat$

The nitrogen–hydrogen mixture is cooled and passed, under pressure, over an iron catalyst. About 15 per cent of the mixture is converted into ammonia which is removed as a liquid. To be converted to ammonia, a mixture of gases has to go round the system about four times. The heat produced goes back into the system. The energy usage is very low because heat recovery is very efficient.

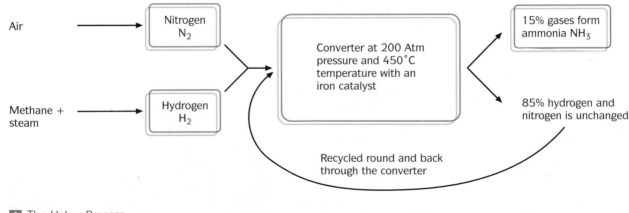

▲ The Haber Process.

Choosing the conditions

When planning an industrial process the working conditions chosen for any chemical reaction depend on the cost, the yield of the product and the rate at which it is made. There is no point in choosing conditions that produce a lot of the product but then having to wait months for the reaction to be completed. Choosing conditions that are expensive reduces profits, and industrial processes *have* to make money. Chemical engineers choose conditions that will give as high a yield of the product as possible at a reasonable rate.

For ammonia

First look at the effect of temperature on the yield of ammonia. The best yields are obtained at low temperatures. The graph on the right, however, tells you nothing about the rate.

▶ *What effect does temperature have on the rate of most reactions?*

▶ *What effect does temperature have on the rate of ammonia production?*

▶ *From the graph what is the effect of pressure on the yield of ammonia?*

In most cases reactions are fast at high temperatures and slow at low temperatures. This reaction is no exception. To make the reaction go at a reasonable rate while producing an acceptable yield, a compromise is reached. Temperatures in the region of 400°C are chosen.

High pressures would seem to be the best choice. As the pressure is raised the yield of ammonia increases. Here the cost plays a part. High-pressure pumps are expensive to buy and to maintain. The pipes and vessels used in the process also have to be strong and have very thick walls. As a compromise between yield and cost, pressures of 150–300 atmospheres are chosen.

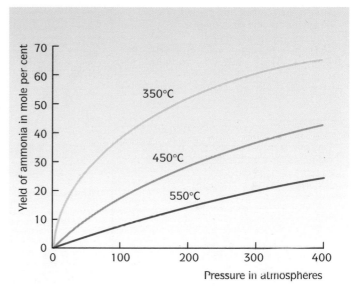

▲ From the graph you can see the yield of ammonia using different temperatures and pressures.

For sulphuric acid

One stage in the manufacture of sulphuric acid (see Chapter Five (Acids and bases)) is the conversion of sulphur dioxide to sulphur trioxide.

$$2SO_2(g) + O_2(g) \rightleftharpoons 2SO_3(g)$$

This is an exothermic reaction. It gives out heat and, as the reaction is reversible, the amount of sulphur trioxide produced depends on the temperature and the pressure. Raised temperatures are used to speed up the reaction but if the temperature is too high the reverse reaction takes place. Sulphur trioxide breaks down forming sulphur dioxide and oxygen. The temperature used must be high enough to get the reaction to go at a reasonable rate and yet not high enough to decompose the newly made sulphur trioxide. To get the best yield a catalyst, vanadium oxide, is used and reaction temperatures of 400–500°C are chosen.

CHEMISTRY

From ammonia to nitric acid

After making ammonia the next step in fertiliser manufacture is the production of nitric acid, HNO_3.

△ The nitrogen fertiliser made at Immingham in Humberside is ammonium nitrate. It is made by reacting together nitric acid and ammonia. The nitric acid is produced on the site.

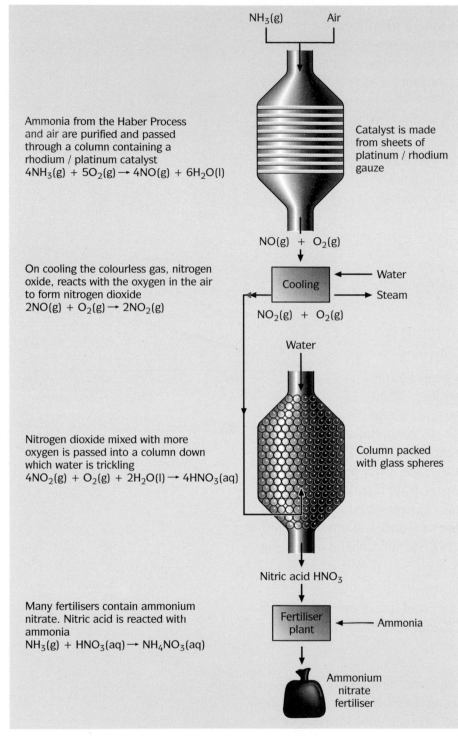

Ammonia from the Haber Process and air are purified and passed through a column containing a rhodium / platinum catalyst
$$4NH_3(g) + 5O_2(g) \rightarrow 4NO(g) + 6H_2O(l)$$

Catalyst is made from sheets of platinum / rhodium gauze

$NO(g) + O_2(g)$

On cooling the colourless gas, nitrogen oxide, reacts with the oxygen in the air to form nitrogen dioxide
$$2NO(g) + O_2(g) \rightarrow 2NO_2(g)$$

Cooling ← Water → Steam

$NO_2(g) + O_2(g)$

Water

Nitrogen dioxide mixed with more oxygen is passed into a column down which water is trickling
$$4NO_2(g) + O_2(g) + 2H_2O(l) \rightarrow 4HNO_3(aq)$$

Column packed with glass spheres

Nitric acid HNO_3

Many fertilisers contain ammonium nitrate. Nitric acid is reacted with ammonia
$$NH_3(g) + HNO_3(aq) \rightarrow NH_4NO_3(aq)$$

Fertiliser plant ← Ammonia

Ammonium nitrate fertiliser

△ Stages in the production of fertiliser from ammonia

The nitrogen fertiliser made at Immingham is ammonium nitrate, which is sold under the trade name Extran. Ammonium nitrate is very soluble in water, and the presence of even a little water makes the particles stick together to produce hard lumps which are difficult to break up. Farmers want their fertilisers to be free flowing so that they can be spread easily by machinery. For this reason, the ammonium nitrate is converted into small granules.

STORE UNDER COVER
PROTECT FROM DIRECT SUNLIGHT

HYDRO

EXTRAN®
34.5% N

PSDS GROUP 1
PRODUCT

△ Extran granules are easy to handle and they contain a drying agent to stop them caking.

COMPOUND FERTILISERS

The three main nutrients required by plants are nitrogen, phosphorus and potassium, NPK. Compound fertilisers contain these nutrients in varying proportions. They are made from ammonia, nitric acid, phosphoric acid and potassium chloride.

▸ *What per cent by mass of nitrogen is in the following fertilisers?*
  a *ammonium phosphate, (NH₄)₃PO₄*
  b *ammonium sulphate, (NH₄)₂SO₄*
  c *urea, CO(NH₂)₂*
  (See Chapter Fifteen (How much?) if you need some help.)

Making use of rocks

Chalk and limestone are forms of calcium carbonate, $CaCO_3$. Vast amounts of chalk and limestone are quarried in the UK, often with very detrimental effects on beautiful countryside. Much limestone is used in the construction industry and in building our ever-extending road networks. The rest is used in the manufacture of chemicals and in agriculture.

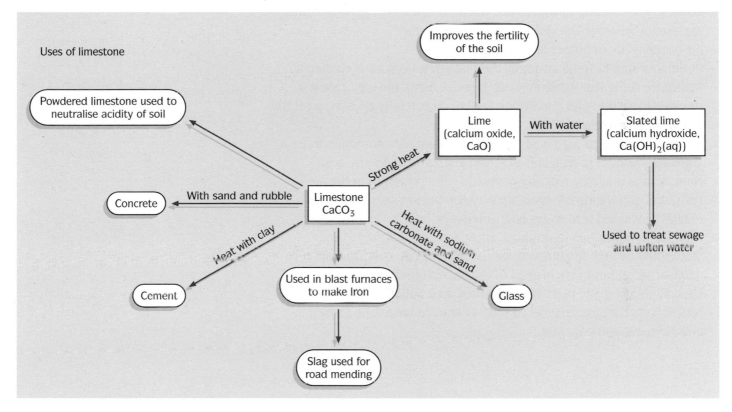

▸ *What chemical test uses calcium hydroxide dissolved in water? Explain the test and write the word and, if you can, the symbol equation for the reaction.*

Thermal decomposition

Strong heating can sometimes split up or decompose compounds into simpler substances. You may be given a worksheet to help you test the effects of strong heating on calcium carbonate.

Debating issues

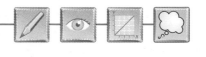

Organise a debate on the issues surrounding the increased quarrying of limestone. Decide whether you support increased quarrying or whether you are against it. Take turns to argue your case to the rest of the group.

Summary

- Chemical reactions are used to turn raw materials into useful products.
- Brine is a solution of salt (NaCl) in water. Electrolysis of brine is used to make sodium hydroxide, chlorine and hydrogen.
- You should know some examples of how sodium hydroxide, hydrogen and chlorine are used in the production of substances like PVC, bleach, soaps and detergents, paper and margarine.
- Reactions that can go backwards and forwards are called reversible reactions.
- The yield in a reversible reaction depends on the conditions of temperature and pressure. Some manufacturing processes involve reversible reactions. For these reactions conditions have to be chosen to give the highest yield at the lowest possible cost.
- Fertilisers containing nitrogen, and often potassium and phosphorus, are used to improve the yield and quality of crops.
- Air contains about 80 per cent nitrogen.
- In the first step in fertiliser production nitrogen from air is reacted with hydrogen, using the Haber Process, to make ammonia gas. This is a reversible reaction and conditions have to be carefully chosen to get the best yield of ammonia.
- Ammonia is reacted with acid to make fertilisers. Ammonium nitrate, a commonly used fertiliser, is made from ammonia and nitric acid.
- Nitric acid is made by reacting ammonia with oxygen from the air.
- Fertilisers containing nitrogen are very soluble in water and so can readily be washed into rivers and waterways.
- High levels of nitrates in drinking water can have harmful effects.
- You should be able to comment on the advantages and disadvantages of using artificial fertilisers instead of organic fertilisers.
- Limestone has many uses. It can be used as a building material or heated to make lime and slaked lime. Powdered limestone is used to make cement and concrete.

Revision Questions

1 Heating blue cobalt chloride, $CoCl_2.6H_2O$, drives water from the crystals, turning it pink. Adding water to the pink crystals reverses this reaction.
   a Write a word and a symbol equation for this reversible reaction.
   b Explain how paper impregnated with pink cobalt chloride could be used to test for the presence of water.

2 Heating calcium carbonate is a reversible reaction:

   $$CaCO_3(s) \rightleftharpoons CaO(s) + CO_2(g)$$

   a What is a reversible reaction?
   b Which industry depends on this reaction?
   c How are the following made from calcium carbonate:
      i slaked lime
      ii mortar
      iii cement?
   d In the manufacture of lime, the newly formed carbon dioxide is constantly removed from the kiln. Explain why.
   e Powdered lime, CaO, is sometimes used to neutralise acidity due to dilute sulphuric acid, H_2SO_4. Write the word and symbol equations for this reaction.

3 Electrolysis is used in the chlor-alkali process.
   a What is the raw material used in this process?
   b How is this raw material recovered from under the ground?
   c Give the names and formulae of the three main products of the reaction.
   d What is formed at the positive electrode in this process?
   e The equation for the electrolysis is:

   $$2NaCl(aq) + 2H_2O(l) \rightarrow Cl_2(g) + H_2(g) + 2NaOH(aq)$$

      i What does (aq) after a chemical symbol tell you?
      ii What mass of sodium chloride would you need to start with in this process to produce 284 tonnes of chlorine?
      iii Name some uses of chlorine.

   f What solution is left in the cell after electrolysis?
   g Name some of the main uses of sodium hydroxide.

4 Write the word and balanced symbol equation for the reaction of limestone described on page 201. Make a poster describing the uses of limestone using those given on page 201 and other sources in your school library.

5 The data in the table below shows how the world's population has grown, and how the United Nations think it will grow, from 1950 to 2010.

Year	Population in billions
1950	2.5
1960	3.0
1970	3.7
1980	4.5
1990	5.3
2000	6.3
2010	7.2

▲ Predictions for population growth.

   a Draw a graph of this data. Include the year 2030 on your axis.
   b From the graph estimate what the population will be in 2025.
   c From 1950 how long did it take for the population to:
      i double
      ii treble?
   d How are these figures linked to the importance of fertiliser manufacture?

6 The data in the table show the effects of applying fertiliser at different rates to a cereal crop.

Application rate (kg/ha)	Grain yield (tonnes/ha)
0	2.34
300	2.51
600	3.84
900	4.36

a Draw a graph showing application rate (kg/ha) on the x-axis and grain yield (tonnes/ha) on the y-axis.

b What grain yield would you expect from a fertiliser application of 450 kg/ha?

c What percentage increase in grain yield can be expected by applying 300 kg/ha of fertiliser?

7 a Why is nitrogen from the air not used by most green plants?

b Explain a natural process by which atmospheric nitrogen can be used by plants.

c What are the three most important nutrients in fertilisers?

d What are the differences between organic and inorganic fertilisers?

e What are the advantages and disadvantages of using inorganic artificial fertilisers?

8 The Haber Process is used to convert nitrogen from air into ammonia. Look at the graph on page 199 showing the per cent yield of ammonia using different operating conditions of temperature and pressure.

$N_2(g) + 3H_2(g) \rightleftharpoons 2NH_3(g)$
This is an exothermic reaction.

a What does the use of this sign $\rightleftharpoons$ tell you about this reaction?

b The reaction is exothermic. What does this mean?

c What is the effect of using an iron catalyst in this reaction?

d How many moles of nitrogen are needed to react with 1 mole of hydrogen?

e How is the yield of ammonia affected by:
   i temperature
   ii pressure?

f In practice, temperatures of around 400 °C are chosen for this process. Explain why temperatures of 350 °C are not used.

g Why are pressures above 300 atmospheres rarely used in this process?

h How is ammonia used?

9

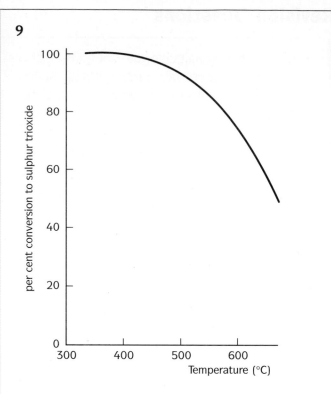

▲ The yield of sulphur trioxide at different temperatures.

$$\text{sulphur dioxide} + \text{oxygen} \rightarrow \text{sulphur trioxide}$$
$$\overset{400-500°C}{2SO_2(g) + O_2(g) \rightleftharpoons 2SO_3(g) + heat}$$

This reaction is one stage in the manufacture of sulphuric acid.

a What effect does temperature have on the yield of sulphur trioxide in this reaction?

b What temperature gives the maximum yield? Explain why this temperature is not used in the manufacturing process.

c What else is done to increase the rate of this reaction?

Structure & bonding

Hydrogen is joined to carbon in candle wax. The wax is soft and melts easily when heated.

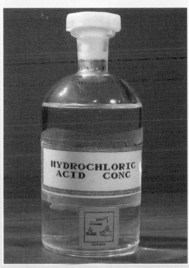

When hydrogen is joined to chlorine you get a gas which dissolves to form a highly corrosive, fuming liquid.

When chlorine joins to sodium you get a white crystalline solid. It melts only when heated to high temperatures and then it conducts electricity.

Table salt is sodium chloride.

The properties of compounds differ greatly and yet they are all made from the same basic elements. There are only about a hundred elements, whose properties also vary widely. All elements and compounds are made from atoms. Their properties depend on which atoms they contain, and how they are joined together.

Review

Before going any further, read this page and attempt the tasks. Write the answers in your notes.

Molten compounds of metals that are joined to non-metals conduct electricity. This type of compound is made from charged particles called ions. When the compounds are melted the ions are freed, and so an electric current can pass through. Metals form positive ions, for example $Na - e^- \rightarrow Na^+$ and $Mg - 2e^- \rightarrow Mg^{2+}$. Non-metals form negative ions, for example $Cl + e^- \rightarrow Cl^-$ and $O + 2e^- \rightarrow O^{2-}$. You can read about ions in Chapter Five (Acids and bases).

Molecules and atoms are tiny little pieces that things are made of. They are so small that you can't see them, and one atom is the smallest part of a material that you can get. Atoms are combined to make molecules.

When substances react, the atoms in them become rearranged. When they stick together in a new arrangement, the new substance might be totally different to the ones you started off with. For example two gases might make a liquid, or two safe atoms might make a poisonous molecule.

Atoms are stuck together in billions of different ways, in all kinds of substances, whether they are artificial or natural. The way they are stuck together decides what the substance will be like, whether it will be heavy, strong, liquid, solid, flexible and so on. It also decides whether the substance will conduct electricity.

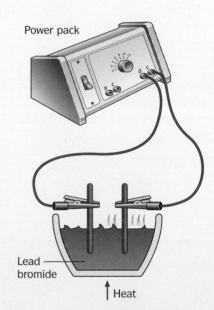

Power pack

Lead bromide

↑ Heat

CHECK FOURTEEN

1 The student above was going over what he could remember about particles in compounds and elements, before his chemistry class.
  a What two types of particles did he mention?
  b What other types of particle can you think of that he did not mention?
  c Can you think of a harmless substance made from a poisonous gas and a very reactive metal?
  d Can you name a liquid made from two gases?
  e A sample of a substance can be heavy or light. What other pairs of contrasting properties do you know?

2 a What is an ion?
  b What type of ion is made by:
    i metals
    ii non-metals?
  c Show what happens when an atom forms an ion, for:
    i a non-metal
    ii a metal.
  d Why are solid compounds of metals joined to non-metals poor conductors of electricity?

Individual properties

Gold is a shiny yellow metal with a high melting point. Sulphur is also a yellow solid, but it is brittle, dull and melts if you heat it gently with a bunsen flame. If you heat shiny black iodine crystals, clouds of brilliant purple toxic gas appear. Nitrogen is a colourless, inert gas at room temperature. We are only reminded of it by the N on fertiliser packets. These substances are all elements and yet their properties are very different.

The materials we use and take for granted every day are mostly compounds. Their individual properties decide how they will be used. Shampoos have a neutral pH, feel soapy to the touch and they clean and condition your hair. Wash-basins and baths might be plastic or ceramic but they must be water resistant and easily cleaned. Water is a liquid that is very good at dissolving things and, when pure, does not conduct electricity. Table salt is a white solid with a high melting point that conducts electricity when it is molten, but perhaps its most obvious property is the way it flavours food.

Compounds are made when two or more elements chemically join together. They are all made from the same 92 elements but, as you can see from the few examples given and your own experience, their properties vary widely.

⬛ The gold here has lasted through the centuries.

$$\text{hydrogen} + \text{oxygen} \rightarrow \text{water}$$

$$2H_2(g) + O_2(g) \rightarrow 2H_2O(l)$$

$$\text{colourless gas} + \text{colourless gas} \rightarrow \text{colourless liquid we use for drinking and washing}$$

$$\text{sodium} + \text{chlorine} \rightarrow \text{sodium chloride}$$

$$2Na(s) + Cl_2(g) \rightarrow 2NaCl(s)$$

$$\text{shiny reactive metal} + \text{yellow/green toxic gas} \rightarrow \text{white solid used to flavour food}$$

▶ *Describe the elements that make up the compounds listed below.*
  a *One form of copper oxide is a black powdery solid.*
  b *Lead iodide is a bright yellow solid.*
  c *Ethanol (C_2H_6O) is the colourless, addictive liquid in many drinks.*

Notice

- The properties of a compound are completely different from the elements that make it up.
- There is wide variation in the properties of different elements and compounds.

⬛ Heating turns solid iodine directly into a purple gas.

Elements and compounds

We now know that elements can't be chemically broken down into other substances. It doesn't matter whether you dissolve them, heat them or pass electricity through them, elements cannot be decomposed into simpler substances. In contrast, compounds can be broken down into simpler parts. Years ago people thought many compounds like water and barium oxide were elements because they couldn't be broken down easily by the methods available then.

▶ *How could you try to show that copper is an element and copper carbonate is a compound?*

▲ The mineral malachite contains green copper carbonate, $CuCO_3$. It can be broken down to black copper oxide, CuO, and carbon dioxide, CO_2, by gentle heating.

▲ Water can be broken down into its elements, hydrogen, $H_2(g)$, and oxygen, $O_2(g)$, by passing a current through acidified water, $H_2O(l)$.

Properties are different

You have seen that there are differences between the elements and that they change their properties when they join together to make compounds. Compounds also vary widely. Some are volatile liquids like ethanol, and others are solids with high melting points like sodium chloride. The next section will help you to understand these differences.

▶ *Use the information given on pages 248 and 249 to classify the following substances.*

sodium chloride	calcium oxide	ammonia
bromine	magnesium chloride	ethanol
sodium	nitrogen	glucose
water	methane	

Give a reason for your grouping and, if you can, include some other examples of your choice.

▲ The properties of different substances.

Substances seem to fall roughly into groups according to their properties.

- Elements are metals or non-metals.
- Compounds with high melting and boiling points, and which conduct electricity when they are melted or dissolved in water, are made from a metal joined to a non-metal.
- The other group, which are gases, liquids or solids with low melting points, are compounds made from non-metals.

These differences depend to some extent on the way the atoms are joined (or **bonded**) together in the compound or element.

Compounds of metals with non-metals

When elements react with one another the outer shell electrons are rearranged. One or more electrons are either given or taken so that the outer shell arrangement is the same as that of the nearest noble gas (group 0 element).

Metals, on the left-hand side of the periodic table, react forming positive ions, for example $Na - e^- \rightarrow Na^+$. Electrons are removed from their outer shell leaving an arrangement similar to the nearest noble gas. Non-metals on the right-hand side of the table react by accepting electrons to form negative ions which also have an electronic structure similar to the nearest noble gas, for example $Cl + e^- \rightarrow Cl^-$. You may have read about this in Chapter Nine (Atoms).

Ionic compounds

Na, (2,8,1) + Cl (2,8,7) $\longrightarrow$ Na$^+$(2,8) Cl$^-$(2,8,8)

The top diagram shows what happens when sodium reacts with chlorine to form sodium chloride. One electron is removed from the outer shell of the sodium atom to form a positively charged sodium ion. This electron is transferred to the chlorine atom, completing its outer shell and forming a negatively charged chloride ion. Oppositely charged particles attract one another (**electrostatic attraction**) which means that positively charged particles are attracted to negatively charged particles. These newly formed ions are held firmly together by strong forces called **ionic bonds**. Compounds formed in this way are called **ionic compounds**.

Ions are packed closely together in the solid in a 3-dimensional structure called a **giant lattice** of ions. Each positive ion is surrounded by negative ions. Each negative ion is surrounded by positive ions.

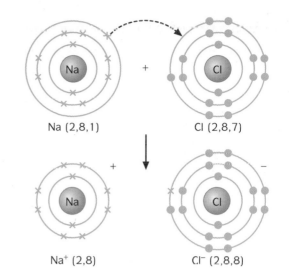

▲ Dot and cross diagram for the formation of sodium chloride from sodium and chlorine.

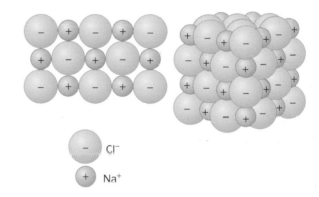

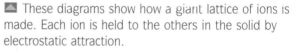

▲ These diagrams show how a giant lattice of ions is made. Each ion is held to the others in the solid by electrostatic attraction.

▲ Both of these models show how sodium and chloride ions are joined in crystalline sodium chloride. In the ball-and-stick model (on the right), lines are used to represent each ionic bond to give you an idea of how the ions are joined together. The space-filling model (on the left) is more realistic because the ions are packed closely together in the crystal.

▲ You can see from the shape of this crystal how it clearly reflects the arrangement of sodium and chloride ions in the models of sodium chloride. The crystal shape of a compound depends on how the ions are arranged within it.

More than one electron can be transferred. Magnesium reacts with fluorine forming magnesium fluoride.

$$Mg\,(2,8,2) + 2F\,(2,7) \rightarrow Mg^{2+}(2,8) + 2F^-(2,8)$$

▶ *Draw dot and cross diagrams to describe the formation of:*
   a *sodium oxide, Na₂O, from sodium Na (2,8,1) and oxygen O (2,6)*
   b *calcium oxide, CaO, from calcium Ca (2,8,8,2) and oxygen O (2,6).*

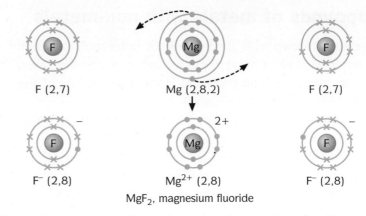

F (2,7)   Mg (2,8,2)   F (2,7)

F⁻ (2,8)   Mg²⁺ (2,8)   F⁻ (2,8)

MgF₂, magnesium fluoride

🔺 Dot and cross diagram for the formation of magnesium fluoride from magnesium and fluorine.

Properties and bonding in ionic compounds

The table below helps to show how the properties of ionic compounds back up the theory of ionic bonding.

Property of ionic compounds	Explanation using the theory of ionic bonding
High melting point and boiling point	In the solid, ions are held together in a giant lattice by very strong bonds. Much energy is needed to prise the ions apart
Do not conduct electricity as solids	Ions are strongly fixed into the giant lattice and so cannot move
Are good conductors of electricity when melted or dissolved in water	Melting or dissolving in water frees ions from the giant lattice and allows them to move. Positive ions move to the cathode (–) and negative ions move to the anode (+)

Compounds of non-metals

There is a whole range of compounds and elements with properties that are completely different from ionic compounds. The atoms in these substances are held or bonded together in a different way. Small groups of atoms join together to form **molecules**.

A hydrogen atom has one electron in its outer shell. A chlorine atom has seven electrons.

$$H(1) + Cl\,(2,7) \rightarrow H—Cl$$

atom + atom → molecule

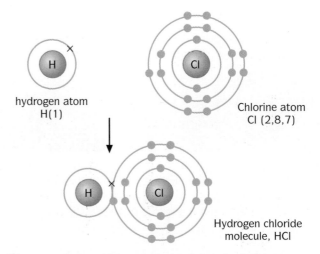

hydrogen atom
H (1)

Chlorine atom
Cl (2,8,7)

Hydrogen chloride
molecule, HCl

🔺 Dot and cross diagram for the formation of hydrogen chloride from hydrogen and chlorine.

Covalent bonds

To become stable, hydrogen and chlorine react to form an arrangement in which each atom has a full outer shell. The two atoms come close together and share two electrons with each atom giving one electron to the pair. The two atoms are held together because each nucleus holds on to its share of the electron pair. The shared pair forms a part of the outer shell of each atom and so the arrangement is like that of the nearest noble gas. This type of bond is called a **covalent bond** and is described on diagrams by a short line —, for example H—Cl. You may have read about covalent bonds in alkanes in Chapter Two (Oil). The new substance formed is a molecule.

Examples of covalent molecules

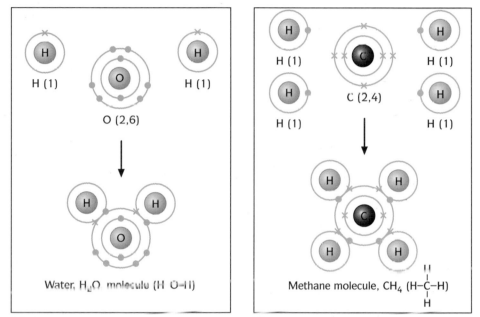

Water, H_2O molecule (H O—H)

Methane molecule, CH_4 (H–C–H)

△ Covalent bonds in water. △ Covalent bonds in methane.

▶ *Draw a dot and cross diagram for the formation of ammonia, NH_3, from N (2,5) and hydrogen H (1). Draw the structural formula for ammonia. If you need help to draw a structural formula, refer to page 17.*

More than one electron pair can be shared. When two electron pairs are shared this is called a **double bond** and is shown as =. Two carbon atoms double bond with one oxygen atom to make a carbon dioxide molecule:

C (2,4) + O (2,6) + O (2,6) → O=C=O

▶ *Check that the outer shell of electrons is full for each atom in the carbon dioxide molecule shown on the right.*

▶ *How many double bonds are in a molecule of carbon dioxide?*

▶ *Draw the structural formula for ethene, C_2H_4. Make a dot and cross diagram for ethene.*

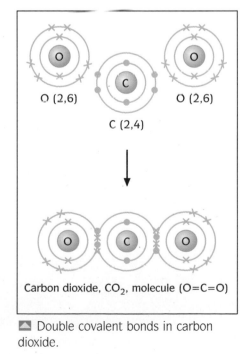

Carbon dioxide, CO_2, molecule (O=C=O)

△ Double covalent bonds in carbon dioxide.

CHEMISTRY

Covalent bonding in elements

Some non-metal elements are molecules, such as chlorine, Cl_2.

$$Cl\ (2,7) + Cl\ (2,7) \rightarrow Cl—Cl$$

More than one electron pair can be shared.

$$O\ (2,6) + O\ (2,6) \rightarrow O{=}O$$

▶ *Draw a dot and cross diagram for hydrogen, H_2.*

▶ *Why don't the atoms in noble gases bond to each other?*

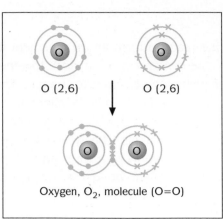

O (2,6)   O (2,6)

Oxygen, O_2, molecule (O=O)

⬛ Dot and cross diagram for the formation of chlorine gas.

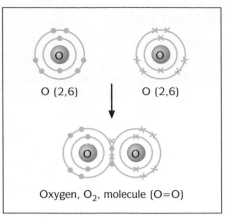

O (2,6)   O (2,6)

Oxygen, O_2, molecule (O=O)

⬛ Dot and cross diagram for the formation of oxygen gas.

Linking properties and theories

Link the properties of compounds to the theory of ionic and covalent bonding. You may be given a worksheet to help you with this.

Properties of covalent molecules

In covalent bonding electrons in the atoms' outer shells form bonds where electrons are shared and the new electron arrangement is like the nearest noble gas. The test of any theory is to match it against properties you can observe. Below you can see how the properties of covalent compounds can be explained by this theory of bonding.

Property of covalent compounds	Explanation using the theory of covalent bonding
Poor conductors of heat and electricity	Electrons are shared and ions are not formed. There are no mobile ions, or electrons, as in metals. Molecules do not carry an electric charge
Gases, liquids or solids with low melting points	Molecules are groups of atoms tightly joined together. Covalent bonding within the molecule is strong but forces between the molecules are weak. Less energy is needed to separate the molecules

⬛ The ball-and-stick model of ethanol (C_2H_6O) tells you about the covalent bonding in the molecule. The space-filling model tells more about the space taken up by the atoms.

▲ This molecule makes you laugh. Its formula is N_2O.

▲ This molecule makes you cry. It is called bromoacetone. Can you see the bromine atom in the molecule?

▲ This molecule smells rotten. Its formula is C_2H_6S. Can you see the one sulphur atom in the molecule?

Metallic bonding

In Chapter Three (Metals) you may have read that metals are good conductors of electricity and heat and that they have high melting points and boiling points. Most are strong structures like titanium while a few, like sodium, can be cut with a knife.

Metals are giant structures of atoms held together by bonds that are neither ionic nor covalent. Metal atoms have one, two or three electrons in their outer shell. These outer shell electrons move around from one atom to another. Each atom still has its share of negative charge but the electrons drift around among the atoms. The atoms in this 'sea' of mobile electrons are held together strongly by the attraction of the positive nucleus (see page 33). These attractive forces are called **metallic bonds**. The mobile outer shell electrons allow metals to conduct heat and electricity.

▶ *Use this model of metallic bonding to explain the properties of metals (see Chapter Three (Metals) if you need some help).*

Giant covalent structures

You have probably already noticed that melting point and boiling point are important clues about the structure of a substance. A low melting point tells you that you are probably looking at a substance made from molecules. It could be a non-metal element, like bromine, or a compound of a non-metal joined to another non-metal, like candle wax. There are, however, exceptions to this rule.

Carbon

Carbon is unusual in that it exists in more than one form.

Diamond is found naturally and most of us know it as the brilliant, shiny stone used in jewellery. Most diamonds, however, are used in a much less exciting way. Diamond is the hardest substance known. It also has a very high melting point which means that diamonds are ideally suited for making drills and cutting tools.

CHEMISTRY

This flawless (perfect) diamond was recently sold for £8.02 million pounds.

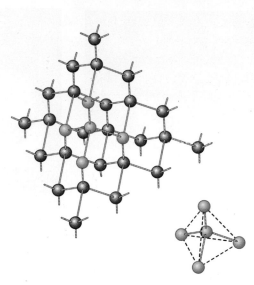

Three-dimensional structure of diamond

Carbon has four electrons in its outer shell. In diamond each carbon atom is covalently bonded to four others and tightly joined into a **giant structure of atoms**.

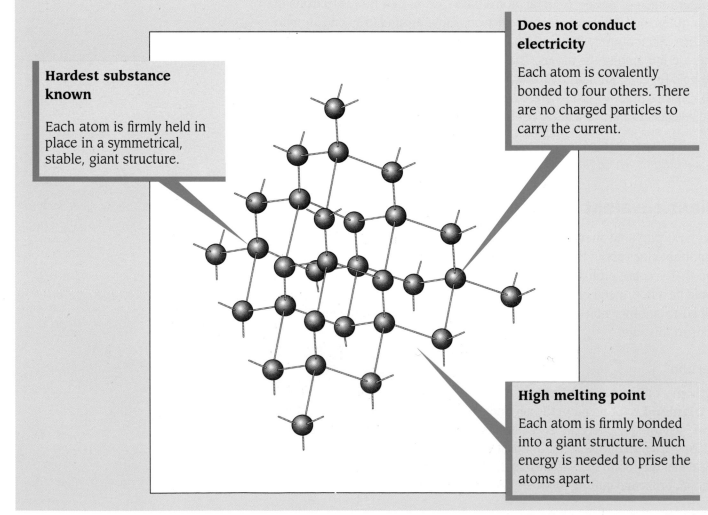

Hardest substance known

Each atom is firmly held in place in a symmetrical, stable, giant structure.

Does not conduct electricity

Each atom is covalently bonded to four others. There are no charged particles to carry the current.

High melting point

Each atom is firmly bonded into a giant structure. Much energy is needed to prise the atoms apart.

Properties of diamond.

Graphite, another form of carbon, is used as the 'lead' in pencils and, probably, in the electrodes you use for electrolysis in class experiments. Graphite is a soft, dull, black solid. It makes a mark if you rub it on paper. Like diamond, it has a high melting point but unlike diamond it is a good conductor of electricity.

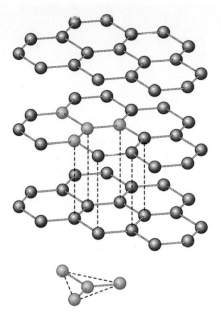

Layered structure of graphite

🔺 The layered structure of graphite.

Smooth, flaky and slippery. Marks surfaces. Used as a lubricant

The layers of carbon atoms are loosely held and so easily slide over one another.

High melting point

The atoms in graphite are held together in a giant structure and so much energy is needed to free them.

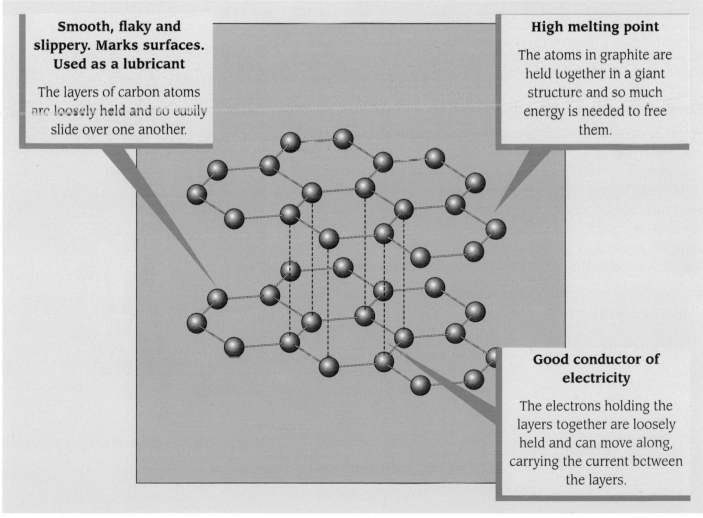

Good conductor of electricity

The electrons holding the layers together are loosely held and can move along, carrying the current between the layers.

🔺 Properties of graphite.

🔺 In graphite fibres, layers of carbon atoms are arranged along the length of the fibre making them stronger than steel. Since it is much lighter than many other strong substances, carbon fibre is widely used to make sports equipment.

Covalent elements with giant structure

From the descriptions of diamond and graphite it is clear that not all non-metal elements are small molecules.

In graphite, each carbon atom is covalently bonded to three other carbon atoms and these are joined together into flat layers. The remaining bonding electron of carbon is used to hold these layers together, in parallel sheets. The carbon atoms in the layers are tightly joined together by covalent bonds. The bonds between the layers are weaker and so the layers are only loosely held together.

▶ *Compare the properties of diamond and graphite. If you can, relate these to differences in their structure.*

Covalent compounds with giant structures

Carbon is an exceptional element. As you have just read, it has more than one form. It also reacts with hydrogen and oxygen to form enormous molecules like polythene and starch. You may have read about polymers in Chapter Two (Oil). In the periodic table, elements like carbon and silicon are in the same group, in the middle of the table, near the division between metals and non-metals. Both the elements and their compounds have some unexpected properties.

You know quite a lot about carbon dioxide, CO_2. It is a gas at room temperature and it is a covalent molecule containing carbon and oxygen. Silicon dioxide, SiO_2, is quite different. Sand, one form of silicon dioxide, has a melting point of 1610°C, a boiling point of 2230°C, and it is a poor conductor of electricity. Quartz and flint are other forms of silicon dioxide.

▶ *What prediction would you make about the structure of silicon dioxide?*

In crystal silicon dioxide each silicon atom is covalently bonded to four oxygen atoms. Each of these oxygen atoms is bonded to another silicon atom in a giant structure.

🔺 Opal is a form of silicon dioxide, that is used to make jewellery because of its attractive sheen.

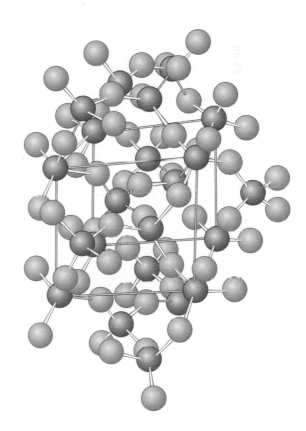
🔺 Silicon dioxide is a giant covalent structure of silicon and oxygen atoms joined together in a similar way to diamond.

🔺 Quartz is a form of silicon dioxide that is used in jewellery and in electronic components.

Summary

- New substances form when atoms join together.

- The new substances can have properties that are completely different from the substances that have made them.

- In the formation of ionic bonds, electrons are given or taken by atoms to form ions.

- In compounds made from metals joined to non-metals, the ions are held together by the attraction of oppositely charged ions. The ions are firmly held by bonds called ionic bonds into a structure called a giant lattice of ions.

- Covalent bonds are formed when atoms of non-metals share electrons.

- Substances containing covalent bonds can be either small molecules or giant structures of atoms.

- You can predict the type of bonding in a compound by looking at its boiling and melting points and whether or not it conducts electricity.

Revision Questions

1 Copy and complete the following sentences giving an example of each type of substance.
  a The elements in compounds of metals and non-metals are joined by _____ bonds, for example _____.
  b Elements in compounds of non-metals with non-metals are joined by _____ bonds, for example _____.
  c In metals the atoms are joined together by _____ bonds, for example _____.

2

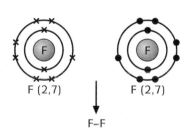

Li (2,1)   F (2,7)

Copy and complete the diagram above with:
  a a label to show an atom and an ion where appropriate,
  b an arrow to show electron transfer
  c charges on the ions formed.

3

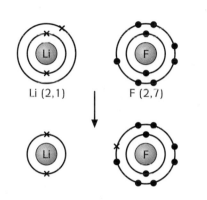

F (2,7)   F (2,7)

F–F

Copy and complete this dot and cross diagram to show the formation of fluorine, F_2.
What name is given to this type of bond?

4

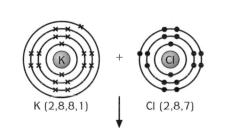

K (2,8,8,1)   +   Cl (2,8,7)

Copy and complete the dot and cross diagram at the bottom of the last column, to show the formation of potassium chloride.
What type of bonding would you expect between:
  a potassium and iodine in potassium iodide
  b sulphur and oxygen in sulphur dioxide
  c zinc and oxygen in zinc oxide
  d nitrogen and oxygen in nitrogen dioxide
  e mercury and sulphur in mercury sulphide?

5

> Hydrogen chloride, nitrogen, iodine, silicon chloride, helium, sulphur, silicon dioxide, carbon, carbon dioxide, phosphorus

  a Look up the melting point and boiling point of each substance in the box above.
  b Predict which will be molecules and which will have giant structures.

6

$$Cl - C - Cl$$

This is the structural formula for tetrachloromethane (carbon tetrachloride). Draw a dot and cross diagram showing how the covalent bonds in this molecule are formed.

7 Copy the summary below of the structure and bonding of substances. Fill in one or more example of each type, including elements and compounds.

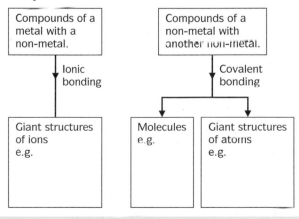

Compounds of a metal with a non-metal.

Ionic bonding

Giant structures of ions e.g.

Compounds of a non-metal with another non-metal.

Covalent bonding

Molecules e.g.

Giant structures of atoms e.g.

8

Compound	Melting point (°C)	Boiling point (°C)	Electrical conductivity (when molten)
A	2072	2980	good
B	−50	55	poor
C	1610	2230	poor
D	620	993	good
E	−77	−34	poor

Which of the above compounds is or are:
a a liquid at room temperature
b a gas at room temperature
c likely to be molecular in structure
d likely to be a giant structure of ions
e likely to be a giant structure of atoms?

9 Draw dot and cross diagrams for the formation of ionic bonds in:
a magnesium chloride, $MgCl_2$
b sodium sulphide, Na_2S
c magnesium oxide, MgO
d beryllium fluoride, BeF_2.

10 Draw a dot and cross diagram for the formation of:
a hydrogen sulphide, H_2S
b phosphine, PH_3.

11 Silicon, Si, is in the same group of the periodic table as carbon. It also has four electrons in its outer shell. Look up its properties. Make a prediction about its structure from its properties.

12 Draw dot and cross diagrams for the formation of covalent bonds in:
a trichloromethane (chloroform), $CHCl_3$
b ethane, C_2H_6
c propene, C_3H_6 ($CH_3CH=CH_2$)
d nitrogen, N_2. (Hint: N_2 contains a triple bond.)

13 a Explain why you can often smell covalent compounds and but not ionic compounds.
b Look at the diagrams showing the structure of diamond and graphite on pages 214 and 215 and use them to explain why:
   i diamond is the hardest substance known
   ii graphite is a good electrical conductor.

14 Suppose you were asked to draw a dot and cross diagram to describe the formation of an ionic compound made from elements X and Y.
a The following are the steps you would have to take. They are not in any order. Put them in the correct sequence.
   A Draw dot and cross diagrams for the newly formed ions and put the correct charge on them.
   B Draw in arrows showing how electrons were transferred from the atom to the ion.
   C Draw dot and cross diagrams for X and Y.
   D Look up the atomic number of X and Y.
   E For each of X and Y decide whether electrons should be given or taken to complete their outer shells.
   F Decide how many atoms of X and Y are needed to make the compound.
   G If more than one atom is needed draw the extra dot and cross diagram or diagrams.
b If X has an atomic number of 12 and Y has an atomic number of 9 check the order of your steps by drawing a dot and cross diagram for the compound formed between X and Y.

How much?

■ Measuring quantities

Whatever people make, they have to work out how much raw material they will need to produce their final product and, especially if they are trying to sell the product, how much of their product they are going to get. A baker buys flour by the tonne. She has to work out how many loaves can be made from each tonne of flour. Then, she can decide on a price to charge for each loaf which will leave her with a profit.

Scientists and manufacturers are no different. To understand chemical reactions and to convert raw materials economically into useful products they have to be able to work out how much of their raw material they will need and how much of their product they will get.

Whenever you do a job, you have to work out what raw materials you need, how much of them you need to make the products you want, and how much it will all cost.

If you decide to re-paper your room you will have to do a number of things to prepare. You might have to ask your parents, and then you will have to work out how much wallpaper you need. You will have to find out how big your room is and how much paper there is in one roll. Only then can you work out how many rolls you need. You will also have to check that you have enough money. There's no point in choosing a fantastic paper if you can only afford enough of it to cover three walls.

Review

Before going any further, read this page and attempt the tasks. Write the answers in your notes.

Chemical equations and symbols are used by scientists all over the world.

$$NaOH(aq) \quad + \quad HCl(aq) \quad \longrightarrow \quad NaCl(aq) \quad + \quad H_2O(l)$$

வன்காரமான சோடியம் ஐதரொட்சைட், வன் அமிலமான ஐதரோக்குளோரிக் அமிலத்துடன் முற்றுகத் தாக்கமடைந்து சோடியம் குளோரைட் உப்பையும் நீரையும் விளைவிக்கும்.

▲ You may not be able to speak Tamil but you should be able to make a good guess as to what the words describing this equation say.

Using symbols

Elements and compounds can be represented by formulae which allow you to work out how many atoms are present.

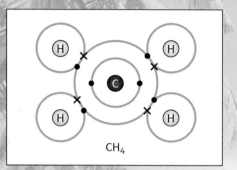
CH₄

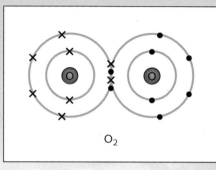
O₂

▲ Shorthand for elements and compounds.

All elements are made from atoms. In some elements, particularly metals, atoms are packed closely together. In other elements small groups of atoms are joined tightly together. These groups are called molecules. The formula tells you how many atoms are joined in one molecule. For example oxygen consists of two atoms joined together. The formula for oxygen gas is O_2.

Using symbols and numbers you can represent compounds as well as elements. For example, the formula for methane is CH_4. This tells you that the elements hydrogen and carbon are joined together in methane. The formula also tells you that in the smallest particle (a molecule) of methane, the ratio of carbon to hydrogen is 1:4.

For some compounds the formula includes brackets, for example, calcium hydroxide $Ca(OH)_2$. The small 2 here refers to everything inside the brackets.

CHECK FIFTEEN

1 How many atoms there are in a molecule of each of the following elements?
  a hydrogen H_2
  b iodine I_2
  c phosphorus P_4
  d sulphur S_8
  e carbon C_{60}

2 Write down the names and the ratio of the elements joined together in these compounds:
  a carbon dioxide CO_2
  b sodium sulphide Na_2S
  c potassium hydroxide KOH
  d sulphuric acid H_2SO_4
  e glucose $C_6H_{12}O_6$
  f magnesium hydroxide $Mg(OH)_2$
  g aluminium sulphate $Al_2(SO_4)_3$
  h ammonium sulphate $(NH_4)_2SO_4$

Formulae for ionic substances

The name of an ionic compound depends on the metal and the acid from which it is made (see Chapter Five (Acids and bases)). Ammonium salts are different. They do not contain metal ions, but instead contain the ammonium ion, NH_4^+, joined to an ion from an acid. An example of an ammonium salt is ammonium nitrate, NH_4NO_3.

If you know the ions in a substance, you can work out its formula.

- Every ionic compound contains positive ions combined with negative ions.
- The total positive charge must equal the total negative charge so, overall, the compound is uncharged.
- Ionic compounds have giant structures of millions of ions joined together so they are described by writing down the simplest ratio of the elements in the compound. You can read about ionic structures in Chapter Fourteen (Structure and bonding).

To solve the problems in this chapter you will need to consult the data section in Chapter Sixteen (Chemistry help).

| Positive ions | | Negative ions | |
Name	Formula	Name	Formula
Hydrogen	H^+	Chloride	Cl^-
Sodium	Na^+	Bromide	Br^-
Silver	Ag^+	Fluoride	F^-
Potassium	K^+	Iodide	I^-
Lithium	Li^+	Hydroxide	OH^-
Ammonium	NH_4^+	Nitrate	NO_3^-
Barium	Ba^{2+}	Oxide	O^{2-}
Calcium	Ca^{2+}	Sulphide	S^{2-}
Copper(II)	Cu^{2+}	Sulphate	SO_4^{2-}
Magnesium	Mg^{2+}	Carbonate	CO_3^{2-}
Zinc	Zn^{2+}	Hydrogencarbonate	HCO_3^-
Lead	Pb^{2+}		
Iron(II)	Fe^{2+}		
Iron(III)	Fe^{3+}		
Aluminium	Al^{3+}		

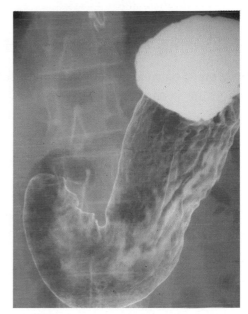

▲ Barium sulphate, $BaSO_4$, is the salt used in barium meals. X-rays cannot pass through this substance, so an X-ray photograph shows up the shape of the patient's digestive system.

Working it out

- What is the formula of magnesium chloride?

Formulae for ions present	Mg^{2+}	Cl^-
Is the formula	MgCl?	
Charges	2+ and 1– so overall charge would be	1+
Is the formula	$MgCl_2$?	
Charges	2+ 2 × 1– so overall charge would be zero	

So the formula for magnesium chloride is $MgCl_2$.

- What is the formula for calcium nitrate?

Formulae for ions present	Ca^{2+}	NO_3^-
Is the formula	$CaNO_3$?	
Charges	2+ and 1– so overall charge would be	1+
Is the formula	$Ca(NO_3)_2$?	
Charges	2+ 2 × 1– so overall charge would be zero	

So the formula for calcium nitrate is $Ca(NO_3)_2$.

Notice that the small 2 outside the bracket refers to everything inside it. In this case, in calcium nitrate, for every calcium ion there are 2 nitrate ions.

▲ Copper sulphate, $CuSO_4$, is used as a fungicide on potatoes and grapes.

▶ *Write down the formulae of the following compounds:*
 a *potassium chloride*
 b *sodium oxide*
 c *magnesium bromide*
 d *aluminium chloride*
 e *calcium hydroxide*

Balancing chemical equations

To write a balanced symbol equation for a chemical reaction, you should follow the steps in the table below.

What is the balanced equation for the reaction of sodium with water?	
■ Write down the equation in words. To do this you have to know the names of the reactants and products	reactants → products sodium + water → sodium hydroxide + hydrogen
■ Write down the formulae for the reactants and products	$Na + H_2O \rightarrow NaOH + H_2$ These are the correct formulae – you cannot change them when you balance the equation
■ Check to see if the equation needs balancing. Count the atoms of each type on both sides of the equation. If the equation is balanced, these should be the same	*Left-hand side* *Right-hand side* 1 Na atom 1 Na atom 2 H atoms 3 H atoms 1 O atom 1 O atom This equation is *not* balanced
■ You can balance the equation by writing numbers in front of the formulae. These numbers refer to the whole formula. (Use pencil here as it's hit or miss at first)	$2Na + 2H_2O \rightarrow 2NaOH + H_2$ *Left-hand side* *Right-hand side* 2 Na atoms 2 Na atoms 4 H atoms 4 H atoms 2 O atoms 2 O atom This equation is balanced: there are the same numbers of atoms on both sides
■ Add state symbols: (s) = solid, (l) = liquid, (g) = gas, (aq) = dissolved in water. These show the state of the substance at room temperature.	$2Na(s) + 2H_2O(l) \rightarrow 2NaOH(aq) + H_2(g)$

Copy and balance the symbol equations below. (Remember you must not change any of the formulae to balance the equation.)
a $Mg(s) + O_2(g) \rightarrow MgO(s)$
b $H_2(g) + O_2(g) \rightarrow H_2O(l)$
c $Fe(s) + HCl(aq) \rightarrow FeCl_2(aq) + H_2(g)$
d $CuO(s) + HNO_3(aq) \rightarrow Cu(NO_3)_2(aq) + H_2O(l)$

🔺 Balancing equations can be hit or miss at first.

Relative mass

Atoms of different elements

Hydrogen is the lightest of all atoms, so scientists decided that it would have a **relative atomic mass** of 1. A_r is the symbol for relative atomic mass. For example, $A_r(H) = 1$.

All the other elements have atoms that are heavier than hydrogen atoms. An atom of carbon is 12 times heavier than a hydrogen atom so its relative atomic mass is 12. $A_r(C) = 12$. Notice that relative atomic mass has no units because it is a ratio. The mass of each atom is being compared to that of another element.

The relative atomic mass of magnesium is 24. So a magnesium atom is 24 times heavier than a hydrogen atom and twice as heavy as an carbon atom. $A_r(Mg) = 24$.

🔺 One of these people is twice as heavy as the other.

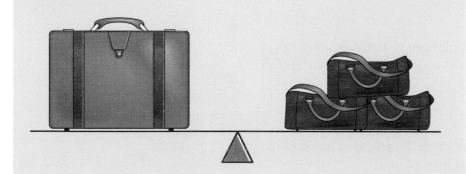

🔺 The packed suitcase is three times as heavy as one packed sports bag.

How many times heavier than hydrogen atoms are atoms of:
a carbon
b magnesium
c bromine
d barium
e lead?

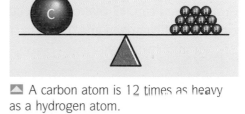

🔺 A carbon atom is 12 times as heavy as a hydrogen atom.

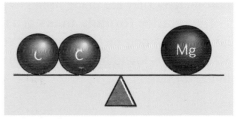

🔺 A magnesium atom is twice as heavy as a carbon atom.

CHEMISTRY

Relative mass of molecules and compounds

Molecules are made when atoms join together. Sometimes the atoms are the same. Most non-metal elements are found as molecules, for example, oxygen, O_2, and sulphur, S_8.

When the combining atoms are different, a compound is made. Most compounds of non-metals with other non-metals are molecules. Examples include water, H_2O, carbon dioxide, CO_2, and tetrachloromethane, CCl_4.

The **relative molecular mass** tells how heavy each molecule is compared to one hydrogen atom. The relative molecular mass (M_r) of a non-metal element or a compound of non-metals can be found from the formula. You add up the relative atomic masses of the elements in the molecular formula to find it. Again, notice that the relative molecular mass has no units because the mass of each molecule is being compared to a hydrogen atom. It tells you how many times heavier each molecule is than a hydrogen atom.

▲ Sulphur, S_8, has a relative molecular mass of 256. Every day tonnes of sulphur are deposited on the crater of this volcano in Java.

Working it out

■ What is the relative molecular mass of nitrogen, N_2?

Formula of compound	nitrogen, N_2
Atoms in the formula	$2 \times N$
A_r for the elements	$A_r(N) = 14$

Add up the masses of the elements in the formula to find M_r for nitrogen

$$2 \times N = 2 \times 14 = 28$$
$$M_r = 28$$

■ What is the relative molecular mass of glucose, $C_6H_{12}O_6$?

Formula of compound	glucose, $C_6H_{12}O_6$
Atoms in the formula	$6 \times C, 12 \times H, 6 \times O$
A_r for the elements	$A_r(C) = 12, A_r(H) = 1, A_r(O) = 16$

Add up the masses of the elements in the formula to find M_r for glucose

$$(6 \times 12) + (12 \times 1) + (6 \times 16) = 180$$
$$M_r = 180$$

From M_r you can tell that one molecule of nitrogen is 28 times heavier than one atom of hydrogen and one molecule of glucose is 180 times heavier than one atom of hydrogen.

▲ One molecule of glucose is 180 times heavier than one atom of hydrogen.

Relative mass of ionic compounds

Salts are ionic compounds usually made from metals joined to one or more non-metals. They are made from giant structures of ions.

The **relative formula mass** of a salt is the same as the relative molecular mass of a non-metal element or compound, and also has the symbol M_r. M_r of a salt is found by adding up the relative atomic masses of the elements in the formula.

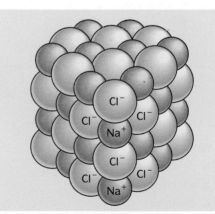

▲ Sodium chloride is a giant lattice of Na^+ ions and Cl^- ions.

Working it out

What is the relative formula mass of calcium nitrate?

Formula of compound	$Ca(NO_3)_2$
Atoms in the formula	$1 \times Ca, 2 \times N, 6 \times O$
A_r for the elements	$Ca = 40, N = 14, O = 16$
M_r for compound	$(1 \times 40) + (2 \times 14) + (6 \times 16)$
	$= 164$

▶ *What is the relative formula mass of:*
  a *potassium chloride, KCl*
  b *sodium oxide, Na_2O*
  c *aluminium bromide, $AlBr_3$*
  d *calcium hydrogencarbonate, $Ca(HCO_3)_2$*
  e *iron sulphate, $Fe_2(SO_4)_3$?*

Moles of atoms

You know from science investigations that, whatever you are doing, it has to be a fair test. If you are comparing substances or their reactions you have to start with the same amount of each substance. When using chemicals it is important to know that you are working with a standard amount of each substance. For chemists this means the same number of particles. The standard amount of any substance contains the same number of particles as there are atoms in 1 g of hydrogen.

Scientists chose 1 g of hydrogen as the standard chemical amount of that element. Atoms are minute and it is extremely difficult to deal with small numbers of them. A gram of hydrogen contains 6×10^{23} atoms – that's 600 000 000 000 000 000 000 000 atoms – more than you can imagine.

For carbon $A_r = 12$ so each carbon atom is 12 times heavier than a hydrogen atom. So 12 g of carbon contains the *same number* of atoms as 1 g of hydrogen. So if you were trying to compare hydrogen atoms and carbon atoms the test would be fair if you started with 1 g of hydrogen atoms and 12 g of carbon atoms.

△ One gross tells you that there are 144 packets in this carton. Can you think of any other words that always describe the same number of items?

▶ *Someone says that comparing 1 g of hydrogen atoms with 12 g of carbon atoms is not a fair test. Explain why it is.*

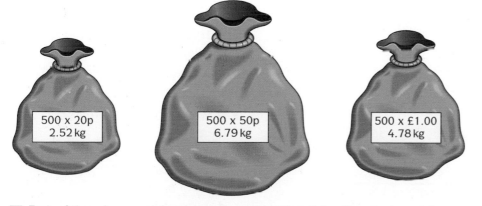

500 x 20p 2.52 kg	500 x 50p 6.79 kg	500 x £1.00 4.78 kg

△ Each of these bags contains the same number of particles. They each contain 500 coins.

Scientists now take the relative mass of one-twelfth of an atom of carbon–12 as being 1. This gives hydrogen an A_r of a little more than 1.

CHEMISTRY

The unit of chemical amount of a substance is the **mole**. The symbol for this unit is **mol**. One mole of a substance contains 6×10^{23} particles of that substance.

You can work out the mass in grams of one mole (mol) of atoms from the relative atomic mass of the elements. One mole of atoms of an element has the same mass, in grams, as the relative atomic mass. You know, then, that this amount of the element always contains the same number of particles. One mole of any substance contains the same number of particles.

▲ Each beaker contains one mole of atoms.

Element	Relative atomic mass, A_r	Mass of 1 mol of atoms (g)	Mass of 3 mol of atoms (g)
Carbon	12	12	36
Oxygen	16	16	48
Magnesium	24	24	72
Lithium			
Argon			

▶ *Copy and complete the last two rows of the table above for lithium and argon.*

Mass into moles

Working it out

Sometimes you need to convert the mass of a substance into moles.

■ How many moles are in 24 g of carbon, $A_r(C) = 12$?

1 mole = 12 g

So 24 g = $\frac{24}{12}$ = 2 mol

■ How many moles are in 96 g magnesium, $A_r(Mg) = 24$?

1 mole = 24 g

So 96 g = $\frac{96}{24}$ = 4 mol

Look at the above examples to check the equation below.

$$\text{number of moles of substance} = \frac{\text{mass of the substance (g)}}{\text{mass of 1 mole (g)}}$$

If you know how many moles you need, you can work out what mass this is, using this equation:

mass of substance (g) = number of moles × mass of 1 mole (g)

If you know the mass of a substance, you can work out how many moles this is, using this equation:

$$\text{number of moles of substance} = \frac{\text{mass of the substance (g)}}{\text{mass of 1 mole (g)}}$$

▲ In your body each atom, ion or molecule has a job to do. In hospital laboratories amounts are measured in moles because they want to know how many of each particle are present, not what they weigh.

▶ *How many moles are in 27 g beryllium, $A_r(Be) = 9$?*

▶ *What is the mass of:*
  a *1 mol of sodium atoms*
  b *10 mol of chlorine atoms*
  c *0.1 mol of iodine atoms*
  d *0.5 mol of iron atoms*
  e *0.125 mol of bromine atoms?*

▶ *How many moles of atoms are there in:*
  a *27 g of aluminium*
  b *20 g of calcium*
  c *4 g of bromine*
  d *140 g of zinc?*

Moles of compounds

The mass of one mole of molecules of a substance is equal to its relative molecular mass in grams. For example, M_r for glucose is 180. The mass of one mole of glucose molecules is 180 g.

The mass of one mole of an ionic salt is equal to its relative formula mass in grams. For calcium nitrate, $M_r = 164$ so the mass of one mole of calcium nitrate is 164 g.

If you know the formula of a substance, you can work out the mass of one mole or any number of moles of the substance.

Compound	M_r	Mass of 1 mol (g)	Mass of 3 mol (g)
Water	18	18	$3 \times 18 = 54$
Calcium nitrate	164	164	$3 \times 164 = 492$
Glucose	180	180	
Carbon dioxide (CO_2)	44		
Sulphuric acid (H_2SO_4)	98		

▶ *Copy and complete the table above.*

You can also work out how many moles there are in a given mass of the substance.

Compound and formula	M_r	Mass (g)	Moles (mol)
Water, H_2O $A_r(H) = 1$, $A_r(O) = 16$	18	18 180 9	$\frac{18}{18} = 1$ $\frac{180}{18} = 10$ $\frac{9}{18} = 0.5$
Carbon dioxide, CO_2 $A_r(C) = 12$	44	44 88 4.4	$\frac{44}{44} = 1$ $\frac{88}{44} = 2$ $\frac{4.4}{44} = 0.1$
Magnesium oxide, MgO $A_r(Mg) = 24$	40	40 160 4 60	

▶ *Copy and complete the table on the left.*

You can use the equations, given in the box on page 228, to work out the moles or mass of any substance, whether it is an element or a compound.

▶ *What is the mass of:*
  a *1 mol of zinc sulphide, ZnS*
  b *0.5 mol of lead nitrate, $Pb(NO_3)_2$*
  c *5 mol of sodium sulphate, Na_2SO_4*
  d *0.1 mol of ammonium chloride, NH_4Cl?*

▶ *How many moles of molecules are there in:*
  a *6.4 g of sulphur dioxide, SO_2*
  b *56 g of carbon monoxide, CO*
  c *14 g of nitrogen, N_2?*

▶ *How many moles are in 480 g of iron oxide, Fe_2O_3?*

▲ These each contain one mole of molecules of the compounds.

CHEMISTRY

▲ Each of these beakers contains one mole of an ionic compound.

Finding the formula of magnesium oxide

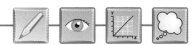

Most people know that H_2O is the formula for water. They do not think it is H_3O or HO_5 or some other ratio of atoms. In your science course you have probably become accustomed to using tables to work out the formulae for different compounds. Using tables you could work out that sodium chloride is NaCl and that magnesium chloride is $MgCl_2$. These formulae have been determined over the years by scientists taking very careful measurements.

Find the formula of magnesium oxide. You may be given a worksheet to help you.

Finding formulae

To do an experiment to find the formula of a compound like lead bromide you have to:

■ measure the masses of the elements which combine to make it. For example, for lead bromide, you have to find the mass of lead and the mass of bromine that combine

■ convert these combining masses into moles. For example, for lead bromide, you must use A_r for lead and bromine to convert these masses into moles

■ find the ratio of the combining moles to give you the number of atoms combining. For example, if you found that lead combined with bromine in the ratio 1:2, then the formula would be $PbBr_2$.

You know that equal numbers of moles contain equal numbers of particles. This means that the ratio of the moles that combine to form a compound gives you the number ratio of the atoms combining. You may find this difficult to follow. Look at the example on the next page to see how these ideas are used to find the formula of ammonia.

▲ Magnesium combines with oxygen from the air to form magnesium oxide. These students are checking the formula of magnesium oxide.

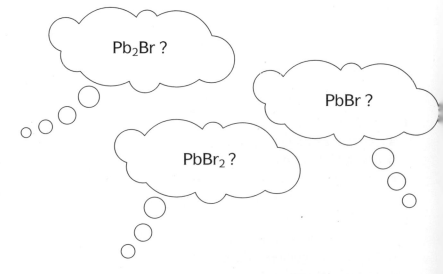

Pb_2Br ?

$PbBr$?

$PbBr_2$?

▲ What is the formula of lead bromide?

Working it out

In an analysis of ammonia, which is a compound of nitrogen and hydrogen, a scientist found that 2.8 g of nitrogen combines with 0.6 g of hydrogen. If $A_r(N) = 14$ and $A_r(H) = 16$, what is the formula of ammonia?

	nitrogen	**hydrogen**
Write down the masses of the elements combining	2.8 g	0.6 g
Use A_r to find the mass of 1 mol of the elements	14 g	1 g
Convert the masses combining into moles	$\dfrac{2.8\,g}{14\,g}$	$\dfrac{0.6\,g}{1\,g}$
	$= 0.2$ mol	$= 0.6$ mol
Divide both numbers by the smaller number. This gives you the simplest ratio of the number of moles combining	$\dfrac{0.2}{0.2}$	$\dfrac{0.6}{0.2}$
	$= 1$	$= 3$
Write the formula	N:H = 1:3	
	The formula is NH_3	

▶ In an analysis of sodium oxide, a chemist found that 1.38 g of sodium combines with 0.48 g of oxygen. What is the formula of sodium oxide? ($A_r(Na) = 23$, $A_r(O) = 16$)

The results of analysing a compound are often given as its percentage composition. For example, in an analysis a scientist found that methane is 75 per cent carbon and 25 per cent hydrogen, by mass. This means that 100 g of methane contain 75 g of carbon and 25 g of hydrogen. So the formula can be worked out in just the same way.

Working it out

	Carbon	**Hydrogen**
Per cent composition	75 per cent	25 per cent
Write down the masses combining in 100 g	75 g	25 g
Mass of 1 mol of the elements	12 g	1 g
Work out the moles combining	$\dfrac{75\,g}{12\,g}$	$\dfrac{25\,g}{1\,g}$
	$= 6.25$	$= 25$
Find the ratio of the moles (divide by the smaller number)	$\dfrac{6.25}{6.25}$	$\dfrac{25}{6.25}$
	$= 1$	$= 4$
Find the formula	C:H = 1:4	
	The formula is CH_4	

▶ Work out the formula of:
a silicon oxide, given that 6.0 g of the oxide contains 2.8 g of silicon
b magnesium nitride, in which 3.6 g of magnesium combines with 1.4 g of nitrogen.

▶ This compound is a black powder, often used as a catalyst and found as a mineral. Its composition by mass is Mn = 63.2 per cent; O = 36.8 per cent. Find its formula.

Using formulae

Formulae are useful in a number of ways. For example, gardeners may need to find out which fertiliser, from a whole range of nitrogen compounds, is the one that contains most nitrogen. Metallurgists need to calculate the amount of metal in a compound in an ore. These calculations can be done using the formula. Once this is known for a compound, it is possible to calculate its percentage composition by mass.

Working it out

Ammonium nitrate, NH_4NO_3, is commonly used in fertilisers to supply nitrogen to plants. What is the percentage of nitrogen in ammonium nitrate? $A_r(N)=14$, $A_r(H)=1$, $A_r(O)=16$.

Formula	NH_4NO_3
Work out M_r	$(2 \times 14) + (4 \times 1) + (3 \times 16) = 80$
Work out the relative mass of the element in the compound	$N = 2 \times 14 = 28$
Work out the percentage mass of the element in the compounds	percentage mass of nitrogen $= \frac{28}{80} \times 100$ $= 35$ per cent

▶ *What would you have to know about the brands of toothpaste in the photo to calculate which contains the most fluorine?*

▶ *Calculate the percentage of nitrogen in the following compounds, which are used as fertilisers:*
   a *ammonia, NH_3*
   b *urea, $CO(NH_2)_2$.*

▶ *What percentage of the ore Wolframite, $FeWO_4$, is tungsten? (The symbol for tungsten is W, and $A_r(W) = 184$.)*

Quantities

In investigations you might have had to work out how much of a substance to use. You might have been adding metal to acid or trying to reduce a metal oxide with carbon. The exact amounts might not seem to matter too much as you can always change your plans and try an experiment again. In a massive chemical plant reactants have to be added together in the correct amounts to ensure a good yield of product without any waste. This is where balanced equations are very important.

Working it out

■ How much lime, CaO, can you get by heating 500 g of limestone, $CaCO_3$? (A_r(Ca) = 40, A_r(C) = 12, A_r(O) = 16.)

Write the balanced equation for the reaction	$CaCO_3(s) \rightarrow CaO(s) + CO_2(g)$
Under the equation write the reacting moles	1 mol → 1 mol
Work out the mass of the reacting moles	(40 + 12 + 48) → (40 + 16) 100 g → 56 g
Scale the quantities up to the amount in the question	500 g → (5 × 56) = 280 g

Heating 500 g of chalk produces 280 g of lime. The maximum possible yield is 280 g.

■ In the UK some of the limestone quarried is converted to lime by heating it in a kiln.

■ How much sodium is needed to react with 364 tonnes of titanium chloride? (A_r(Ti) = 48, A_r(Cl) = 35.5, A_r(Na) = 23.)

Write the balanced equation for the reaction	$TiCl_4 + 4Na \rightarrow Ti + 4NaCl$
Pick out out the substances referred to in the question and write them in moles under the equation	1 mol + 4 mol i.e. 1 mol $TiCl_4$ reacts with 4 mol Na
Convert the amounts in moles to masses	1 mol $TiCl_4$ = 40 + (4 × 35.5) g = 182 g 4 mol Na = (4 × 23 g) = 92 g 1 mol $TiCl_4$ combines with 4 mol Na 182 g $TiCl_4$ reacts with 92 g Na
Scale the masses to the quantities in the question	The question refers to 364 tonnes of titanium chloride. (First find how much reacts with 364 g titanium chloride and then scale it up.) This is $\frac{364}{182}$ = 2 times the amount in the equation. So, scale up the mass of sodium needed. Mass of Na needed for 364 g $TiCl_4$ = 2 × 92 = 184 g Mass of Na needed for 364 tonnes $TiCl_4$ = 184 tonnes

So, 184 tonnes of sodium are needed to react with 364 tonnes of titanium chloride.

▶ *To demonstrate the thermit reaction a teacher weighed out 8 g of iron oxide. How much aluminium powder should be added to the iron oxide?*

$2Al(s) + Fe_2O_3(s) \rightarrow Al_2O_3 + 2Fe(s)$

■ Expensive sodium is used to extract titanium from its ore. Titanium is used in nuclear reactors and supersonic aeroplanes. This picture shows a titanium ingot.

▶ *What mass of copper oxide is made when 128 g of copper is completely oxidised?*

$2Cu(s) + O_2(g) \rightarrow 2CuO(s)$

CHEMISTRY

Molar gas volume

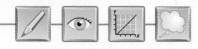

One mole of any substance, whether an element or a compound, contains the same number of particles. One mole of any gas also fills the same volume, provided the temperature and pressure are constant (kept the same). The volume is called the **molar gas volume**.

You may be given a worksheet to help you learn about molar gas volume.

Summary

- Given the symbol and charge on the ions in a compound, you can write down the compound's formula.
- Word equations and balanced symbol equations are shorthand ways of describing reactions.

    reactants → products

- In balanced equations the total number of each type of atom on either side of the equation is the same.
- The relative atomic mass, A_r, of an element is its mass compared to those of other elements. You can find A_r for each element from data tables.
- The relative formula mass, or relative molecular mass, of a compound, M_r, is found by adding together the relative atomic masses of all the atoms in the compound.
- One mole (mol) of atoms of an element is its relative atomic mass expressed in grams. For example, $A_r(Na) = 23$, so one mole of sodium atoms = 23 g.
- The mass of one mole of a compound is its relative formula mass, M_r, expressed in grams. For example, $M_r(H_2O) = 18$, so one mole of water = 18 g.
- Number of moles of a substance (g) = mass of the substance (g) ÷ mass of one mole (g).
- Mass of a substance (g) = number of moles × mass of one mole (g).
- One mole of any substance contains the same number of particles, be they atoms or molecules (or ions).
- You can find the formula of a compound from the masses of the elements that are combined in it.
- You can work out the percentage by mass of each element in a compound from its formula.
- Given the balanced symbol equation for a reaction you can work out the quantity of each substance reacting and how much of the product will be made.

Revision Questions

1 Look at these formulae. For each, decide which is an atom, a molecule or an ion.
   a Ar
   b CO_2
   c SO_3
   d K^+
   e Zn
   f HCO_3^-
   g N_2

2 Here are the formulae for the ions of some elements:

   sodium Na^+ magnesium Mg^{2+}
   sulphur S^{2-} iodine I^-

   Use these to write down the formulae for the following compounds:
   a sodium iodide
   b sodium sulphide
   c magnesium sulphide
   d magnesium iodide.

3 Which of these equations are balanced?
   a $C(s) + O_2(g) \rightarrow CO_2(g)$
   b $NaOH(aq) + H_2SO_4(aq) \rightarrow$
      $Na_2SO_4(aq) + H_2O(l)$
   c $CH_4(g) + 2O_2(g) \rightarrow CO_2(g) + 2H_2O(l)$
   d $Li(s) + H_2O(l) \rightarrow LiOH(aq) + H_2(g)$

4 These elements are listed in alphabetical order:

   aluminium, argon, chlorine, magnesium, phosphorus, silicon, sulphur.

   Arrange them in order of relative atomic mass, putting the lightest first.

5 Write the formulae for these compounds:
   a zinc carbonate
   b calcium nitrate
   c sodium sulphate
   d calcium hydrogencarbonate
   e ammonium sulphate
   f aluminium oxide.

6 Copy and balance the symbol equations below.
   a $Ca(OH)_2(aq) + HCl(aq) \rightarrow CaCl_2(aq) + H_2O(l)$
   b $KHCO_3(s) + H_2SO_4(aq) \rightarrow$
      $K_2SO_4(aq) + CO_2(g) + H_2O(l)$
   c $Al(s) + Cl_2(g) \rightarrow AlCl_3(s)$

7 How many times heavier is:
   a a magnesium atom than a carbon atom
   b a nitrogen atom than a lithium atom
   c a sulphur atom than a helium atom
   d a bromine atom than an argon atom
   e an iron atom than a nitrogen atom?

8 What is the relative molecular mass of:
   a oxygen, O_2
   b water, H_2O
   c hydrogen iodide, HI
   d tetrachlorosilicon, $SiCl_4$?

9 Write balanced symbol equations for the following reactions. Include the state symbols where you can.
   a copper with oxygen to give copper oxide, CuO
   b calcium oxide with water to give calcium hydroxide solution, $Ca(OH)_2$
   c hydrogen peroxide, H_2O_2, decomposing to give oxygen and water
   d nitrogen with hydrogen to give ammonia, NH_3
   e iron with chlorine to give solid iron chloride, $FeCl_3$
   f calcium carbonate with dilute hydrochloric acid forming carbon dioxide, calcium chloride and water.

10 a What mass of carbon contains the same number of atoms as 39 g of potassium?
   b What mass of fluorine contains the same number of atoms as 4000 g of helium?
   c How many moles of lithium contain the same number of atoms as 320 g of oxygen?
   d How many moles of phosphorus contain the same number of atoms as 2.0 g of neon?

11 What is the mass of:

    a 1 mole of chlorine molecules, Cl_2

    b 2 moles of water molecules, H_2O

    c 0.5 moles of sulphur molecules, S_8

    d 0.25 moles of phosphorus molecules, P_4?

12 How many moles of molecules are there in:

    a 160 g of bromine, Br_2

    b 4.0 g of hydrogen fluoride, HF?

13 Work out the formula of:

    a methane, given that in 0.8 g of the gas there is 0.6 g of carbon and the rest is hydrogen

    b iron bromide, if 0.378 g of iron reacts with bromine to form 2.00 g of the compound.

14 Calculate the formulae for red and black copper oxide using the results below.

	Mass of copper (g)	Mass of oxygen (g)
black copper oxide	8.0	2.0
red copper oxide	3.74	0.47

15 a What mass of sodium hydroxide would you need to neutralise 490 g of sulphuric acid?

    b Titanium chloride can be reduced by magnesium to titanium metal.

$$TiCl_4(l) + 2Mg(s) \rightarrow 2MgCl_2(s) + Ti(s)$$

    What mass of titanium chloride would be needed to produce 480 kg of titanium metal?

    c What mass of ethanol is formed when 9.0 g of glucose is fermented?

$$C_6H_{12}O_6(aq) \rightarrow 2C_2H_6O(aq) + 2CO_2(g)$$

Chemistry help

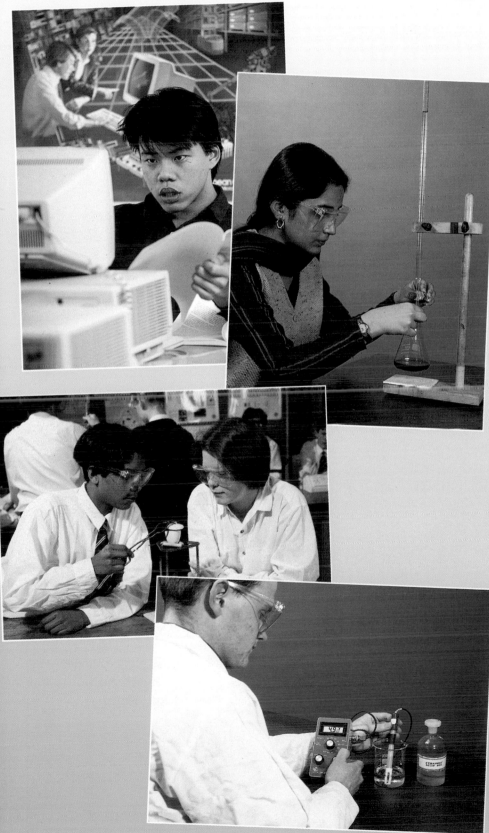

This chapter contains the planning, observations, results and conclusions from five different investigations carried out by students.

You can work through the chapter evaluating the students' work and answering the questions. This will help you practise some of the skills needed for doing investigations and it might give you ideas too.

Alternatively, your teacher might help you set up some of the investigations so that you can carry them out for yourself.

Review

Before going any further, read this page and attempt the tasks. Write the answers in your notes.

Putting your thoughts in order

Class 10B had a brain storming session. The class had been asked what important things they should think about or do when carrying out an investigation. Their teacher wrote the suggestions on the board in the order that the class thought of them.

1. repeat readings where necessary

2. any information you have to find or preliminary work you have to do before starting

3. some indication of what you think might happen (a prediction)

4. what could you do to improve your investigation if you had more time?

5. indicate what measurements you are going to make and how often

6. any variables you feel are outside your control in a school laboratory for reasons of time, equipment or safety

7. make sure you have enough results and that they are accurate enough to test your ideas

8. what your results show — is there any pattern or trend?

9. make a suggestion for further work to extend your investigation

10. an explanation of why it is a fair test

11. can you explain your results quantitatively? (This means using numbers like 'for every 5°C rise in temperature twice as much solid dissolves'.)

12. can you use knowledge you already have to explain your results?

13. compare your results with other data

14. some details of the scientific background that guided your investigation

15. any factors you feel might affect the accuracy or validity of your results

16. an outline of what you're investigating

17. make a comment on how good, bad, reliable and accurate your results are

18. clear details of any apparatus you are going to use

19. plan of a safe, fair way of testing your ideas

20. a way to record results and observations (tables, graphs)

CHECK SIXTEEN

1 Use the headings given below to group the statements above so that they can be used to help check investigation work, step by step.

 Planning

 Obtaining evidence

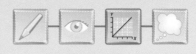 Analysing evidence and drawing conclusions

 Evaluating evidence

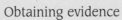

Investigating Hot Cans

▲ Piercing a 'Hot Can' provides a hot meal.

▲ Hot food is welcome when you are cold and hungry.

Adding water to lime is an exothermic reaction. (You can read about this in Chapter Twelve (Energy in reactions)). 'Hot Cans' make use of the energy transferred in this exothermic reaction. Piercing the lid of the can allows water and lime to mix and sets off a reaction that heats up the food and keeps it warm for a reasonable time. The lime industry produces many grades of lime. Hot Cans have to contain the right sort of lime as some sorts react with water too quickly and some react too slowly. The mass of lime used must be at least half the mass of water.

Class 10B were provided with three samples of lime labelled grade 1, 2 and 3. Grade 1 was thought to be purest and grade 3 the poorest quality lime. The students investigated the samples to find out which was most suitable for use in a Hot Can.

Safety

If you carry out this investigation, do not let lime get onto your skin as it can burn.

▲ The exothermic reaction between lime and water provides enough heat to warm up food.

Planning

The purpose of a Hot Can is to heat the food inside without needing a fire or a camping stove. The water bag is pierced allowing water to flow on to the lime. From cookery books, it seems that the ideal temperature to warm food is about 80°C. Lime is calcium oxide. The reaction between calcium oxide and water is exothermic. This means that energy is transferred to the surroundings when the reaction takes place.

calcium oxide + water → calcium hydroxide

$$CaO + H_2O \rightarrow Ca(OH)_2$$

▶ *Carry out a risk assessment for calcium oxide.*

PREDICTIONS

The amount of energy transferred to the food will depend on the amount of pure lime in each sample. As grade 1 lime is the purest, I think that it will be best at heating the food.

The more water is added to the lime the more the food will be heated until all the lime has reacted. The addition of even more water will cool the food. In this investigation I am going to use water as 'food'.

Independent variable (I am going to change this)	Controlled variable (I am going to keep this the same)	Dependent variable (I am going to measure this)
The grade of lime	Volume of 'food' Volume of water added	Temperature rise

I am going to use 10 cm³ of water as the 'food' in the test tube. I am going to add 10 cm³ of water to 20 g of each of the three grades of lime in turn.

I am going to take the temperature of the 'food' and then add 10 cm³ water to the calcium oxide and then take the temperature of the 'food' every 30 seconds.

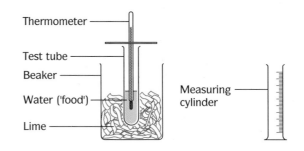

▲ Class 10B used this apparatus to test the heating effectiveness of different grades of lime.

Results

▸ *Present the results in the table in a clearer way.*

▸ *Make a comment on these results. Should any readings be repeated? Are there enough readings to allow a reliable conclusion to be reached?*

Time (s)	Temp (°C) lime 1	Temp (°C) lime 2	Temp (°C) lime 3
0	20	20	20
30	23.5	28	20
60	50	36	24
90	69	43	27
120	74	43	30
180	80	43	33

Looking at the evidence and drawing conclusions

▸ *What pattern or trend can you see?*

▸ *Do the results support the original prediction?*

▸ *What improvements could you suggest?*

▸ *Write a report on the effectiveness of different grades of lime for heating Hot Cans.*

▸ *Make detailed plans to investigate other variables that should be tested regarding the use of lime in a self-heating can. Make it plain what variables will be changed and what will be kept the same.*

Using precipitation reactions

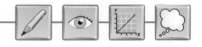

thiosulphate ions + hydrogen ions → sulphur dioxide + sulphur + water

$$S_2O_3^{2-}(aq) + 2H^+(aq) \rightarrow SO_2(aq) + S(s) + H_2O(aq)$$

Hydrochloric acid, HCl, and sodium thiosulphate, $Na_2S_2O_3$, react together forming a solid precipitate of sulphur, which is yellow. Some students from class 10B were asked to investigate factors affecting the rate of this reaction. They were given a solution of sodium thiosulphate (50 g/dm³), and some dilute hydrochloric acid.

🔺 You can monitor the reaction between sodium thiosulphate solution and dilute hydrochloric acid, by timing how long it takes for the yellow precipitate formed to completely block out a marker under the flask.

Planning

> I found out from a textbook that this reaction takes place quite slowly. When you add acid to the thiosulphate solution, sulphur is made. As the solid sulphur precipitate is formed, the solution becomes cloudier and cloudier until you can't see through it. From the same book I found out how you can follow the rate of the reaction. You draw a black cross on a piece of paper. Then you carry out the reaction in a conical flask and place it on the paper. I am going to mix the thiosulphate and acid together and time how long it takes before I can't see the cross.

▶ *What would you vary in this investigation? Make a prediction, using your knowledge of the collision theory to support your ideas.*

PREDICTION FOR TEST 1

I think that the higher the concentration of thiosulphate the quicker the reaction will happen. The more thiosulphate ions in the solution the more likely there is to be a collision with the hydrogen ions from the acid, and the more likely there is to be a reaction.

I predict that when the concentration doubles the rate of the reaction will be doubled.

Independent variable (I am going to change this)	Controlled variable (I am going to keep this the same)	Dependent variable (I am going to measure this)
Concentration of thiosulphate	Concentration of acid Temperature	Time taken for solution to become too cloudy to see the cross

I also predict that increasing the temperature will increase the rate of the reaction. Heating transfers energy to the particles in solution. The particles move faster and so there will be more collisions. As they are moving faster the collisions will be a lot harder and have more energy. Both of these factors are likely to increase the rate of the reaction so I think raising the temperature will have more effect on this reaction than increasing the concentration. From a textbook I have found out that raising the temperature by 10 °C doubles the rate for many reactions. I can test this in a second experiment.

Independent variable (I am going to change this)	Controlled variable (I am going to keep this the same)	Dependent variable (I am going to measure this)
Temperature	Concentration of thiosulphate Concentration of acid	Time taken for the solution to become too cloudy to see the cross

▶ *What preliminary test should you do before deciding exactly how much of each solution to add together?*

TEST 1

I am going to find out what effect the concentration of thiosulphate has on the rate of the reaction. To make this a fair test I am going to add water to the flask to dilute the thiosulphate and keep the volume the same each time. I am going to use the same flask.

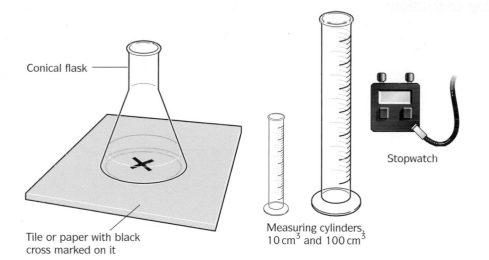

Conical flask

Stopwatch

Tile or paper with black cross marked on it

Measuring cylinders, $10\,cm^3$ and $100\,cm^3$

▲ This is the apparatus the students used to investigate the reaction of sodium thiosulphate solution with dilute hydrochloric acid.

▸ *Explain why it is important to keep the volume the same in each test.*

▸ *Why should the same flask be used each time?*

> I am going to measure the thiosulphate solution and water using measuring cylinders and mix them together in a conical flask.
>
> I used the same conical flask for each test. $5\,cm^3$ dilute acid was added with a little swirl to mix it and the flask was placed on a paper marked with a cross. I timed how long it was before I couldn't see the cross. The amounts of water and thiosulphate solution used each time are shown in the table of results. The total volume of solution in the flask each time was $55\,cm^3$.

Collecting results

Volume of thiosulphate solution (cm^3)	Volume of water (cm^3)	concentration of thiosulphate in flask (g/dm^3)	Time (s)	1/time
50	0	45.5	~~34.91~~ 35	
40	10	36.4	40	
30	20	27.3	~~52.63~~ 53	
20	30	18.2	~~79.82~~ 80	
10	40	9.1	~~196.85~~ 197	

▸ *Why were different amounts of water added in each test?*

▸ *On marking this work, as you can see above, the teacher crossed out the time taken and put in the nearest whole number. Explain why.*

CHEMISTRY

Looking at the evidence and drawing conclusions

▸ *Plot the results on a graph.*

▸ *What pattern can you see in the results?*

▸ *Copy the results table on the previous page, and complete the last column.*

▸ *Draw a graph of concentration (g/dm³) against 1/time. Does the reaction rate double when the concentration doubles? How does this result match up to the original prediction?*

EVALUATION

One of my problems was that sometimes the thiosulphate and the water went cloudy before the acid was added.

I also felt uncertain about exactly when the cross vanished. It didn't just suddenly disappear and I had some trouble deciding exactly when to stop the clock.

▸ *Why do you think the student had the problems described above?*

▸ *How do you suggest she tries to solve these problems?*

▸ *What could you do to check the reliability of these results?*

Collecting results

TEST 2

This test was to find out what effect temperature has on the rate of reaction between thiosulphate and acid.

The student carried out test 2 in this investigation, and got the results shown below. She did not have time to write it up properly showing exactly what she did and analysing her results.

Temperature of solution (°C)	Time taken for cross to be hidden (s)
18	79
27	53
37	33
47	21
57	16
67	12

▸ *Using test 1 to help you, write a plan for test 2 in detail.*

▸ *Analyse and comment on these results. Do they agree with the student's original predictions?*

▸ *How could you compare these results with those from other sources?*

Investigating crystal size in rocks

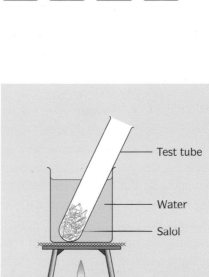

At room temperature salol is a white crystalline solid. The melting point of salol is below 100 °C and so it can be melted in a water bath.

Different rocks contain crystals of different sizes, because of the way the rocks were formed. Igneous rocks form as molten magma cools. How fast it cools affects the kinds of crystals formed.

Planning

> I am going to use salol as my rock. As liquids cool down crystals are formed. I am going to investigate the effect of different cooling temperatures on the crystal size. I think when the liquid cools quickly the crystals will be large. When it cools slowly the crystals will be small.

Independent variable (I am going to change this)	Controlled variable (I am going to keep this the same)	Dependent variable (I am going to measure this)
Temperature of cooling		The size of the crystals

▸ *Try to support this student's prediction using your knowledge of particles.*

▸ *If you carried out this investigation, what would you keep the same? What else could affect crystal size?*

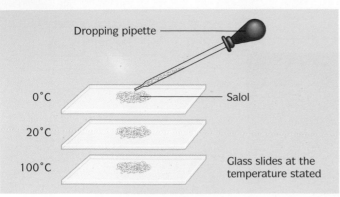

You can look at the crystals under a microscope.

I am going to put 3 spatula loads of salol in a test tube and melt it in a water bath. I am going to drop the liquid salol on to 3 slides, one at room temperature, one that has been kept in the fridge overnight and one that has been placed in boiling water for a few minutes and thoroughly dried. Once the crystals have formed I will look at them under the microscope.

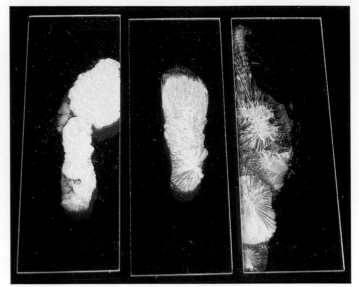

Salol crystal sizes formed at different temperatures.

Collecting results

Temperature	Time to cool (mins)	Drawing of crystals as viewed under microscope	Description of crystals
Room temperature (20°C)	3		Crystals are long and quite small
Boiling point of water (100°C)	0.5		Crystals were needle shaped but very small
Freezing point of water (0°C)	4		Crystals were long and large

Looking at the evidence and drawing conclusions

▶ *How could you stop the problem the student describes on the right?*

▶ *What can you learn from the results above?*

▶ *Do the results support the original prediction? What should the student do to check whether or not his results are valid ?*

▶ *How could he have improved on this investigation?*

▶ *What do you know about rock formation that supports these findings?*

One problem I had was that the salol sometimes solidified inside the pipette before I could drop it on the slide.

Appendix

THE PERIODIC TABLE OF THE ELEMENTS

Key:

| Mass number A | 1 **H** |
| Atomic number Z | 1 |

Group 1	2											3	4	5	6	7	0
																	4 **He** 2
7 **Li** 3	9 **Be** 4											11 **B** 5	12 **C** 6	14 **N** 7	16 **O** 8	19 **F** 9	20 **Ne** 10
23 **Na** 11	24 **Mg** 12											27 **Al** 13	28 **Si** 14	31 **P** 15	32 **S** 16	35 **Cl** 17	40 **Ar** 18
39 **K** 19	40 **Ca** 20	45 **Sc** 21	48 **Ti** 22	51 **V** 23	52 **Cr** 24	55 **Mn** 25	56 **Fe** 26	59 **Co** 27	59 **Ni** 28	64 **Cu** 29	65 **Zn** 30	70 **Ga** 31	73 **Ge** 32	75 **As** 33	79 **Se** 34	80 **Br** 35	84 **Kr** 36
85 **Rb** 37	88 **Sr** 38	89 **Y** 39	91 **Zr** 40	93 **Nb** 41	96 **Mo** 42	99 **Tc** 43	101 **Ru** 44	103 **Rh** 45	106 **Pd** 46	108 **Ag** 47	112 **Cd** 48	115 **In** 49	119 **Sn** 50	122 **Sb** 51	128 **Te** 52	127 **I** 53	131 **Xe** 54
133 **Cs** 55	137 **Ba** 56	139 **La** 57	178 **Hf** 72	181 **Ta** 73	184 **W** 74	186 **Re** 75	190 **Os** 76	192 **Ir** 77	195 **Pt** 78	197 **Au** 79	201 **Hg** 80	204 **Tl** 81	207 **Pb** 82	209 **Bi** 83	(210) **Po** 84	(210) **At** 85	(222) **Rn** 86
226 **Ra** 88	**Fr** 87	227 **Ac** 89															

Lanthanides:

140 **Ce** 58	141 **Pr** 59	144 **Nd** 60	**Pm** 61	150 **Sm** 62	152 **Eu** 63	157 **Gd** 64	159 **Tb** 65	162 **Dy** 66	165 **Ho** 67	167 **Er** 68	169 **Tm** 69	173 **Yb** 70	175 **Lu** 71

Actinides:

232 **Th** 90	231 **Pa** 91	238 **U** 92	**Np** 93	**Pu** 94	**Am** 95	**Cm** 96	**Bk** 97	**Cf** 98	**Es** 99	**Fm** 100	**Md** 101	**No** 102	**Lr** 103

The value used for mass number is that of the commonest isotope, e.g ^{35}Cl not ^{37}Cl.

Atomic numbers and approximate relative atomic masses

Element	Symbol	Atomic number	Relative atomic mass (A_r)
Aluminium	Al	13	27
Argon	Ar	18	40
Barium	Ba	56	137
Bromine	Br	35	80
Caesium	Cs	55	133
Calcium	Ca	20	40
Carbon	C	6	12
Chlorine	Cl	17	35.5
Copper	Cu	29	63.5
Fluorine	F	9	19
Germanium	Ge	32	73
Gold	Au	79	197
Helium	He	2	4
Hydrogen	H	1	1
Iodine	I	53	127
Iron	Fe	26	56
Lead	Pb	82	207
Lithium	Li	3	7
Magnesium	Mg	12	24
Mercury	Hg	80	201
Nitrogen	N	7	14
Oxygen	O	8	16
Phosphorus	P	15	31
Potassium	K	19	39
Rubidium	Rb	37	85
Silicon	Si	14	28
Silver	Ag	47	108
Sodium	Na	11	23
Strontium	Sr	38	88
Sulphur	S	16	32
Tin	Sn	50	119
Titanium	Ti	22	48
Zinc	Zn	30	65

*Carbon (as either graphite or diamond) does not melt but sublimes (i.e. changes directly from solid to gas); the temperature is approximate.

Gas densities are quoted at 25 °C and atmospheric pressure.

Properties of elements

Element	Melting point (°C)	Boiling point (°C)	Density (g/cm³) (× 1000 kg/m³)
Aluminium	660	2470	2.7
Argon	−189	−186	0.0016
Barium	725	1640	3.5
Bromine	−7	59	3.1
Caesium	29	669	1.9
Calcium	840	1490	1.5
Carbon			
*Graphite	sublimes	4800	2.3
*Diamond	sublimes	4800	3.5
Chlorine	−101	−35	0.0029
Copper	1084	2570	8.9
Fluorine	−220	−188	0.0016
Germanium	937	2830	5.4
Gold	1064	3080	19.3
Helium	−272	−269	0.00017
Hydrogen	−259	−253	0.00008
Iodine	114	184	4.9
Iron	1540	2750	7.9
Lead	327	1740	11.3
Lithium	180	1340	0.5
Magnesium	650	1110	1.7
Mercury	−39	357	13.6
Nitrogen	−210	−196	0.0012
Oxygen	−218	1183	0.0013
Phosphorus (white)	44	760	1.8
Potassium	63	760	0.86
Rubidium	39	686	1.5
Silicon	1410	2355	2.32
Silver	960	2212	10.5
Sodium	98	880	0.97
Strontium	769	1384	2.6
Sulphur (rhombic)	113	445	2.1
Tin (grey)	232	2270	7.3
Titanium	1660	3290	4.5
Zinc	420	907	7.1

Formulae and properties of compounds (under normal conditions)

Name	Melting point (°C)	Boiling point (°C)	Electrical conductivity (molten)	Density (g/cm³) (× 1000 kg/m³)	Structure
Aluminium oxide	2072	2980	Good	3.97	Giant
Ammonia	−77	−34	Poor	0.0007	Molecular
Barium chloride	963	1560	Good	3.9	Giant
Calcium chloride	782	1600	Good	2.15	Giant
Calcium oxide	2614	2850	Good	3.35	Giant
Carbon dioxide	sublimes	−78	Poor	0.0018	Molecular
Carbon monoxide	−191	−119	Poor	0.0012	Molecular
Copper(II) chloride	620	993	Good	3.39	Giant
Copper(II) sulphate	dec.	dec.	−	2.28	Giant
Ethanol	−117	79	Poor	0.789	Molecular
Glucose	150	−	Poor	1.562	Molecular
Hydrogen chloride	−114	−85	Poor	0.0015	Molecular
Iron(III) oxide	1565	−	Good	2.9	Giant
Lead(II) chloride	500	950	Good	5.85	Giant
Lithium chloride	605	1340	Good	2.07	Giant
Lubricating oil	−	250 to 350	Poor	0.8*	Molecular
Magnesium chloride	714	1412	Good	2.32	Giant
Methane (natural gas)	−182	−161	Poor	0.00066	Molecular
Methylated spirit	−100	80	Poor	0.79	Molecular
Paraffin wax	50 to 60	dec.	Poor	0.8*	Molecular
Petrol	−60 to −40	40 to 75	Poor	0.6	Molecular
Potassium chloride	770	1500	Good	1.98	Giant
Silicon dioxide (sand)	1610	2230	Poor	2.65	Giant
Sodium chloride	801	1413	Good	2.17	Giant
Sugar (sucrose)	161	dec.	Poor	1.5	Molecular
Sulphur dioxide	−73	−10	Poor	0.0026	Molecular
Water	0	100	Poor	1.00	Molecular
*Approximate values					

Mineral data

Name	Chemical formula	Hardness (Mohs' scale)*	Density (g/cm³) (× 1000 kg/m³)
Quartz	SiO_2	7	2.65
Feldspar	Complex metal silicate	6	2.6 2.56 to 2.70
Mica	Complex metal silicate	2½	2.9 2.85 to 3.00
Haematite	Fe_2O_3	5½	5.2
Magnetite	Fe_3O_4	6	5.2
Halite	$NaCl$	2½	2.16
Fluorite	CaF_2	4	3.18
Calcite	$CaCO_3$	3	2.71
Gypsum	$CaSO_4.2H_2O$	2	2.3
Barite	$BaSO_4$	3	4.5
Galena	PbS	2½	7.5
Pyrite	FeS_2	6	5
Sphalerite	ZnS	4	4.1
Chalcopyrite	$CuFeS_2$	4	4.2

*Hardness increases from 1 to 10 on the Moh's scale. The hardness of a mineral can be found by attempting to scratch it with standard minerals – a mineral can only be scratched by harder minerals and will itself scratch softer minerals.

Fractions from oil and their uses

Name of fraction	Boiling point range		Uses	Length of carbon chain
LPG (liquefied petroleum gas)	most runny liquid	up to 25°C	Calor gas, camping gaz, propane gas	C_1 to C_4
Gasoline (petrol)		20 to 200°C	Petrol for cars	C_4 to C_{12}
Kerosine (paraffin)		174 to 275°C	Jet fuel, petrochemicals	C_{11} to C_{15}
Gas oil (Diesel)		200 to 400°C	Central heating fuel, petrochemicals	C_{15} to C_{19}
Mineral oil (lubricating oil)		over 350°C	Lubricating oils, petrochemicals	C_{20} to C_{30}
Fuel oil		over 400°C	Fuel for ships and power stations	C_{30} to C_{40}
Wax, grease		solid	Candles, grease for bearings, polish	C_{41} to C_{50}
Bitumen	least runny liquid	solid	Roofing, roads	C_{50} and longer

Energy needed to break bonds

Bond	Energy needed (kj/mol)
C—C	347
C=C	612
C—H	413
C—Cl	346
C—O	336
C=O	805
C—N	286
N—N	158
N=N	410
N≡N	945
H—H	436
H—N	391
H—O	464
H—Cl	432
H—Br	366
H—I	298
Cl—Cl	243
Br—Br	193
I—I	151
O=O	497

Index

acid rain 36, 61, 63, 65
acids 61–76
    metals reaction 36
    periodic table 121
    properties 64
activation energy 153, 183
addition polymerisation 23
addition reactions 21
aerobic bacteria 166
alcohol 159, 163–5
alkali metals 116
alkalis 67–76, 121
alkanes 17–20, 21
alkenes 20, 21, 22
alloys 29
aluminium
    acid rain 65
    dilute acid reaction 36
    extraction from ore 53, 54–5
    iron oxide reaction 37
    properties 34
    water reaction 35
aluminium oxide, iron reaction 38
amino acids 24
ammonia 68
    breakdown 196–7
    fertilisers 196, 200
    formulae 231
    nitric acid production 200
    production 196–9
ammonium nitrate
    fertilisers 200, 232
    water reaction 173
amoebae 158
amylases 165, 166, 169
analysis 3, 11
anode 55, 57
antacids 68
Antarctica 45
anticlines 15, 97
antioxidants 42
apparatus, drawing 4
atmosphere 102–3
atomic mass 112, 113, 129
atomic numbers 115, 128, 248
Atomic Theory 115
atomic volume 113
atoms 14, 125–40, 206, 222
    metals 33
    moles 227–8

bacteria 157, 158, 162
baking 166–7
baking powder 167
bar charts 6, 9
basalt 83
bases 61–76
bauxite 54, 55
beer 163–5
Bhopal gas tragedy 143
biodegradable products 26
biotechnology 159
blast furnaces 51
blister copper 56
Bohr, Niels 131
boiling 165
boiling points 14, 17, 248
bonding 205–20
bonds
    breaking 181–2, 249
    covalent 211–12

double 20, 21, 211
    energy 182
    ionic 209
    making 181–2
    metallic 32, 213
Braer 13
brewing
    beer 163–5
    vinegar 165–6
brine 191, 192
bromine
    double bond test 20
    properties 117–18
Buchner, Edward 160
Buckminsterfullerine 109
burning 41, 63, 174
    alkanes 18
    energy release 183
    fuels 175–6, 183
    hydrocarbons 18, 184
    methane 181
butane 17

calcite 81
calcium
    dilute acid reaction 36
    oxygen reaction 35, 37
calcium carbonate 48
    acid reaction 71, 146
    rocks 201
calcium chloride, sodium carbonate
    reaction 73
calcium hydroxide, hydrochloric
    acid reaction 65
calcium nitrate 223
calcium oxide 67
    water reaction 239–40
carbon 213–17
    chain 18
    cycle 104, 186
    forms 109
    lead oxide reaction 50
    oxygen reaction 52
    reduction of metal ores 52
carbon dioxide 217
    atmosphere 104, 185
    covalent bonds 211
    testing for 67
carbon monoxide, iron oxide
    reaction 52
carbonates 65, 68
catalysts 19, 120, 150–1, 153,
    159–60, 183
catalytic converters 151
cathode 55, 57
cellulose 24
chalk 201
cheese
    making 161–2
    rennet 160, 161–2
chemical weathering 84
chlor-alkali process 192
chlorine
    isotopes 130
    properties 117–18
    sodium bromide reaction 118
    sodium reaction 209
    uses 193
chloroethane 23
chocolates 168
citric acid 64, 73

clay minerals 84
cloth manufacture 169
cold packs 173
collision theory 151–3
collisions 183
combustion 175
compound fertilisers 200
compounds 14, 207–12, 226
    moles 229
    properties 249
concentration, reaction rates 148,
    149, 152
conclusions 246
condensation 179
conditioning 165
conduction 33
conductivity, metals 33, 34
conservation, metal reserves 29
constructive plate margins 99
continental crust 80, 99
Continental Drift theory 100
continental plates 98
controlled variables 8
convection currents, Earth
    movements 100, 101, 102
copper 34, 35, 36, 48, 56–7
copper chloride, electrolysis 54
copper sulphate, zinc reaction 38
core 79
corrosion 40
cotton 169
covalent bonds 211–12
covalent molecules 211–12
covalent structures 213–17
cracking 19, 21
crust 79, 80, 99
cryolite 55
crystals 31, 83
    size 245–6
curd 162

dairy microbes 161–3
Dalton, John 115
decane 19, 21
decay, food 42
denaturation 161
density 32, 34, 80, 87, 248
dependent variables 8
destructive plate margins 99
diamond 213–14
diatomic gases 119
diffraction 127
dilution 148
displacement reactions 38–9, 118
distillation 15, 16, 177
Döbereiner, Johann 111, 115, 117
double bonds 20, 21, 211

Earth 79–80, 93–108
earthquakes 93, 95–6
electrical conductivity, metals 33,
    34
electricity 33, 34, 65
electrolysis 190
    acids 65
    brine 192
    copper 57
    lead bromide 53–4
    sodium chloride 136–7
electronic structure 132, 133, 134,
    136

electrons 33, 127, 128, 132
electrostatic attraction 209
elements 14, 30, 208
    covalent bonds 212
    properties 208, 248
endothermic reactions 178, 180–1,
    182
energy
    changes 182
    level diagrams 180
    reactions 173–88
    transfer 175, 177, 179
    UK sources 175
enzymes 150, 157–72, 183
epicentre 95
equations, balancing 224
erosion 84, 85
eruptions 82, 103
ethane 17
ethanoic acid, base reactions 71
ethanol 66, 176
ethene 19–20, 22–3
evaluation, evidence 3, 12, 240,
    244, 246
evaporation 178, 181
evaporites 105
evidence
    analysis 3, 11
    evaluation 3, 12, 240, 244, 246
    obtaining 3, 9
exothermic reactions 66, 141, 179,
    180, 181, 199, 239
experiments 1–12
extinct volcanoes 82
Extran fertilizer 200
extrusive rocks 83

fallow fields 194
fats 22
fatty acids 22
faults 97
feldspar 81
fermentation 73, 159, 160, 165
fertilisers 194–6, 200
fibres 25
fixing 104
flexibility, metals 33
fluorine 118
folding rocks 97
food decay 42
formulae 17, 18, 249
    ionic substances 223
    letters 64
    working out 230–2
fossil fuels 176, 184
fractional distillation 15, 16
fractionating column 15
fractionation 15
fromage frais 162
froth flotation 49
fruit juice 169
fruits 64
fuels 16, 18, 175–7, 183, 184
fungi 157, 158

galena 80–1
galvanised metals 40–1
gases 14, 119, 177
germination 165
giant covalent structures 213–17
glucose 66

gneiss 85
gold 34, 35, 36, 47
Gondwanaland 100
granite 81, 83
graphite 215–16
graphs 7, 9–10
greenhouse effect 184
Group 0 elements 119
Group 1 elements 115–16
Group 7 elements 117–18

Haber, Fritz 196, 197
Haber process 104, 196, 197–8
halogens 117–18
hardness, minerals 81
heat 14
    conduction 33
    transfer 177
heat-resistance, metals 32
Holmes, Arthur 101, 102
Hot Cans 239–40
hot packs 173
hydrocarbons 15, 17–23, 184
hydrochloric acid
    base reactions 71
    calcium carbonate reaction 146
    calcium hydroxide reaction 65
    magnesium reaction 144
    sodium hydroxide reaction 67,
        70, 71
    sodium thiosulphate reaction
        241–4
    zinc reaction 149
hydrogen
    nitrogen reaction 196–8
    oxygen reaction 152, 207
    production 197–8
    uses 193
hydrogen peroxide, breakdown 151
hydrogenation reaction 22
hydrogencarbonates 65, 68
hydroxides 67, 68
hypotheses 3

igneous rocks 82–3, 88
ilmenite 45
immobilised enzymes 167
impermeable rock 15
independent variables 8
indicators 62, 69
industry, fuels 177
inert gases 119
information
    presentation 6
    recording 6
inhibitors 150
inner core 79
inorganic fertilisers 194–5
insoluble salts 71
intrusive rock 83
invertase 168
investigations 1–12
iodine 117–18
ionic bonds 209
ionic compounds 209–10, 226
ionic equations 70, 72
ionic substances, formulae 223
ions 126, 190, 206
    atom conversion 136–7
    electricity 65
    lead bromide 54
    neutralisation 69–70
    periodic table 133–4, 135
    precipitation 73
    in salts 71
iron 36, 48
    aluminium oxide reaction 38

extraction from ore 51–2, 52
oxygen reaction (rusting) 35,
    40–1, 173
properties 34
water reaction 35
iron oxide
    aluminium reaction 37
    carbon monoxide reaction 52
irreversible reactions 197
isotopes 130, 131

joules 174

kilojoules 174

lactase 168
lactic acid 162
Lactobacillus bulgaris 162
lactose 162, 168
lattice 31, 209
lava 82–3
Law of Octaves 112
lead
    extraction from ore 52
    ore 48
    properties 34
lead bromide 53–4, 230
lead nitrate, potassium iodide
    reaction 72
lead oxide
    carbon reaction 50
    oxygen 50
lead shot 109
length 5
lime 67, 233, 239–40
limestone 81, 85, 201, 233
limewater 67
line graphs 7, 9–10
liquids 14, 177
litmus 62
lock and key model 159, 161
lubricants 17

Madagascar 45
magma 82–3, 97
magma chamber 89
magnesium
    acid reaction 36, 147–8
    copper oxide reaction 50
    hydrochloric acid reaction 6, 144
    oxygen reaction 37, 40
    sulphuric acid reaction 64
    water reaction 35
magnesium carbonate, acid
        reactions 71
magnesium chloride 223
    sodium hydroxide reaction 73
magnesium oxide 230
magnetic surveys 102
malleablity 33
malting 165
mantle 79
manufactured goods 189, 204
marble 85
margins 97, 99
mashing 165
mass
    measurement 5, 144
    moles 228
    number 128
    spectrometry 130
measurement 221–36
    accuracy 12
    length 5
    mass 5, 144
    pH 5
    reaction rates 144

speed 145
temperature 5
time 5, 144
volume 5, 144
melting 178, 181
melting points 14, 248
    alkanes 17
    metals 34
membrane, electrolysis 192
Mendeléev, Dimitri 114, 115
Mercalli scale 96
metallic bonds 32, 213
metals 29–44
    acid rain 36
    compounds 209
    dilute acids 36
    extraction 49–57
    ions 133–4, 190
    ores 45–60
    oxygen 35, 37
    properties 30, 32–4
    reactions 35–6
    reactivity 134
    reactivity list 37–9
    reserves 29
    water 35
metamorphic rocks 85, 88
methane 17, 231
    covalent bonds 211
    oxygen reaction 18, 41, 181–2
    steam reaction 197–8
Meyer, Lothar 113, 115
mica 81
microbes 157–8
milk 161
milk sugar 162
milling 165
minerals 47, 77–92, 249
    identification 81–2
    mining 49
    ores 45–60
    reserves 45
    streaks 82
mining 49, 191
models 2
Moho discontinuity 79
Mohs' scale of hardness 81
molar gas volume 234
molecules 14, 206, 210, 222, 226
moles 227–31
monatomic gases 119
monomers 23

native metals 47
natural fibres 25
natural polymers 24
neutral solution 62
neutralisation 65, 67, 68, 69–70,
    179
neutrons 127, 128
Newlands, John 112, 115
nitrates 196
nitric acid
    base reactions 71
    production 200
    silver reaction 141
nitrogen
    cycle 104
    fertiliser 200
    fixers 194
    hydrogen reaction 196–8
nitrogen oxides 63
nitrogenous fertilisers 196
noble gases 119
non-metals 30
    compounds 209, 210–12
    ions 135

reactivity 136
nucleus 127, 128
nutrients 194
nylon 25

oceanic crust 80
oceanic plates 98
octane 19–20
oil 13–28, 249
olivine 81
orbits 131
ores 45–60
organic fertilisers 194–5
outer core 79
oxidation 40–2, 46, 50
oxides 35, 40–42, 67, 176
oxidising agents 40
oxygen 63
    see also burning
    calcium reaction 35, 37
    hydrogen reaction 152, 207
    iron reaction 173
    lead oxide 50
    magnesium reaction 37, 40
    metals reaction 35, 37
    methane reaction 18, 41, 181–2
    oxidation 40–2, 46, 50
    production 103
    sulphur reaction 40
    zinc reaction 46

Pangaea 100
particles 125
pasteurisation 161, 162
pectinase 169
pectins 169
periodic table 109–24, 131, 247
    electronic structure 133
    ions 135
permeable rock 15
pH 5, 61, 62, 69, 163
physical weathering 84
pie charts 7, 9
pig iron 52
planning 3, 8, 239, 241–3, 245–6
plant nutrients 194
plastics 24, 26
plate movement 100
plate tectonics 102
plates 97–9
pollution 13
    see also acid rain
polymerisation 22–3
polymers 23–5
polypropene 24
polystyrene 23
polythene 22–3, 24
potassium 35
potassium iodide, lead nitrate
    reaction 72
precipitate 71, 144
precipitation reactions 71–3, 241–4
presentation, results 6–7, 10
pressure, reaction rates 149
propane 17
propene 20
proteases 167
protein catalysts 159
proteins 24
protons 14, 33, 127, 128
protozoans 158
PTFE 23
purification
    citric acid 73
    copper 56
    salts 71, 73
PVC 23

quarks 125, 127
quartz 81, 86–7

raising agents 167
rare gases 119
rates of reaction 141–56
reaction energy 173–88
reaction intermediates 161
reactivity
    list 37–9
    metals 35, 53, 134
    non-metals 136
recycling
    metals 29
    plastics 26
redox reactions 50
reducing agents 50
reduction 50, 52
refinery 15
relative atomic mass 112, 113, 129,
    131, 225, 248
relative formula mass 226
relative molecular mass 226
rennet 160, 161–2
results
    collection 243–4, 246
    presentation 9–10, 240
reversible reactions 66, 196, 197
Richter scale 96
ridges 97
rifts 101
risk assessment 4, 36–7
rocks 47, 77–92, 97, 245–6
    cycle 86
    impermeable 15
    permeable 15
    record 88
    uses 201
Rothamsted Experimental Station
    195
rubbish 26
rusting 40–1

safety 4
salami 159
salt 105, 191, 192
    see also sodium chloride
salts 68, 70, 71, 73
sand 77, 86
saturated compounds 20
saturated fats 22

scale 73
schist 85
scree 84
seawater 105
sediment 83
sedimentary rocks 15, 83–4, 89
seisomometers 95
semtex 175
shells 131
shock waves 95
Shrinking Earth theory 100
silicon 87
silicon dioxide 217
silver
    nitric acid reaction 141
    oxygen reaction 35
slag 52
slurry 49
smelting 49
sodium
    chlorine reaction 207, 209
    dilute acid reaction 36
    ore 48
    oxygen reaction 35, 143
    titanium chloride reaction 57,
    233
    water reaction 35, 224
sodium bromide, chlorine reaction
    118
sodium carbonate, calcium chloride
    reaction 73
sodium chloride 70
    catalyst 173
    electrolysis 53, 136–7, 191
    precipitation 72
    production 190
    water reaction 192
sodium hydroxide
    acid reactions 71
    hydrochloric acid reaction 67,
    70, 71
    uses 193
sodium sulphite 36
sodium thiosulphate, hydrochloric
    acid reaction 241–4
soft-centred chocolates 168
soils 61, 67, 194
solidification 179
solids 14, 177
solutes 148
solution mining 191

solutions 190
speed, measurement 145
stalactites 85
stalagmites 85
starch 24, 163, 166, 169
state changes 177
statistics 1
steam, methane reaction 197–8
strength
    acids 63
    metals 32, 34
Streptococcus thermophilus 162
structure 205–20
styrene 23
sub-atomic particles 127
subduction 97
substrates 159
sulphates 223
sulphur, oxygen reaction 40
sulphur dioxide 36, 40, 63, 66, 199
sulphur trioxide 66, 199
sulphuric acid 66
    base reactions 71
    magnesium reaction 64
    production 199
    zinc oxide reaction 65
surface area 145–6
    reaction rates 152
symbols 222
synclines 97
synthetic fibres 25
synthetic polymers 24
syrups 168

temperature 5, 69
    Earth 104, 184–5
    enzymes 161
    reaction rates 8–12, 147, 152
tensile strength, metals 32, 34
TFE 23
thermal decomposition 201
thermit reaction 38
thermoplastic polymers 24
thermosetting plastics 24
thermosoftening plastics 24
Thomson, G. 127
Thomson, J.J. 127
time, measurement 5, 144
titanium 34, 57
titanium chloride, sodium reaction
    233

transition elements 120–21
transportation 84
tremors 95
trenches 97

UHT see ultra heat treatment
ultra heat treatment 161
universal indicators 62
unreactive metals 35, 56
unsaturated compounds 20
unsaturated fats 22

variables 3, 8, 242
vinegar, brewing 165–6
viruses 158
viscosity 17
volcanoes 63, 82, 96, 97, 103
volume, measurement 5, 144

washing powders 167
waste product, fuels 176
water
    ammonium nitrate reaction 173
    calcium oxide reaction 239–40
    covalent bonds 211
    cycle 104
    decomposition 182
    freezing/melting 197
    metals 35
    sodium reaction 224
weathering 83, 84, 143
Wegner, Alfred 100–1, 102
whey 162, 168
wool 25
wort 165

yeast 160, 166, 167
yoghurt 162–3

zinc 36, 48
    copper sulphate reaction 38
    corrosion 41
    extraction from ore 52
    hydrochloric acid reaction 149
    oxygen reaction 35, 46
    properties 34
zinc hydroxide, acid reactions 71
zinc oxide, sulphuric acid reaction
    65